THE
WORLD
ATLAS &
ENCYCLOPEDIA

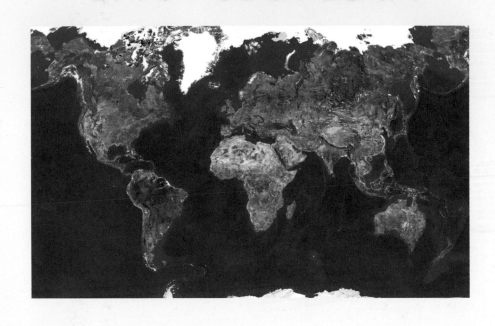

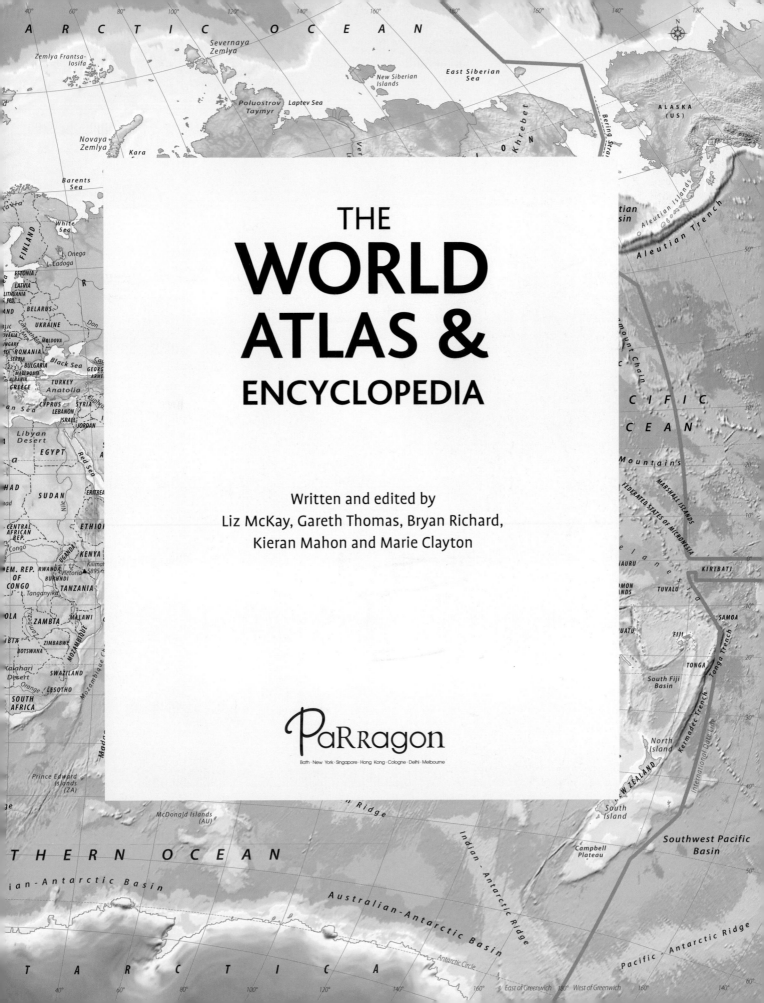

THE
WORLD
ATLAS &
ENCYCLOPEDIA

Written and edited by
Liz McKay, Gareth Thomas, Bryan Richard,
Kieran Mahon and Marie Clayton

PaRragon

Bath·New York·Singapore·Hong Kong·Cologne·Delhi·Melbourne

This edition published by Parragon in 2010

Parragon
Queen Street House
4 Queen Street
Bath, BA1 IHE UK

Maps © Parragon Books Ltd 2009.
Maps created by Compare Infobase Ltd (with the exception of the maps showing India, Pakistan and China)
Satellite maps © PlanetObserver – www.planetobserver.com All rights reserved.
For details of copyright in the photographs see page 336
Text © Parragon Books Ltd 2009

Produced by Atlantic Publishing

ISBN: 978-1-4454-0880-4

Printed in Malaysia

CONTENTS

HOW TO USE THIS BOOK

There is more information about the world than ever before and it can be overwhelming. *The World Atlas and Encyclopedia* offers a careful balance between the quantity and value of information, making it easier for the reader to locate important geographic detail then to absorb and remember it.

The atlas is structured in an unusual way with a world map section followed by continental sections; within each continent the countries are presented by regions that follow the definition of the United Nations. This not only gives a clearer geographical understanding of the world, it also enables countries to be compared with each other using a number of criteria, ranging from area and population to political and

VICTORIA FALLS, SOUTHERN AFRICA
Situated on the Zimbabwe–Zambia border, the falls are one of the seven natural wonders of the world. Their local name translates as 'the smoke that thunders'.

economic activity, set out in fact files. Highly illustrated country entries give the reader an informative and engaging real-life snapshot.

Gathering the data for any atlas is difficult when the world changes so quickly and different countries produce their annual statistics in varied formats and at different times – all of which make it difficult for people to grasp facts about their world. This atlas offers a consistent approach and although in theory it is an encyclopedia of autonomous, self-ruling countries, entries are also included for dependent territories that are important as popular destinations or have a rich history – such as Gibraltar. The countries are grouped in regions and the order they are listed is not alphabetical but generally as if one were flying over them from north-west to south-east.

Readers may be surprised to find the entire Russian Federation included in Europe when the eastern part of this vast country is geographically in Asia. This is mainly because the Russian Federation is classified by the United Nations in this way and also because this encyclopedic atlas is based on country entries. There are some other anomalies: for instance, in accordance with United Nations classification there is no regional layer to South America. The USA also gets special treatment with a regional division based on the US Census Bureau. The atlas also separates Central America and the Caribbean as a region, which is unusual but is considered by the editors to be a useful perspective. The Polar Regions are treated as a continental area although there is no formal political or social geography for Antarctica or a single land mass for the Arctic.

Map Key

LUXEMBOURG	Country Name
BELGIUM	Neighbouring Country
▣ LUXEMBOURG	National Capital
● Valdez	Major Town
○ Coburg	Other Town
T E X A S	Province or State Name
North Sea	Sea Name
ATLANTIC OCEAN	Ocean Name
Massif Central	Physical Feature
Canary Islands (SPAIN)	Island Name
▲ 493	Mountain Peak Name
0 150 300 Km / 0 75 150 Miles	Scale Bar
✈ (circled)	International Airport
✈	Regional Airport
— · — · — · — · —	International Boundary
· · · · · · · · · · · · ·	Disputed Boundary
· · · · · · · · · · · · · · · ·	Ceasefire Boundary
———————	Province/State Boundary
——————	Railway
═══════	Major Road
——————	Other Road
——————	Major River
——————	Minor River
——————	Coastline
▭	Lake
✦ (N)	North Symbol
	Ice Cap
	Depression Below Sea Level
· · · · · · · · · · · · · · · ·	Seasonal River
	Seasonal Lake
	Swamp
	Mash land

World Maps

The world map section (pp14-47) needs little explanation; it is a set of maps using Van der Grinten projection with the world overview centred on the prime meridian (or Greenwich meridian). The map of the world is scaled at 1:92,700,000. The larger scale continental maps that follow all use the Van der Grinten projection at a scale of 1:37,000,000, with the exception of the Polar Regions which are scaled at 1:48,000,000 and use the Polar Stereographic projection. The satellite images that alternate in the world map section are at the identical projection and scale as the topographic maps.

Continental Sections

Continental sections open with two pages containing a brief text, continent map and an index listing countries with the pages on which each entry can be found. Dependent territories are indicated by the sovereign state in brackets in short code. The continent locator shows position on a thumbnail. The tabs are a different colour for each continent and show at the edge of the page to help navigate quickly to a continent section.

Subregional Sections

With the exception of South America and the Polar Regions, each continent is subdivided into the regions defined by the United Nations. The region section has a brief text, a larger scale region map and an index list of countries. Tabs show the region name and the locator shows the position of the region in the continent.

Country Entries

In each country entry the header contains the country's flag and its international name, the longitude and latitude at the country's centre, the area of the country and the local time as UTC +/- the hour. UTC is the international convention for local time and is short for Universal Coordinated Time. A globe locator shows the position of the country blocked in red. The fact file is in two parts – every country has key facts but only the largest have the second level of information that gives administrative and commercial details. Dependent territories that have their own entry have a modified fact file. To save space very small percentages of ethnic or religious groups have been left out. The threshold for recording these percentages is 3 per cent, below which they are rarely shown unless they are of particular interest – most often in the case of indigenous populations where the editors consider that the reader will be interested. This means that the total of the percentages given does not always reach 100 per cent. A detailed explanation of the fact file can be found along with the index at the end of the book.

MOUNT McKINLEY, ALASKA
Mount McKinley is the highest peak in North America.

INTRODUCTION

CLIMATE ZONES

Weather is created by the constant movement in the Earth's atmosphere and it is usually defined as the state of the atmosphere in a particular place and time. In contrast, climate is the longer-term state of the atmosphere. It takes into consideration long-term averages in order to eliminate the effects of 'freak' events and so give a clearer picture of what to expect. The most important conditions that affect climate are the average monthly temperatures and average monthly rainfall. The world is divided into regions according to their climate, although the boundaries are not sharply defined, as one type of climate gradually merges into the next.

The climatic region known as the tropics lies between the Tropics of Cancer and Capricorn. In this zone the sun is directly overhead so that temperatures are always high (except in highland areas) and the

CLIMATE ZONES

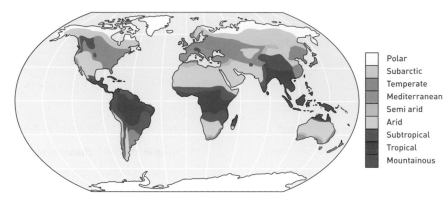

| Polar |
| Subarctic |
| Temperate |
| Mediterranean |
| Semi arid |
| Arid |
| Subtropical |
| Tropical |
| Mountainous |

seasons are marked by changes in wind and rainfall. These conditions are ideal for vegetation and consequently these areas contain the greatest rain forests in the world. The most well known are the Amazon rain forest of Brazil, the Congo basin of Central Africa and the jungles of Malaysia and Indonesia. In moist tropical rain forests it rains nearly every day and is hot and humid throughout the year. The subtropics are the zones of the Earth immediately north and south of the Tropics of Cancer and Capricorn and include the regions of coastal California, southern Florida, northern India, coastal Australia and coastal South Africa. Subtropical regions usually have distinctly wet or dry seasons.

The arid regions contain the hot deserts and semi-desert regions that occupy one-fifth of the world's land surface. Deserts are made in different ways, but are always formed because there is not enough water – they receive an average annual precipitation of less than 250 millimetres. They usually have an extreme temperature range: daytime temperatures can be over 50°C but nights are

often extremely cold. Deserts are thought to support very little life, but in fact they are often home to a high diversity of animal life; many of these remain hidden during daylight hours to control body temperature or to limit moisture needs. The semi-arid regions are found in the interiors of the continents and contain vast areas of grassland. They develop where there is too little precipitation for trees to grow. The soil is too moist to be a desert, but too dry to support normal forest life. Various names are given to these grasslands, including prairie (North America), steppe

DESERT LANDSCAPES
Sand dunes in the Namib Desert, South Africa.

SUBTROPICAL FOREST
Tree ferns thrive in hot and humid conditions.

(Russia), veld (South Africa) and pampas (South America).

Despite the name, regions with a Mediterranean climate are not limited to countries fringing the Mediterranean Sea. There are Mediterranean climates between 30° and 40° north and south of the Equator, for example parts of the USA including California, much of South Africa and southern Australia, northern parts of Chile and Argentina and much of the North Island, New Zealand. Summers are hot and winters are usually warm enough for plants to grow. Frost and snow are rare except over mountains. The Mediterranean climate is ideal for growing many fruits, especially grapes, melons and citrus and many of these areas are important wine producers.

The temperate regions of the world lie between the tropics and the polar circles. The changes in climate between summer and winter are generally relatively subtle; however, a temperate climate can have very unpredictable weather. Temperate climates include northern Europe, British Columbia, Oregon and Washington State in North America, southern Chile, Tasmania and South Island, New Zealand. Conditions are generally favourable for abundant plant and animal life and approximately 80 per cent of the world's population live in temperate zones.

The subarctic climate is characterized by long, cold winters, and brief, warm summers. In winter temperatures can drop to −40°C and in summer they may exceed 30°C. With six to seven consecutive months when the average temperature is below freezing, all moisture in the soil and subsoil freezes solidly to depths of many metres. Vegetation consists almost entirely of conifers, which survive extreme cold and are not easily damaged by snow. Animal such as deer, brown bears and wolves can survive in these conditions.

The polar climate is the harshest climate on Earth and it occurs within the Arctic and Antarctic circles. These regions are cold, icy deserts – the lowest temperature recorded being −89°C. The Antarctic region around the South Pole includes a huge continent

ANTARCTIC
Crab-eater seals lie on the Antarctic ice.

TEMPERATE CLIMATE
Plentiful rainfall and mild temperatures mean that a great variety of plants grow in temperate zones.

almost covered with ice and snow and a deep ocean partly covered by floating ice even in the summer. Antarctica has such a harsh climate that people have never settled there permanently. The northern polar region is an ocean basin surrounded by land. Floating ice covers much of the Arctic Ocean all year round. In warmer parts of the Arctic territory, ice and snow disappear in summer and tundra plants grow on the stony ground. During the summer months in the polar regions, many types of small plants and millions of insects enjoy their brief life cycle, especially in the Arctic as migratory birds fly in. Year-round natural inhabitants are mostly restricted to seals, sea lions and penguins in the south, and polar bears, seals and walruses in the north.

Mountain climates often differ from one another – a mountain on the Equator will experience a different weather pattern from one nearer the poles – but in general mountain regions are characterized by cooler temperatures, higher winds and more precipitation than the surrounding area. The colder temperature means that precipitation often falls as snow in the mountains.

THE EARTH

The Earth formed about 4.6 billion years ago in a disc of interstellar dust and gas surrounding our newborn Sun. Over a long period of time, the dust and gas began to coalesce as a result of gravity, eventually forming large clumps of rock or gas that became planets of the Solar System. Much of the remaining debris was cleared out of the Solar System by solar winds or it crashed into the developing planets leaving large craters. Any such impact events on Earth have long since been covered up by its ever-changing surface, but the heavily cratered surface of the moon hints at the intense level of bombardment the Earth might have suffered early in its history. Indeed the

EARTH
The Earth viewed from space. The Earth is the fifth largest planet in the solar system and the only one known to support life.

moon itself may have been created when an exceptionally large object collided with the Earth early in its history causing a part of the planet to break away and so create its own satellite. Some of the debris remains within the solar system and is evident as meteor showers and comets.

The Earth is 12,756 kilometres in diameter. At its centre lies a solid iron inner core about 2,300 kilometres in diameter. This is enveloped by a molten iron-nickel outer core 2,270 kilometres thick. Man has never been to these depths, but we have learned about the internal makeup of the planet by observing the behaviour of shockwaves as they make their way through the Earth following an earthquake.

Surrounding the outer core is a semi-molten layer of rock and magma called the

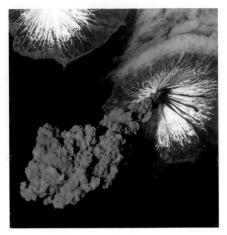

MOUNT CLEVELAND VOLCANO
Smoke pours out of the Mount Cleveland volcano in the Aleutian Island chain, Alaska, at the start of an eruption in 2006. Volcanic activity in the region is caused when the Pacific Plate slides beneath the North American plate in a process known as subduction.

mantle, which is about 2,885 kilometres thick, and above the mantle is the Earth's crust, which averages just 30 kilometres in depth. Compared to the thickness of the crust the variations on the Earth's surface are slight: The tallest mountain, Everest, is 8,850 metres high while the deepest trench, the Mariana in the Pacific Ocean, is 11,034 metres deep. In contrast the exosphere, the outer limit of the Earth's atmosphere, extends to a height of approximately 2,000 kilometres.

The surface of the Earth, the crust, is not static but is composed of a series of interlocking plates which are in a continual state of motion. The energy that drives this movement originates from the nuclear reactions that take place deep within the Earth's core. This energy creates convection currents that force magma up between some plates which forces them apart. This process, known as seafloor spreading, is taking place

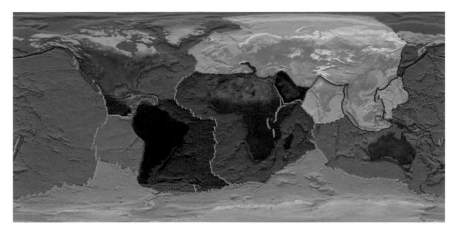

THE MAJOR PLATES
The location of the major plates of the Earth. The areas along the boundaries between the plates often experience volcanic or earthquake activity or both.

in mid Atlantic and is causing the distance between the continents of America and Europe to gradually increase. As the plates spread apart at one edge so they are pushed together at others. The exact consequence of these collisions depends upon the nature of the plates involved. Oceanic plates are made of basaltic rocks, which are heavier than the rocks found on continental plates and so when a collision occurs, the oceanic plate is forced beneath the lighter continental plate into the mantle below. This causes a build-up of pressure, which is eventually released through volcanic eruptions near the

coast on the continental plate. The water that is displaced during this process can cause tsunamis, such as the Asian tsunami of December 2004, which killed an estimated quarter of a million people. When two oceanic plates collide they behave in a similar manner; one is forced beneath the other, but the addition of water can create an even

SAN ANDREAS FAULT
The San Andreas Fault is approximately 1300 kilometres long and runs across the coastal area of California, one of the most populated areas on Earth. The largest earthquake to hit the area was in San Francisco in 1906 but the most recent major tremor was 1989, when an 800-metre stretch of road in the city collapsed.

more devastating build-up of pressure until there is an almighty volcanic eruption. The most famous example of this is Krakatoa, near Indonesia, in 1883. The eruption was so powerful that it was reportedly heard in Australia and Africa. When two continental plates collide the result is somewhat different; the plates buckle, either causing earthquakes or the formation of mountains. The world's greatest mountain range, the Himalayas, was formed in just such a fashion when the Indian plate crashed into the Eurasian plate. Alternatively, the plates can slide past each other, causing friction that can result in powerful earthquakes, such as those along the San Andreas Fault in California.

The movement of the plates has resulted in the original single continental landmass named 'Pangea' breaking up into the seven continents that we know today. It has also been responsible for the formation of the four vast oceans; the Pacific, Atlantic, Indian and Arctic Oceans which account for the majority of the 71 per cent of the Earth's surface that is covered with water. While the movement of the Earth's plates has created the familiar pattern of land and sea, the landscapes that give the Earth its character are the result of other forces, mainly associated with climate, that through erosion and deposition have reduced mountains to plains, diverted rivers and created and destroyed seas.

WORLD POPULATION

Since the earliest beginnings of humankind the peoples of the Earth have been in constant movement, spreading their influence across the globe. It is generally accepted that humankind emerged from eastern and southern Africa around 100,000 years ago. From these beginnings, *Homo sapiens* or 'wise man' began to migrate, heading initially into Asia becoming the ancestors of the Mongoloid people. Some 40,000 years ago the ancestors of the Caucasian peoples began to migrate into western Asia and then Europe; the Negroid peoples remained in Africa. Lowered sea levels during the last great Ice Age exposed land bridges, enabling the spread of populations into the Americas and parts of Australasia. The development of important new technologies such as boat building provided access to the more remote lands of Oceania by people who were ethnically related.

At first our ancestors were hunter-gatherers, constantly moving in search of food, living in caves or making shelters from wood and animal skins. Developing agriculture, realizing the power of harnessing nature and other species, allowed people to settle in one place and begin to build permanent settlements, a major step towards a more advanced civilization. The earliest civilizations are generally considered to have sprung up within the fertile regions of the Middle East around 10,000 years ago and there is evidence of civilized communities appearing in parts of China, South-east Asia, Africa, Greece and Meso-America within the next several thousand

LASCAUX CAVES
The paintings on the walls of the caves at Lascaux are believed to date back at least 15,000 years.

years. Although these earliest communities were, by today's standards, primitive they developed quickly over the coming millennia. With the advent of trade, cultural developments could be shared and histories became entwined as wars and invasions became a common feature. What we now consider to be the four world religions, Christianity, Islam, Hinduism and Judaism, were all born and spread across the globe, in many cases extinguishing far older and disparate cultural practices.

During the period usually referred to as the Dark Ages, following the fall of the Roman Empire, Europe was at the centre of a period of growth and development and nation states began to form. The European discovery of the Americas by Christopher Columbus in 1492 changed the demographic history of the 'New World' forever; the face of the Americas would be profoundly

changed yet again by the African diaspora that resulted from the slave trade begun in the sixteenth century and lasting until 1865. Societies shifted away from purely agrarian based economies and urban centres began to evolve; in 1800 only 3 per cent of the world's population lived in cities, by the end of the twentieth century this number had risen to 47 per cent and the percentage is still rising. According to United Nations figures, some 3.2 billion people live in cities today and one third of this number survive in slums and shanty towns.

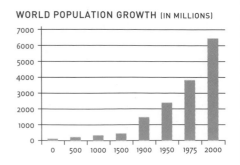

WORLD POPULATION GROWTH (IN MILLIONS)

POPULATION GROWTH
The population of the world has risen rapidly during the twentieth century.

The world's population began to grow steadily with the most rapid growth rates seen during the twentieth century when developments in science and medicine resulted in decreasing mortality rates. At the time of writing, the world's population is estimated to be around 6.80 billion, with China and then India being the two most highly populated countries. In developed nations these vast numbers are managed, despite the challenges created by large urban sprawls. Undeveloped countries struggle with issues related to population sizes; for instance in parts of Africa where a lack of clean water increases the risk of diseases such as typhoid and where famine remains a constant threat for many millions.

Although today we may consider that international boundaries are fixed this is not necessarily so. Since the tumultuous wars of the twentieth century, and despite the

WORLD'S MOST POPULATED AREAS (population in thousands)

1950		2000		2015 (PROJECTED FIGURE)	
NEW YORK	12,339	TOKYO	26,444	TOKYO	27,190
LONDON	8,733	MEXICO CITY	18,066	DHAKA	22,766
TOKYO	6,920	SÃO PAULO	17,962	MUMBAI	22,577
PARIS	5,441	NEW YORK	16,732	SÃO PAULO	21,229
MOSCOW	5,356	MUMBAI	16,086	DELHI	20,884
SHANGHAI	5,333	LOS ANGELES	13,213	MEXICO CITY	20,434
RHEIN-RUHR NORTH	5,296	CALCUTTA	13,058	NEW YORK	17,944
BUENOS AIRES	5,042	SHANGHAI	12,887	JAKARTA	17,268

Statistics from the UN

emergence of powerful economic blocs such as the USA, the Soviet Union, and China, assertions of independence have continued. Independent countries re-emerged as colonial powers lost their hold as has been seen in Africa, India and Pakistan and South America, whilst ethnic divisions have resulted in splits such as with the Balkan states once belonging to the former Republic of Yugoslavia. In the wake of the Second World War, the United Nations was formed to ensure stability and to encourage peace through international arbitration. First convening

in 1946, the United Nations consists of a network of international organizations including the Security Council, the General Assembly, the Economic and Social Council and the International Courts of Justice. Over the course of the past six decades it has had plenty of work; from dealing with the tensions in the Middle East to responding to natural disasters such as the Asian tsunami in 2004 and the Aids Crisis in Africa.

The countries in this book are organized according to the United Nations census areas and in each entry there is a summary of the economic and social challenges faced as well as details of the economic strengths of individual nations. As our global community faces up to the challenges presented by a worldwide economic depression, this book clearly outlines the web of trading partnerships and agreements which go some way to explaining the important links between so many nations. And so despite the international boundaries and borders clearly presented by the maps offered here, this book serves to highlight the interconnectedness of the world we live in today.

HONG KONG
Hong Kong is one of the most densely populated territories in the world. Almost 7 million people inhabit an area of just over 1,100 square kilometres.

RUSSIAN
FEDERATION

Chukchi
Sea

Beaufort
Sea

Banks

Queen Elizabeth
Islands

Parry
Islands

Parry Channel

Ellesmere

Nares Strait

Gr

Devon

Greenland
(Kalaallit Nunaat)
(DK)

Ja

Brooks Range

Amundsen
Gulf

Victoria

Baffin
Bay

ALASKA
(US)

Alaska Range
Mt McKinley
6194 m

Mt. Logan
5959 m

Gulf of
Alaska

Yukon

Mackenzie

Great Bear Lake

Baffin

Foxe
Basin

Davis Strait

Denmark Strait

Arctic C

ICELAND

Aleutian
Basin

Bering
Sea

Great Slave
Lake

Hudson
Strait

Faroe Islands (DK)

Aleutian Islands

Aleutian Range

Aleutian Trench

Queen Charlotte
Islands

Coast Mountains

C A N A D A

Hudson
Bay

Labrador
Sea

1. BOSNIA HERZEGOVINA
2. MONTENEGRO
3. KOSOVO
4. LIECHTENSTEIN

REPUBLIC
OF IRELAND

U
KIN

Vancouver

Rocky Mountains

L. Winnipeg

Laurentian
Plateau

Canadian Shield

Newfoundland

Bay of
Biscay

Northeast Pacific Basin

NORTH

PACIFIC

OCEAN

Missouri

Fraser

Coast Ranges

Snake

Sierra Nevada

Great
Salt
Lake

UNITED STATES
OF AMERICA

L. Superior

L. Michigan

L. Huron

L. Ontario

L. Erie

Nova Scotia

North
America
Basin

NORTH

ATLANTIC

OCEAN

Azores
(PT)

PORTUGAL

SPA

Hawai'ian Islands
(US)

Mt. Elbert
4398 m

Appalachian Mtns

Ozark
Plateau

Colorado

Ohio

Bermuda
(UK)

Madeira
(PT)

Strait of Gibr

MOROCCO

Atlas M

Hawai'ian Ridge

Tropic of Cancer

Mt. Whitney
4418 m

Arkansas

Mississippi

Rio Grande

Baja California

Sierra Madre Occidental

Edwards
Plateau

MEXICO

Gulf of
Mexico

THE BAHAMAS

Sargasso
Sea

Nares
Deep

Canary Islands
(ES)

WESTERN
SAHARA

S

MAURITANIA

M

Yucatan

CUBA

HAITI

Greater Antilles

DOMINICAN
REP.

Puerto Rico (US)

CAPE VERDE

SENEGAL

THE GAMBIA

Ni

Equator

BELIZE

GUATEMALA

HONDURAS

EL SALVADOR

NICARAGUA

JAMAICA

Caribbean
Sea

ANTIGUA

DOMINICA

Guadeloupe (FR)

Martinique (FR)

Lesser Antilles

ST. LUCIA

ST. VINCENT

BARBODAS

GRENADA

GUINEA-BISSAU

GUINEA

SIERRA LEONE

LIBERIA

COTE
D'IVOIRE

Gulf

Guatemala
Basin

COSTA RICA

TRINIDAD AND TOBAGO

Guinea
Basin

Cocos Ridge

PANAMA

VENEZUELA

GUYANA

SURINAM

FRENCH
GUIANA
(FR)

Guiana
Basin

Galapagos
Islands
(EC)

Cotopaxi
5896 m

COLOMBIA

Amazon

Îles Marquises

ECUADOR

Chimborazo
6310 m

PERU

Amazon
Basin

São Francisco

P o l y n e s i a

Andes

B R A Z I L

L. Titicaca

Brazilian
Highlands

St Helena
(UK)

Tuamotu Islands

Society Islands

Peru-Chile Trench

Nazca Ridge

BOLIVIA

Paraguay

Brazil
Basin

Austral Islands

East Pacific Rise

Peru
Basin

Atacama Desert

PARAGUAY

Paraná

COOK
ISLANDS

Pitcairn
Islands
(UK)

Tropic of Capricorn

Cerro Aconcagua
6959 m

Andes

CHILE

Uruguay

Pampas

ARGENTINA

URUGUAY

Tristan da
Cunha
(UK)

AT

SOUTH

PACIFIC

OCEAN

Chile Rise

Patagonia

Argentine
Basin

Falkland
Islands (UK)

South
Georgia
(UK)

South Sandwich
Islands
(UK)

South Sandwich Trench

Scotia Ridge

Pacific-Antarctic Ridge

Southeast Pacific Basin

Drake Passage

South Shetland
Islands
(UK)

South Orkney
Islands
(UK)

Van der Grinten Projection
1:92,700,000

Peter I

Bellingshausen Sea

Thurston

Weddell
Sea

A

0   1000   2000   3000 Km

0   500   1000 Miles

East of Greenwich   180°   West of Greenwich

ARCTIC OCEAN

Zemlya Frantsa-Iosifa
Severnaya Zemlya
Poluostrov Taymyr
Laptev Sea
New Siberian Islands
East Siberian Sea
ALASKA (US)
Bering Strait

Novaya Zemlya
Kara Sea
Barents Sea
White Sea
Bering Sea
Aleutian Basin
Aleutian Islands
Aleutian Trench

FINLAND
West Siberian Plain
Central Siberian Plateau
Verkhoyanskiy Khrebet
Kolymskiy Khrebet
Lena
Kolyma
Kamchatka
Emperor Seamount Chain

ESTONIA
LATVIA
LITHUANIA
RUSSIAN FEDERATION
Pechora
Yenisey
Ob'
Stanovoy Khrebet
Sea of Okhotsk
Sakhalin
Kuril Islands
Kuril Trench
Northwest Pacific Basin

L. Onega
L. Ladoga
BELARUS
UKRAINE
Ural Mountains
Volga
Tobol
Irtysh
Angara
L. Baikal
Amur
Manchurian Plain
Hokkaido
Kuril Trench
PACIFIC OCEAN

MOLDOVA
ROMANIA
SERBIA
BULGARIA
KAZAKHSTAN
Syrdar'ya
L. Balkhash
Altai Mountains
MONGOLIA
Gobi Desert
Huang He
NORTH KOREA
Sea of Japan
Honshū
JAPAN
Japan Trench

MACEDONIA
ALBANIA
GREECE
TURKEY
Black Sea
Caucasus
GEORGIA
ARMENIA
AZERBAIJAN
Aral Sea
UZBEKISTAN
KYRGYZSTAN
Tien Shan
Tarim Pendi
Taklimakan Desert
Qilian Shan
Kunlun Shan
YELLOW Sea
SOUTH KOREA
Shikoku
Kyushu
Ryukyu Islands
East China Sea
Mid-Pacific Mountains

Anatolia
CYPRUS
SYRIA
LEBANON
ISRAEL
IRAQ
JORDAN
Caspian Sea
Amudar'ya
TURKMENISTAN
TAJIKISTAN
K2 8611 m
ANSAI CHIN
CHINA
Plateau of Tibet
Yangtze
Xun Jiang
TAIWAN
Luzon Strait
Philippine Basin
FEDERATED STATES OF MICRONESIA
MARSHALL ISLANDS

Libyan Desert
EGYPT
Red Sea
SAUDI ARABIA
Elburz Mts.
Zagros Mts.
IRAN
AFGHANISTAN
JAMMU AND KASHMIR
PAKISTAN
HIMALAYA
NEPAL
Mt. Everest 8850 m
BHUTAN
Brahmaputra
Ganges
Mekong
VIETNAM
LAOS
South China Sea
Luzon
PHILIPPINES
Mariana Islands (US)
Mariana Trench
Philippine Sea
Melanesia

BAHRAIN
QATAR
UAE
OMAN
Arabian Basin
INDIA
Deccan Plateau
Eastern Ghats
Western Ghats
Bay of Bengal
MYANMAR
Irrawaddy
THAILAND
CAMBODIA
Mindanao
PALAU
KIRIBATI

SUDAN
ERITREA
YEMEN
DJIBOUTI
Arabian Sea
MALDIVES
SRI LANKA
Andaman & Nicobar Islands (IN)
BRUNEI
Celebes Sea
NAURU

CENTRAL AFRICAN REP.
ETHIOPIA
SOMALIA
Somali Basin
SEYCHELLES
Carlsberg Ridge
Chagos Archipelago
MALAYSIA
SINGAPORE
Borneo
Sulawesi
New Ireland
New Britain
SOLOMON ISLANDS
TUVALU
SAMOA

DEM. REP. OF CONGO
UGANDA
KENYA
Kilimanjaro 5895 m
Victoria
RWANDA
BURUNDI
TANZANIA
L. Tanganyika
Sumatra
Java Sea
Java
INDONESIA
Java Trench
EAST TIMOR
PAPUA NEW GUINEA
Mt. Wilhelm 4509 m
Coral Basin
VANUATU
FIJI

ZAMBIA
MALAWI
COMOROS
Mayotte (FR)
MOZAMBIQUE
MADAGASCAR
MOZAMBIQUE Channel
Madagascar Ridge
Madagascar Basin
INDIAN OCEAN
Mid-Indian Ridge
Ninetyeast Ridge
West Australian Basin
Timor Sea
Arafura Sea
Torres Strait
Kimberley Plateau
Coral Sea
New Caledonia (FR)
TONGA
South Fiji Basin

ZIMBABWE
BOTSWANA
SWAZILAND
LESOTHO
SOUTH AFRICA
Kalahari Desert
Orange
Réunion (FR)
MAURITIUS
Mid-Indian Basin
Broken Plateau
Great Sandy Desert
Macdonnell Ranges
AUSTRALIA
Great Victoria Desert
Great Dividing Range
Lord Howe Rise
Darling

Perth Basin
Nullarbor Plain
Great Australian Bight
Murray
L. Eyre
Mt. Kosciuszko 2229 m
Bass Strait
Tasman Sea
Tasmania
NEW ZEALAND
North Island
Kermadec-Dacca Late

Amsterdam (FR)
St. Paul (FR)
South Australian Basin
Southeast Indian Ridge

Crozet Islands (FR)
Prince Edward Islands (ZA)
Kerguelen (FR)
McDonald Islands (AU)

SOUTHERN OCEAN

...an-Antarctic Basin
Australian-Antarctic Basin
Indian-Antarctic Ridge
Campbell Plateau
South Island
Southwest Pacific Basin

ANTARCTICA
Antarctic Circle
Pacific-Antarctic Ridge

East of Greenwich   West of Greenwich

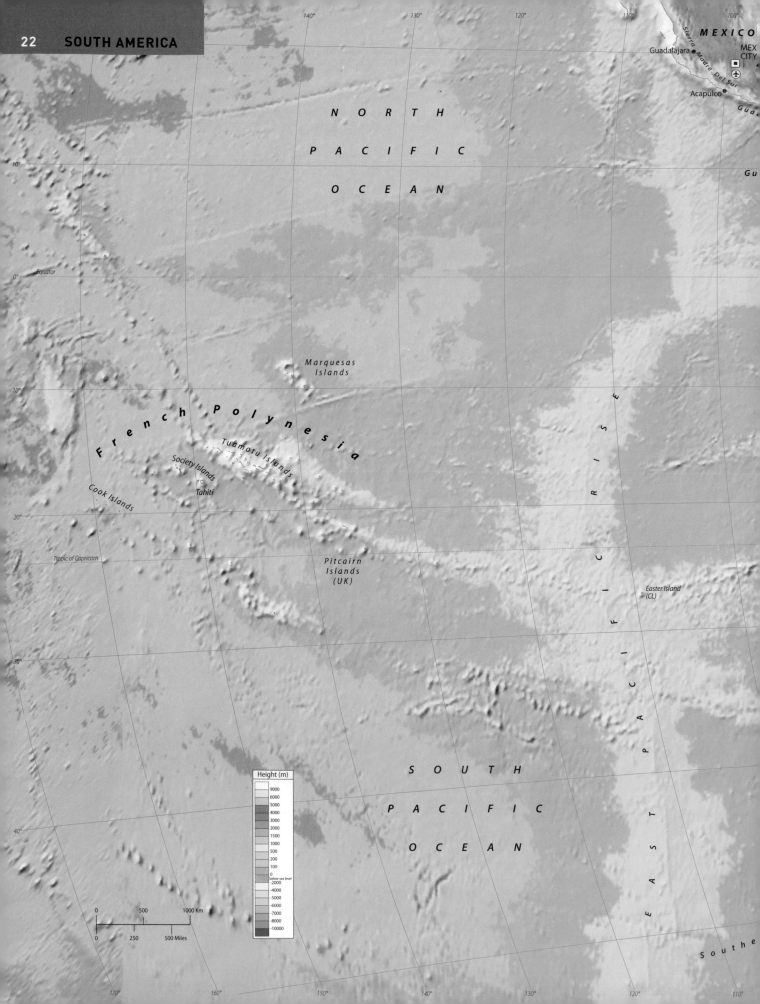

MEXICO

MEX
CITY

Guadalajara

Acapulco

Sierra Madre Del Sur

Gua

Gu

N O R T H

P A C I F I C

O C E A N

Equator

*Marquesas
Islands*

F r e n c h   P o l y n e s i a

Tuamotu Islands

Society Islands

Cook Islands

Tahiti

Tropic of Capricorn

*Pitcairn
Islands
(UK)*

*Easter Island
(CL)*

P A C I F I C   R I S E

E A S T

P A C I F I C

S O U T H

P A C I F I C

O C E A N

Southe

Height (m)

9000
6000
5000
4000
3000
2000
1500
1000
500
200
100
0
below sea level
-2000
-4000
-5000
-6000
-7000
-8000
-10000

0   500   1000 Km

0   250   500 Miles

NORTH

ATLANTIC

OCEAN

CAPE VERDE

HAVANA

Yucatan Channel

Greater Antilles

CUBA

Turks and
Caicos Islands (UK)

Sargasso Sea

DOMINICAN
HAITI
REPUBLIC

PORT-AU-PRINCE

SAN JUAN

Puerto Rico Trench

JAMAICA

KINGSTON

SANTO
DOMINGO

PUERTO RICO
(US)

Leeward Islands

BELIZE

BELMOPAN

Antigua

Guadeloupe (FR)

Venezuelan
Basin

HONDURAS

TEGUCIGALPA

OR

NICARAGUA

MANAGUA

Caribbean Sea

Dominica

Martinique (FR)

St. Lucia

Lesser Antilles

Grenada

Barbados

Windward Islands

L. Nicaragua

COSTA
RICA

SAN JOSÉ

PANAMÁ
CITY

Barranquilla

Maracaibo

CARACAS

PORT-OF-SPAIN

TRINIDAD AND TOBAGO

Cocos Ridge

PANAMA

Gulf of
Panama

Valencia

VENEZUELA

Orinoco

GEORGETOWN

PARAMARIBO

Medellín

BOGOTÁ

COLOMBIA

GUYANA

SURINAME

CAYENNE

French Guiana (FR)

Guiana Highlands

Guiana
Basin

QUITO

ECUADOR

Chimborazo
6310 m

Negro

Macapa

Amazon

Belém

Fortaleza

Gulf of
Guayaquil

Putumayo

Amazon

Represa de
Balbina

Manaus

SOUTH

AMERICA

Natal

Marañón

Amazon
Basin

Madeira

Tapajós

Xingu

Teresina

Recife

PERU

Nevado Huascarán
6768 m

Purus

BRAZIL

Represa de
Sobradinho

Maceió

Aracaju

Chimbote

Ucayali

Feira de
Santana

São Francisco

Salvador

LIMA

Peru Basin

Nazca Ridge

Arica

BOLIVIA

Lake
Titicaca

LA PAZ

SUCRE

Mato Grosso

BRASÍLIA

Araguaia

Cuiabá

Goiânia

Brazilian Highlands

Belo
Horizonte

Vitória

Brazil

Basin

Chile Trench

PARAGUAY

Pilcomayo

Campo
Grande

São José do
Rio Preto

São
Paulo

Rio de Janeiro

Antofagasta

Atacama Desert

Gran Chaco

Paraguay

Paraná

Ourinhos

Santos

ASUNCIÓN

Curitiba

Paranaguá

Chile

Basin

ARGENTINA

Uruguay

Santa
Maria

Porto Alegre

Cerro Aconcagua
6959 m

Mendoza

San
Luis

Río Cuarto

URUGUAY

Río Grande

SOUTH

SANTIAGO

Juan Fernández
Islands
(CL)

San Rafael

BUENOS
AIRES

MONTEVIDEO

Río de la Plata

Argentine Rise

ATLANTIC

Talcahuano

Santa Rosa

Pampa

Mar del
Plata

OCEAN

Concepción

Colorado

Bahía Blanca

Neuquen

Río Negro

u

in

Puerto Montt

Isla de Chiloé

Península
Valdés

Argentine

Basin

Chile Rise

Patagonia

Chica

Gulf of San Jorge

Comodoro Rivadavia

Península de
Taitao

Golfo de Penas

ic Basin

Falkland Islands
(UK)

Stanley

South Georgia
Islands (UK)

South Sandwich Trench

Bahía
Grande

Strait of Magellan

Scotia Ridge

Punta Arenas

Monte Darwin
2438 m

Cape Horn

South Sandwich
Islands (UK)

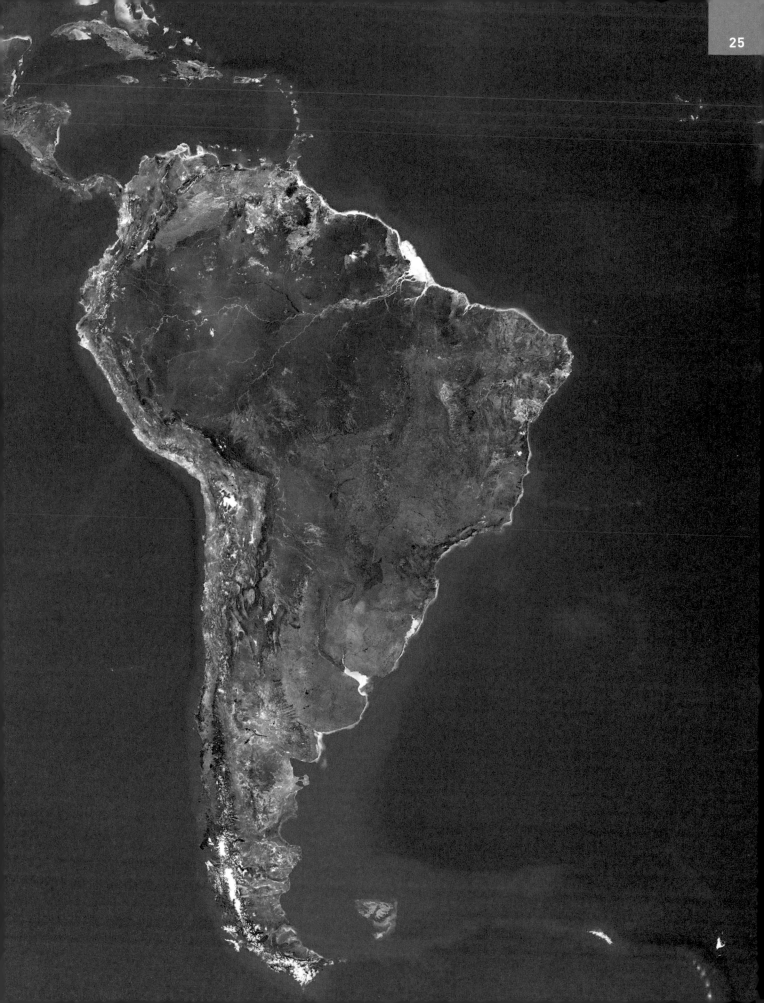

A R C T I C   O C E A N

West of Greenwich | East of Greenwich

Greenland
(Kalaallit Nunaat)
(DK)

Zemlya Frantsa-Iosifa

Nordaustlandet

Spitsbergen

Svalbard
(NO)

Greenland
Sea

Greenland
Basin

Barents
Sea

Jan Mayen (NO)

Norwegian Basin

Murmansk

Kola
Peninsula

Denmark Strait

Arctic Circle

White
Sea

Archangel

ICELAND

REYKJAVÍK

Norwegian Sea

Scandinavia

L. Onega

R

Reykjanes Ridge

Iceland Basin

Faroe Islands (DK)

Shetland
Islands

Orkney
Islands

Outer Hebrides

Wyville Thomson Ridge

Rokall
Bank

SWEDEN

NORWAY

FINLAND

L. Ladoga

St. Petersburg

Bergen

OSLO

HELSINKI

Gulf of Bothnia

Volga

Niz
No

Edinburgh

Belfast

DUBLIN

Manchester

IRELAND

UNITED
KINGDOM

Leeds

Birmingham

Cardiff

North
Sea

DENMARK

COPENHAGEN

Odense

Göteborg

STOCKHOLM

L. Vänern

Baltic Sea

TALLINN

ESTONIA

RĪGA

LATVIA

LITHUANIA

RUS. FED.

VILNIUS

MINSK

BELARUS

MOSCOW

Dnieper

Don

Height (m)
9000
6000
5000
4000
3000
2000
1500
1000
500
200
0
below sea level
-2000
-4000
-5000
-6000
-7000
-8000
-9000
-10000

1. LIECHTENSTEIN
2. KOSOVO
3. MACEDONIA

N O R T H

A T L A N T I C

O C E A N

Van der Grinten Projection
1:37 000 000

Azores
(PT)

Madeira
(PT)

English Channel

LONDON

BRUSSELS

BELGIUM

LUXEMBOURG

NETHERLANDS

AMSTERDAM

Rotterdam

Hamburg

BERLIN

GERMANY

Dresden

PRAGUE

CZECH REPUBLIC

Gdansk

POLAND

Łódź

Wrocław

WARSAW

Kraków

Vistula

KIEV

UKRAINE

Dnipropetrovs'k

Donets'k

Rostov-
na Donu

MOLDOVA

CHIŞINĂU

Odessa

Sea of
Azov

Brest

PARIS

Seine

Strasbourg

Loire

FRANCE

Nantes

VADUZ

BERN

SWITZERLAND

VIENNA

BRATISLAVA

AUSTRIA

SLOVAKIA

BUDAPEST

HUNGARY

Carpathian Mts.

Dniester

ROMANIA

BUCHAREST

Black Sea

GEORGIA

ARME

Bay of
Biscay

Biscay
Abyssal Plain

Lyon

Rhône

Turin

Po

Genoa

SLOVENIA

LJUBLJANA

ZAGREB

CROATIA

BOS.-HERZ.

SARAJEVO

BELGRADE

SERBIA

PODGORICA

MONTENEGRO

SOFIA

BULGARIA

PRISHTINE

SKOPJE

Istanbul

Samsun

Bilbao

Toulouse

Marseille

MONACO

Corsica (FR)

SAN
MARINO

ROME

VATICAN
CITY

ITALY

Naples

TIRANA

ALBANIA

Aegean
Sea

GREECE

ATHENS

Izmir

ANKARA

Anatolia

TURKEY

Erzurum

Adana

Aleppo

Oporto

PORTUGAL

Zaragoza

MADRID

Iberian

Ebro

Pyrenees

ANDORRA
LA VELLA

Barcelona

Tagus

Sardinia
(IT)

M

Ionian
Sea

NICOSIA

CYPRUS

SYRIA

BEIRUT

LEBANON

DAMASCUS

LISBON

SPAIN

Seville

Valencia

Peninsula

Balearic Islands (ES)

Cagliari

Palermo

Sicily

MALTA

VALLETTA

Crete

JERUSALEM

ISRAEL

GAZA

AMMAN

JORDAN

RABAT

Casablanca

Marrakech

MOROCCO

ALGIERS

ALGERIA

TUNIS

TUNISIA

TRIPOLI

LIBYA

Strait of Gibraltar

EGYPT

Mediterranean Sea

500   1000 Km
250   500 Miles

N

E U R O P E

Severnaya Zemlya

Kara Sea

New Siberian Islands

East Siberian Sea

Laptev Sea

Poluostrov Taymyr

R U S S I A N   F E D E R A T I O N

Verkhoyanskiy Khrebet

Verkhoyansk

Noril'sk

Igarka

Vilyuy

Vorkuta

70°

Arctic Circle

Salekhard

Yakutsk

Lena

Aldan

60°

West Siberian Plain

C e n t r a l   S i b e r i a n   P l a t e a u

Ob

Tobol

Yenisey

S t a n o v o y   K h r e b e t

n

Yekaterinburg

Amur

U r a l   M o u n t a i n s

Ufa

Chelyabinsk

Omsk

Novosibirsk

L. Baikal

Angara

Chita

Irtysh

Novokuznetsk

Irkutsk

50°

Ural

ASTANA

Karaganda

Altai Mountains

Uliastay

ULAN BATOR

Harbin

Manchurian Plain

KAZAKHSTAN

L. Balkhash

M O N G O L I A

Aral Sea

Syrdarya

BISHKEK

Almaty

G o b i   D e s e r t

Shenyang

UZBEKISTAN

KYRGYZSTAN

Tien Shan

Baotou

Anshan

TASHKENT

Samarqand

Tarim Pendi

Altun Shan

Huang He

BEIJING

Tangshan

Dalian

TURKMENISTAN

Kashi

Tianjin

Shijiazhuang

Amudarya

TAJIKISTAN

Qilian Shan

Taiyuan

Zibo

AŞGABAT

DUSHANBE

Takla Makan Desert

Qinghai Hu

Yellow Sea

Mountains

Mashhad

Hindu Kush

Kunlun Shan

Lanzhou

Luoyang

TEHRĀN

KABUL

Karakoram Range

8611 m

C H I N A

Xi'an

Herāt

JAMMU AND KASHMIR

AKSAI CHIN

Plateau of Tibet

Yangtze

Nanjing

IRAN

AFGHANISTAN

ISLAMABAD

H I M A L A Y A

Chengdu

Wuhan

Shanghai

Esfahān

Kandahār

Faisalabad

Mekong

Chongqing

Yazd

PAKISTAN

INDIA

Lhasa

Salween

Yangtze

80°

90°

100°

110°

120°

130°

140°

150°

160°

60°

70°

90°

100°

110°

ARCTIC

Zemlya Frantsa - Iosifa

Nordaustlandet

Spitsbergen

Svalbard
(NO)

Severnaya Zemlya

Poluos
Tayn

Novaya Zemlya

Barents
Sea

Kara
Sea

Noril'sk

Norwegian Sea

NORWAY

Murmansk

Kola
Peninsula

Vorkuta

Igarka

Scandinavia

Salekhard

West Siberian
Plain

SWEDEN

White
Sea

Pechora

Arctic Circle

Archangel

R   U   S   S   I   A   N   F   E   D

FINLAND

Central
Ple

HELSINKI

L. Ladoga

L. Onega

Kotlas

Kama

Baltic
Sea

TALLINN

St. Petersburg

Gulf of Bothnia

European Plain

ESTONIA

Perm'

Yekaterinburg

Ural Mountains

LATVIA

RIGA

Volga

Nizhniy
Novgorod

Tobol

Yenisey

LITHUANIA

N O

VILNIUS

MOSCOW

Kazan'

Ufa

Chelyabinsk

Omsk

Novosibirsk

MINSK

Novokuznetsk

BELARUS

Samara

Irtysh

Volga

Ural

Altai Mountains

KIEV

Nikolayevsk

ASTANA

Uliastay

UKRAINE

Khaskiv

Karaganda

Dnieper

MOLDOVA

Donets'k

Volgograd

KAZAKHSTAN

CHIŞINĂU

Don

Rostov-na-Donu

ROMANIA

Odessa

Sea of
Azov

Astrakhan

Syr Dar'ya

L. Balkhash

Ürümqi

BUCHAREST

Elbrus
5642 m

Caspian

Aral
Sea

BULGARIA

Black Sea

GEORGIA

BISHKEK

Almaty

GO
DESL

Istanbul

Samsun

T'BILISI

Amu Dar'ya

UZBEKISTAN

TASHKENT

Ysyk-Köl

Tian Shan

ANKARA

ARMENIA

AZERBAIJAN

KYRGYZSTAN

C H I

Izmir

Erzurum

YEREVAN

Sea

TURKMENISTAN

Samarqand

Kashi

Tarim Pendi

Altun Shan

Qilian Shan

Qing

Anatolia

AZER.

BAKU

TAJIKISTAN

Taklimakan
Desert

TURKEY

Tabriz

AŞGABAT

DUSHANBE

Kunlun Shan

Adana

Murat

Elburz Mountains

Mashhad

Hindu Kush

Aleppo

Mosul

Dasht-e
Kavir

Herât

KABUL

Plateau
of Tibet

NICOSIA

SYRIA

IRAQ

TEHRAN

ISLAMABAD

Yangtze

CYPRUS

Euphrates

Esfahan

IRAN

AFGHANISTAN

Mediterranean

LEBANON

BEIRUT

DAMASCUS

BAGHDAD

Yazd

PAKISTAN

Lhasa

Sea

ISRAEL

GAZA

AMMAN

Kandahâr

INDIA

Alexandria

Giza

JERUSALEM

JORDAN

Basra

Zâhedân

Ganges

NEPAL

CAIRO

SAUDI

KUWAIT

KUWAIT

NEW DELHI

EGYPT

ARABIA

Shîrâz

Zagros Mountains

Tigris

OCEAN

International Date Line

*Laptev
Sea*

New Siberian Islands

*East
Siberian
Sea*

Chukchi
Sea

Wrangel

ALASKA
(US)

Verkhoyansk

Indigirka

Kolyma

Anadyr

Bering Strait

Lena

Vilyuy

Yakutsk

Khrebet Kolymskiy

Verkhoyanskiy Khrebet

O   N

A   T   I   O   N

Magadan

*Bering
Sea*

Stanovoy Khrebet

*Sea
of
Okhotsk*

Kamchatka

*Aleutian
Basin*

Aldan

Sakhalin

Petropavlovsk-
Kamchatskiy

Aleutian Islands

Aleutian Trench

Chita

Amur

Khabarovsk

Yuzhno-
Sakhalinsk

Kuril Islands

Kuril Trench

*Northwest
Pacific
Basin*

Emperor Seamount Chain

International Date Line

İ BATOR

Qiqihar

Manchurian Plain

Sikhote Alin

Sapporo

Hokkaidō

Harbin

Jilin

Shenyang

Vladivostok

*Japan
Basin*

N

Anshan

NORTH
KOREA

Baotou

BEIJING

Tangshan

*Korea
Bay*

P'YŎNGYANG

Aomori

*Sea of
Japan
(East Sea)*

Japan Trench

PACIFIC

Shijiazhuang

Tianjin

Dalian

Bo Hai

SEOUL

Inch'ŏn

SOUTH
KOREA

Honshū

OCEAN

Taiyuan

Jinan

Zibo

Taejŏn

JAPAN

Taegu

Pusan

TOKYO

an

Qingdao

*Yellow
Sea*

Ōsaka

Kyōto

Van der Grinten Projection
1:37 000 000

Luoyang

Korea Strait

Hiroshima

Shikoku

| Height (m) |
| 9000 |
| 6000 |
| 5000 |
| 4000 |
| 3000 |
| 2000 |
| 1500 |
| 1000 |
| 500 |
| 200 |
| 100 |
| 0 |
| below sea level |
| -2000 |
| -4000 |
| -5000 |
| -6000 |
| -7000 |
| -8000 |
| -10000 |

Nagasaki

Kita-
Kyūshū

South Honshū Ridge

0   500   1000 Km

0   250   500 Miles

Yangtze

Wuhan

Nanjing

Shanghai

Hangzhou

Kyūshū

*East
China
Sea*

Nanchang

St. Petersburg
L. Onega
L. Ladoga
ESTONIA
LATVIA
MINSK
BELARUS
KIEV
UKRAINE
Dnipropetrovs'k
Dniester
MOLDOVA
CHISINAU
Odessa
ROMANIA
BUCHAREST
BULGARIA
Istanbul
Black Sea
Samsun
CYPRUS
NICOSIA
Crete
Mediterranean Sea
Alexandria
CAIRO
Suez
Qattara Depression
EGYPT
Aswân
Lake Nasser
Nubian Desert
Port Sudan
SUDAN
KHARTOUM
El Obeid
White Nile
Blue Nile
ERITREA
ASMARA
Ras Dejen 4533 m
DJIBOUTI
DJIBOUTI
Aden
ETHIOPIA
ADDIS ABABA
Ethiopian Highlands
Horn of Africa
SOMALIA
L. Turkana
UGANDA
KAMPALA
Kisangani
RWANDA
KIGALI
BURUNDI
BUJUMBURA
DEM. REP. OF THE CONGO
Ubangi
L. Victoria
KENYA
NAIROBI
Kilimanjaro 5895 m
Mombasa
Dar es Salaam
TANZANIA
DODOMA
L. Tanganyika
L. Malawi
MALAWI
LILONGWE
ZAMBIA
Lubumbashi
Mtwara
COMOROS
MORONI
Mayotte (FR)
MADAGASCAR
MOZAMBIQUE

Kotlas
Perm
MOSCOW
Nizhniy Novgorod
Kazan'
Ufa
Samara
Volga
Don
Volgograd
Astrakhan
Rostov-na-Donu
Kharkiv
Donets'k
Nikolayevsk
Sea of Azov
Caucasus
El'brus 5642 m
GEORGIA
TBILISI
ARMENIA
YEREVAN
AZERBAIJAN
BAKU
ANKARA
Anatolia
TURKEY
Izmir
Adana
Aleppo
SYRIA
BEIRUT
LEBANON
DAMASCUS
ISRAEL
JERUSALEM
GAZA
AMMAN
JORDAN
Eastern Desert
Red Sea
Jiddah
Al Madinah
SAUDI ARABIA
RIYADH
Rub' al Khali
YEMEN
ŞAN'Ā'
Bab al Mandab
Gulf of Aden
Socotra (YE)

Pechora
Ural Mountains
Yekaterinburg
Chelyabinsk
Omsk
Tobol
Irtysh
ASTANA
Karaganda
KAZAKHSTAN
Syrdar'ya
Aral Sea
L. Balkhash
UZBEKISTAN
TASHKENT
Samarqand
Amudar'ya
TURKMENISTAN
AŞGABAT
Mashhad
Elburz Mountains
TEHRĀN
Dasht-e Kavir
IRAN
Esfahān
Yazd
BAGHDAD
IRAQ
Tigris
Euphrates
Zagros Mountains
Basra
KUWAIT
KUWAIT
Shiraz
MANAMA
BAHRAIN
RIYADH
QATAR
DOHA
UAE
ABU DHABI
The Gulf
Oman
MUSCAT
OMAN
Arabian Basin
Arabian Sea
Zāhedān
Kandahār
AFGHANISTAN
Herāt
KABUL
ISLAMABAD
JAMMU AND KASHMIR
Faisalabad
PAKISTAN
Thar Desert
Karachi
Hyderabad
Ahmadabad

Novosibirsk
Novokuznetsk
Irkutsk
Ob
Angara
Yenisey
RUSSIAN FED
Uliastay
Altai Mountains
Gobi
M
BISHKEK
Almaty
KYRGYZSTAN
Tien Shan
Kashi
TAJIKISTAN
DUSHANBE
Tarim Basin
Takla Makan Desert
Altun Shan
Qilian Shan
Kunlun Shan
Hindu Kush
K2 8611 m
AKSAI CHIN
LINE OF CONTROL
Plateau of Tibet
HIMALAYA
Lhasa
NEPAL
Mt. Everest 8848 m
NEW DELHI
Jaipur
Lucknow
Kanpur
KATHMANDU
Ganges
Patna
Varanasi
BHUTAN
THIMPHU
Brahmaputra
BANGLADESH
DHAKA
Khulna
Calcutta (Kolkata)
Chittagong
MYA
INDIA
Nagpur
Bay of Bengal
Mumbai (Bombay)
Deccan Plateau
Pune
Hyderabad
Western Ghats
Eastern Ghats
Vishakhapatnam
YANGON
Bangalore
Madras (Chennai)
Madurai
Andaman & Nicobar Islands (IN)
And S
SRI LANKA
Colombo
SRI JAYEWARDENEPURA KOTTE
MALE
MALDIVES
Chagos-Laccadive Ridge
Mid-Indian Basin
Ninetyeast Ridge
Carlsberg Ridge
Somali Basin
MOGADISHU
SEYCHELLES
VICTORIA
British Indian Ocean Territory (UK)
Chagos Archipelago
Mascarene Ridge
INDIAN OCEAN

Aleutian
Basin
Aleutian Islands
Aleutian Trench
International Date Line

Chita
Aldan
ATOR
Kamchatka
Sea of
Okhotsk
Petropavlovsk-
Kamchatskiy
50°

Qiqihar
Khabarovsk
Amur
Sakhalin
Yuzhno-
Sakhalinsk
Kuril Islands
Kuril Trench
Emperor Seamount Chain
Hess Rise
40°

Harbin
Jilin
Vladivostok
Sapporo
Hokkaidō
Aomori
Northwest Pacific
Basin

Shenyang
Anshan
NORTH
KOREA
Sea of
Japan
(East Sea)
Honshū
PACIFIC
OCEAN

Baotou
Tangshan
BEIJING
Dalian
Korea
Bay
P'YŎNGYANG
Bo
Hai
Japan Trench
J A P A N

Shijiazhuang
Tianjin
Inch'ŏn
SEOUL
SOUTH KOREA
TOKYO

Taiyuan
Jinan
Zibo
Qingdao
Taejon
Taegu
Pusan
Kyōto
Kōbe
Shatsky Rise

Xi'an
Luoyang
Yellow Sea
Hiroshima
Shikoku
Izu-ogasawara Trench
30°

C H I N A
Nanjing
Korea Strait
Nagasaki
Kyūshū
Height (m)
9000
7000
5000
4000
3000
2000
1500
1000
500
200
100
0
below sea level
-2000
-4000
-5000
-6000
-7000
-8000
-10000

Wuhan
Shanghai
East
China
Sea

Chongqing
Hangzhou
Nanchang
Changsha
Fuzhou
Ryukyu Islands
Ryukyu Trench
Van der Grinten Projection
1:37 000 000
0   500   1000 Km
0   250   500 Miles

Guiyang
Xun Jiang
T'AIPEI
TAIWAN
Kaohsiung
Tropic of Cancer
Mid-Pacific Mountains
20°

TNAM
NÕI
Guangzhou
Hong Kong
Luzon Strait
Philippine
Basin

Hainan
Luzon
Philippine
Sea
Pagan
West
Mariana
Basin

Huê
South China
Sea
Saipan
NORTHERN MARIANA
ISLANDS (US)
MARSHALL ISLANDS

AMBODIA
NH
Ho Chi Minh City
Spratly Islands
MANILA
Mindoro
Samar
Panay
Rota
Guam
(US)
Mariana Trench
East
Mariana
Basin

Palawan
Negros
PHILIPPINES
Philippine Trench
Kwajalein
Ralik Chain
Mili

Mekong
Sulu
Sea
Mindanao
Moro
Gulf
MELEKEOK
PALAU
Chuuk
Pohnpei
PALIKIR
Kosrae
Jaluit

BRUNEI
BANDAR
SERI BEGAWAN
Celebes
Sea
West
Caroline
Basin
Caroline Islands
FEDERATED STATES
OF MICRONESIA
KIRIBATI
Gilbert
Islands

Town
ALA-Y-SIA
KUMPUR
SINGAPORE
SINGAPORE
Kuching
Gorontalo
Makassar Strait
Borneo
Molucca Sea
Halmahera
Equator
YAREN
NAURU
TARAWA

Bangka
Balikpapan
Sulawesi
(Celebes)
Taliabu
Obi
New
Ireland
New
Britain
TUVALU

Palembang
Belitung
Java
Sea
Mangole
Buru
Mangole
Seram
Ambon
Banda
Sea
Pegunungan Maoke
PAPUA
New Guinea
Bougainville
SOLOMON
ISLANDS

JAKARTA
Madura
I N D O N E S I A
Kepulauan
Aru
Mt. Wilhelm
4509 m
NEW GUINEA
Choiseul
Santa
Isabel

Bandung
Surabaja
Bali
Bali
Sea
Flores Sea
DILI
Kepulauan
Tanimbar
Gulf
of Papua
PORT
MORESBY
New Georgia
Islands
HONIARA
Malaita
Guadalcanal
San Cristobal

Christmas I.
(AU)
Java
Lombok
Sumbawa
Flores
Sumba
Savu
Sea
EAST TIMOR
Timor
Arafura
Sea
Torres Strait
Cape York
Santa
Cruz Islands

Trench
Ashmore and
Cartier Islands
(AU)
Bathurst
Melville
Timor Sea
Darwin
AUSTRALIA
FIJI
10°

Mid-Atlantic Ridge

1. ANDORRA
2. SWITZERLAND
3. LIECHTENSTEIN
4. SLOVAKIA
5. SLOVENIA
6. CROATIA
7. BOSNIA AND HERZEGOVINA
8. MONTENEGRO
9. MACEDONIA

Azores (PT)

Nantes Loire PARIS GERMANY AUSTRIA VIENNA BRATISLAVA UKRAINE MOLDOVA Dnipropetrovs'k
FRANCE Seine 2 BERN VADUZ LJUBLJANA 5 ZAGREB HUNGARY BUDAPEST CHISINAU
Lyon Rhône 3 1 SAN MARINO 7 SERBIA ROMANIA BELGRADE BUCHAREST Odessa Sea of Azov
Bordeaux Garonne MONACO Genoa ITALY SARAJEVO 6 PODGORICA KOSOVO PRISTINE BULGARIA Black Sea
Bilbao Ebro ANDORRA LA VELLA 1 Marseille Corsica (FR) ROME TIRANA SOFIA SKOPJE 9 Istanbul Samsun
Oporto Douro Barcelona Sardinia (IT) VATICAN CITY Naples ALBANIA Thessaloniki ANKARA TURKEY
PORTUGAL MADRID Balearic Islands (ES) Cagliari Palermo GREECE Izmir Adana Ale
Madeira (PT) LISBON Guadiana SPAIN Valencia Sicily ATHENS Crete CYPRUS SYR LEBAN DAM
Seville Strait of Gibraltar Oran ALGIERS TUNIS VALLETTA MALTA Patras NICOSIA ISRAEL AMM
Canary Islands (ES) Ceuta (ES) RABAT Casablanca MOROCCO TUNISIA Sfax TRIPOLI Benghazi Alexandria JERUSALEM GAZA JORDAN
Marrakech Atlas Mountains Fès Ghadamis Qattara Depression Port Said CAIRO Suez

LAÂYOUNE Tropic of Cancer ALGERIA Sabhā LIBYA Libyan Desert EGYPT Aswān Wadi Halfa Lake Nasser Nubian Desert Port Sudan

WESTERN SAHARA SAHARA Tamanrasset A F R I C A
Nouâdhibou MAURITANIA MALI Timbuktu Niger Agadez NIGER CHAD KHARTOUM ERIT ASMA
NOUAKCHOTT Saint Louis Lake Chad El Obeid Blue Nile
CAPE VERDE PRAIA DAKAR SENEGAL BAMAKO BURKINA FASO NIAMEY Kano N'DJAMENA SUDAN Lake Tana ADD ABA
BANJUL THE GAMBIA BISSAU OUAGADOUGOU BENIN NIGERIA Maiduguri White Nile
GUINEA-BISSAU GUINEA CÔTE D'IVOIRE GHANA TOGO ABUJA Benue CENTRAL AFRICAN REPUBLIC
CONAKRY SIERRA LEONE YAMOUSSOUKRO PORTO-NOVO Enugu Niger UGANDA
FREETOWN MONROVIA LIBERIA ACCRA LOME Lagos Mt Cameroon 4100 m CAMEROON BANGUI KAMPALA K
Abidjan Gulf of Guinea MALABO YAOUNDÉ Ubangi Kisangani Tu
EQUATORIAL GUINEA SÃO TOMÉ Congo RWANDA KIGALI Lake Victoria

Mid Atlantic Ridge Guinea Basin SÃO TOMÉ AND PRÍNCIPE LIBREVILLE CONGO Mbandaka DEMOCRATIC REPUBLIC OF THE CONGO KIGALI Kilimanjaro 5895 m DODOM
Equator Prime Meridian GABON BRAZZAVILLE BURUNDI BUJUMBURA Lake Tanganyika TANZAN
Pointe Noire KINSHASA Kananga Lake
Matadi Kanga Lake Tanganyika

SOUTH ATLANTIC OCEAN St Helena (UK) Angola Basin LUANDA Lubumbashi MALAW
Benguela ZAMBIA LILONG
ANGOLA LUSAKA Luangwa
Walvis Ridge HARARE MOZAM
NAMIBIA ZIMBABWE Bulawayo Beira
Namib Desert WINDHOEK BOTSWANA Livingstone Zambezi
Swakopmund GABORONE Orange
Kalahari Desert PRETORIA MAPUTO
Tropic of Capricorn Johannesburg MBABANE SWAZILAND
Kimberley MASERU LESOTHO
SOUTH AFRICA Bloemfontein Drakensberg Durban
Great Karoo
Cape Town Cape of Good Hope Port Elizabeth

Height (m)
9000
6000
5000
4000
3000
2000
1500
1000
500
250
100
0
below sea level
−2000
−4000
−5000
−6000
−7000
−8000
−10000

N

Van der Grinten Projection
1:37 000 000

0 500 1000 Km
0 250 500 Miles

KAZAKHSTAN

MONGOLIA

Altai Mountains

Gobi Desert

L. Balkhash

Ural
Astrakhan'

Aral Sea

UZBEKISTAN

Syr Darya

Shan

Baotou

BEIJING

KYRGYZSTAN

Almaty

Ürümqi

Tianjin

Caspian Sea

BAKU

Samarqand

BISHKEK

Tarim Basin

Taiyuan

Shijiazhuang

TASHKENT

TAJIKISTAN

Kashi

Altun Shan

Zibo

AZERBAIJAN

TURKMENISTAN

DUSHANBE

Qilian Shan

abriz

AŞGABAT

Amu Darya

Lanzhou

Elburz Mountains

Mashhad

Karakoram Range
8611m

Luoyang

Xi'an

IRAN

*Dasht-e
Kavir*

KABUL

Kun Lun Shan

C H I N A

TEHRĀN

AFGHANISTAN

Herāt

JAMMU
AND

AKSAI
CHIN

Chengdu

Chongqing

Nanchang

Wuhan

Esfahān

Yazd

ISLAMABAD

ZONE OF CONTROL

*Plateau
of Tibet*

Yangtze

Basra

Shiraz

Kandahār

KASHMIR

Lhasa

Changsha

KUWAIT

Zagros Mountains

Zāhedān

Faisalabad

Mt. Everest
8848 m

BHUTAN

Guiyang

PAKISTAN

Indus

NEPAL

THIMPHU

Brahmaputra

Kunming

The Gulf

MANAMA

Karachi

NEW
DELHI

KĀTHMĀNDU

Ganges

Patna

BANGLADESH

Guangzhou

BAHRAIN

DOHA

Jaipur

Lucknow

Xun Jiang

QATAR

ABU
DHABI

Hyderabad

Kanpur

DHAKA

Chittagong

MYANMAR

VIETNAM

Hong
Kong

OMAN

UAE

MUSCAT

Tropic of Cancer

Ahmadabad

Varanasi

Calcutta
(Kolkata)

Khulna

Nay Pyi Taw

HA NÒI

*Rub' al
Khali*

I N D I A

Nagpur

*Bay of
Bengal*

LAOS

Hainan

SAUDI
ARABIA

OMAN

*Arabian
Sea*

Mumbai
(Bombay)

*Deccan
Plateau*

Vishakhapatnam

RANGOON

VIENTIANE

Huê

YEMEN

Pune

Hyderabad

*Andaman
Sea*

THAILAND

SAN'Ā

Gulf of Aden

Socotra
(YE)

Chagos-Laccadive Ridge

Mangalore

Madras (Chennai)

*Andaman & Nicobar
Islands (IN)*

Irrawaddy

BANGKOK

CAMBODIA

Mekong

SOMALIA

Bangalore

*South China
Sea*

Cochin
(Kochi)

Madurai

PHNOM
PENH

Ho Chi
Minh City

DJIBOUTI

SRI
LANKA

SRI JAYEWARDENEPURA
KOTTE

BANDAR SERI
BEGAWAN

Carlsberg Ridge

Colombo

Strait of Malacca

George
Town

M A L A Y S I A

BRUNEI

MALDIVES

MALE

Medan

KUALA
LUMPUR

Kuching

Equator

SINGAPORE

B o r n e o

SINGAPORE

*Somali
Basin*

*Mid-Indian
Basin*

Padang

I N D O N E S I A

Sumatra

Kepulauan Mentawai

VICTORIA

SEYCHELLES

*British
Indian Ocean
Territory*

Chagos Archipelago

Palembang

Bangka

Belitung

Mascarene Ridge

JAKARTA

Java Sea

Madura

OROS
ONI

Mayotte
(FR)

Bandung

Java

Surabaya

Bali

MADAGASCAR

Ninetyeast Ridge

*West Australian
Basin*

Java Trench

IVO

Toamasina

I N D I A N

MAURITIUS

O C E A N

PORT LOUIS

St. Denis

Réunion
(FR)

North West Cape

Tropic of Capricorn

*Great
Sandy Desert*

Southwest Indian Ridge

Mid-Indian Ridge

Broken Ridge

*Perth
Basin*

AUSTRALIA

Perth

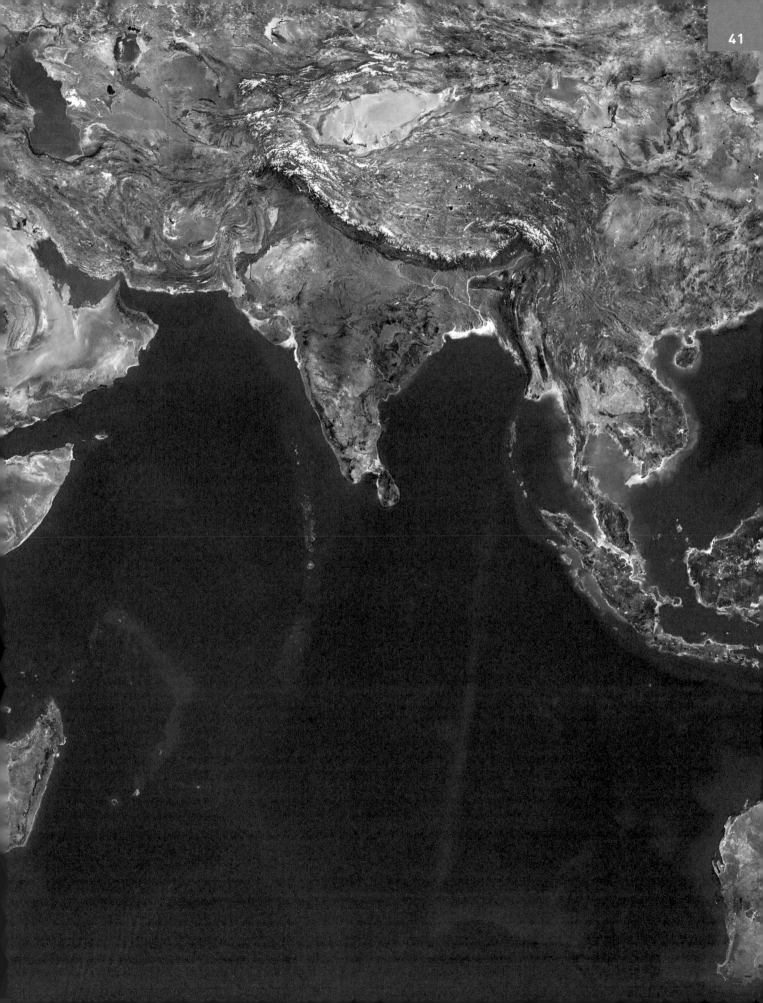

LAOS
VIENTIANE
HA NOI
T'AIPEI
TAIWAN
Kaohsiung
Hong Kong
Hainan
Luzon Strait
South
China
Sea
Philippine
Basin
Mid-Pacific Mountains
Tropic of Cancer
THAILAND
BANGKOK
VIETNAM
CAMBODIA
Huê
Mekong
Philippine
Sea
Manila
Luzon
PHILIPPINES
Mindoro
Samar
West
Mariana
Basin
Pagan
Saipan
Rota
Guam (US)
East
Mariana
Basin
MARSHALL
Gulf of
Thailand
PHNOM
PENH
Ho Chi Minh City
Palawan
Panay
Negros
Sulu
Sea
Mindanao
Moro
Gulf
Sprately Islands
Philippine Trench
MELEKEOK
PALAU
West
Caroline
Basin
Chuuk
Pohnpei
PALIKIR
Kosrae
George
Town
MALAYSIA
Celebes
Sea
Halmahera
Gorontalo
East
Caroline
Basin
FEDERATED STATES
OF MICRONESIA
Melanesian
Basin
YAREN
NAUR
SINGAPORE
Singapore
KUALA
LUMPUR
Kuching
Borneo
Makassar Strait
Sulawesi
(Celebes)
Taliabu
Mangole
Obi
Buru
Seram
Ambon
Strait of Malacca
Sumatra
Padang
Bangka
Belitung
Balikpapan
INDONESIA
JAKARTA
Java Sea
Makassar
Molucca Sea
Maluku
Banda
Sea
Kepulauan
Aru
New
Guinea
Regunungan Maoke
PAPUA
NEW GUINEA
Mt. Wilhelm
4509 m
New
Ireland
New Britain
Bougainville
SOLOMON
ISLANDS
Choiseul
Santa
Isabel
Malaita
Kepulauan Mentawai
Palembang
Bandung
Java
Surabaya
Bali
Madura
Bali
Sea
Flores Sea
Lombok
Sumbawa
Flores
Sumba
Savu
Sea
DILI
EAST TIMOR
Timor
Kepulauan
Tanimbar
Arafura
Sea
Gulf
of Papua
Torres Strait
PORT
MORESBY
Tagula
Solomon Sea
HONIARA
Guadalcanal
San Cristobal
Java Trench
Christmas
(AU)
Cocos
(AU)
Ashmore and
Cartier Islands
(AU)
Timor Sea
Bathurst
Beagle Gulf
Joseph
Bonaparte
Gulf
Melville
Darwin
Arnhem
Land
Cape Arnhem
Groote
Eylandt
Mornington
Gulf
of
Carpentaria
Cape York
Cape
York
Peninsula
Coral
Basin
Coral Sea
Coral Sea
Islands
Territory
(AU)
Banks Islan
Espiritu Santo
VANUATU
Lu
Malakula
PORT VILA
North Australian
Basin
Daly
Kimberley
Plateau
King Leopold Ranges
L. Argyle
Tanami
Desert
Barkly Tableland
Gilbert
Cairns
Great Barrier Reef
West Australian
Basin
Exmouth
Plateau
Eighty Mile
Beach
Great Sandy Desert
Townsville
New Caledonia
(FR)
Iles
Loyauté
Nouméa
Barrow
North West Cape
Chichester Range
Ashburton
L. Mackay
Gibson Desert
AUSTRALIA
Macdonnell Ranges
Alice Springs
Simpson
Desert
Diamantina
Grey Range
Great
Dividing
Lord Howe
(AU)
Dirk Hartog
Gascoyne
Murchison
Musgrave Ranges
Great
Victoria Desert
L. Eyre
(North)
L. Eyre (South)
Sturt
Stony
Desert
Brisbane
Norfolk
(AU)
Perth
Basin
Perth
Nullarbor Plain
L. Gairdner
L. Torrens
Flinders Ranges
L. Frome
Darling
Lord
Howe
Rise
Cape Leeuwin
Great
Australian Bight
Cape Catastrophe
Spencer Gulf
Adelaide
Murray
Murrumbidgee
Sydney
CANBERRA
Mount
Kosciuszko
2229 m
Tasman Abyssal Plain
Kangaroo
Island
Cape
Jaffa
Melbourne
Bass Strait
King
Furneaux
Group
Tasman Sea
Cape Farewell
Nelson
South
Australian
Basin
INDIAN OCEAN
Tasmania
Hobart
South East
Cape
Tasman
Basin
Mt. Cook
3754 m
Southern Alps
South
Island
Ch

Height (m)
9000
6000
5000
4000
3000
2000
1500
1000
500
200
100
0
below sea level
-2000
-4000
-5000
-6000
-7000
-8000
-10000

Southeast Indian Ridge

Indian-Antarctic Ridge

South Tasman Rise

Cape Providence
Foveaux Strait
Stewart

Auckland Islands
(NZ)

Campbell
Plateau

0   500   1000 Km

0   250   500 Miles

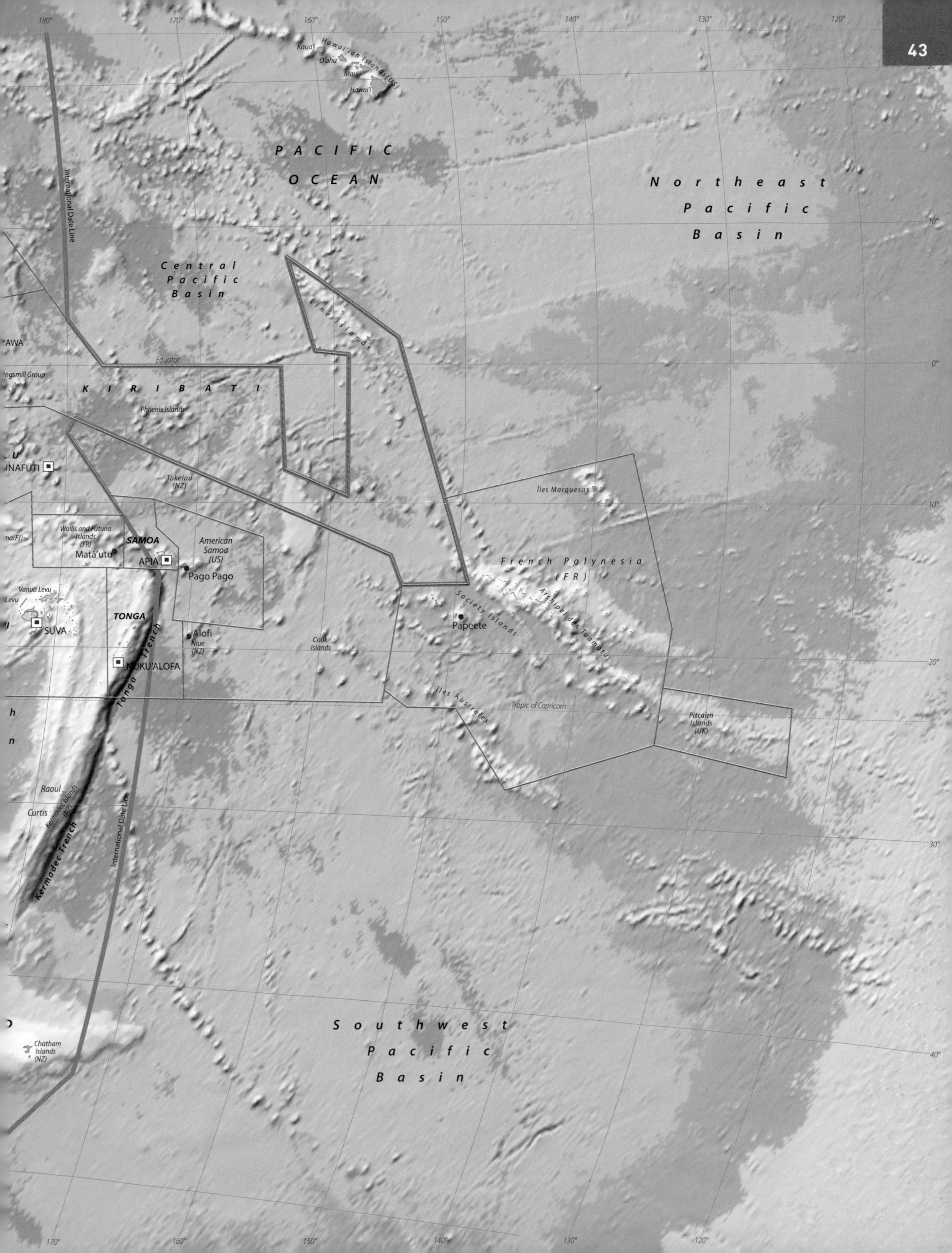

PACIFIC
OCEAN

*Northeast
Pacific
Basin*

*Central
Pacific
Basin*

Line Islands

Equator

K I R I B A T I

Phoenix Islands

AWA

ngsmill Group

Íles Marquesas

Tokelau
(NZ)

INAFUTI

*Wallis and Futuna
Islands
(FR)*

na(FJ)

SAMOA

Matá'utu

*American
Samoa
(US)*

APIA

Pago Pago

*French Polynesia
(FR)*

Society Islands

Archipel des Tuamotu

Papeete

Vanua Levu

Levu

TONGA

SUVA

Alofi
*Niue
(NZ)*

*Cook
Islands*

NUKU'ALOFA

h

Íles Australes

Tropic of Capricorn

Pitcairn
Islands
(UK)

n

Raoul

Curtis

*Kermadec Islands
(NZ)*

Kermadec Trench

Tonga Trench

International Date Line

*Southwest
Pacific
Basin*

*Chatham
Islands
(NZ)*

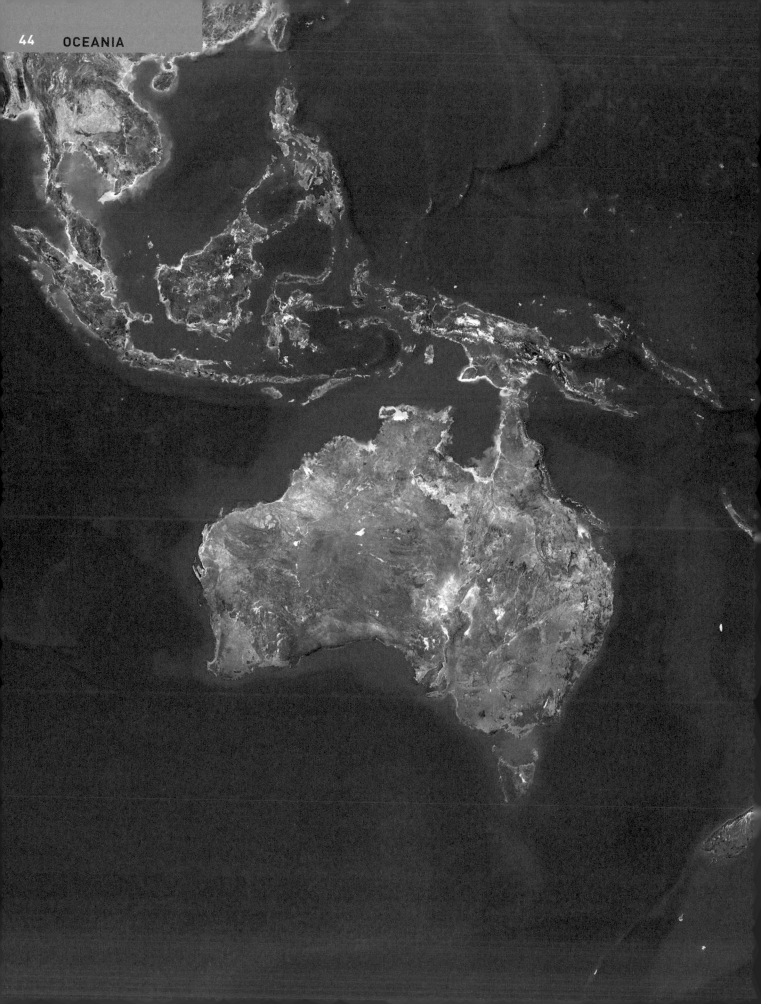

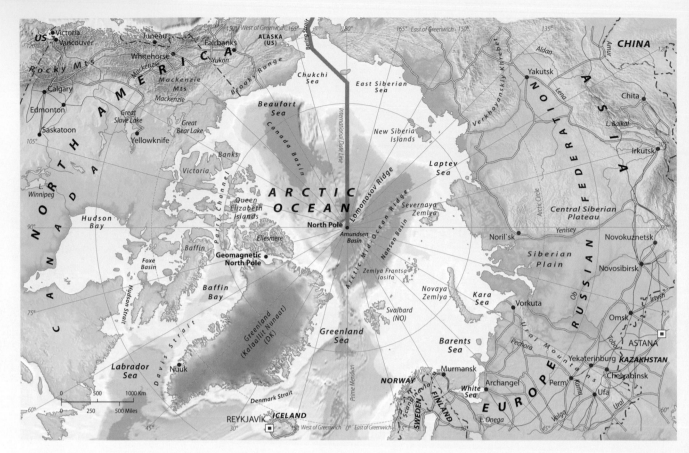

US
Victoria
Vancouver
Juneau
Whitehorse
Fairbanks
ALASKA (US)
Yukon
Rocky Mts
Mackenzie
Mackenzie Mts
Mackenzie
Brooks Range
Chukchi Sea
East Siberian Sea
CHINA
Aldan
Amur
Yakutsk
Lena
Verkhoyanskiy Khrebet
Chita
L. Baikal
Irkutsk
ASIA
Calgary
Edmonton
Saskatoon
Yellowknife
Great Slave Lake
Great Bear Lake
Banks
Beaufort Sea
Canada Basin
New Siberia Islands
Laptev Sea
Severnaya Zemlya
Arctic Circle
Central Siberian Plateau
RUSSIAN FEDERATION
NORTH AMERICA
Victoria
Parry Channel
Queen Elizabeth Islands
ARCTIC OCEAN
Lomonosov Ridge
North Pole
Amundsen Basin
Arctic Mid Ocean Ridge
Nansen Basin
Zemlya Frantsa Josifa
Noril`sk
Yenisey
Siberian Plain
Novokuznetsk
Novosibirsk
L. Winnipeg
Hudson Bay
Baffin
Foxe Basin
Ellesmere
Geomagnetic North Pole
Novaya Zemlya
Kara Sea
Ob
Vorkuta
Ural Mountains
Omsk
Irtysh
CANADA
Baffin Bay
Baffin Bay
Greenland (Kalaallit Nunaat) (DK)
Greenland Sea
Barents Sea
Pechora
Ural Mountains
Tobol
ASTANA
Davis Strait
Labrador Sea
Nuuk
Denmark Strait
Prime Meridian
NORWAY
Svalbard (NO)
Murmansk
Archangel
White Sea
Yekaterinburg
Perm
Kama
KAZAKHSTAN
Chelyabinsk
Ufa
Ural
0   500   1000 Km
0   250   500 Miles
REYKJAVÍK ICELAND
30° 15° West of Greenwich 0° East of Greenwich
SWEDEN FINLAND
L. Onega
Volga
EUROPE

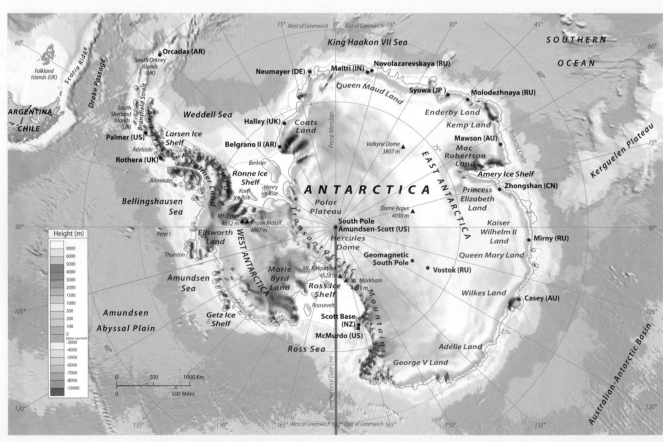

Height (m)
9000
6000
5000
4000
3000
2000
1500
1000
500
200
100
0
below sea level
-2000
-4000
-5000
-6000
-7000
-8000
-10000

60°
Scotia Ridge
Falkland Islands (UK)
Drake Passage
South Orkney Islands (UK)
Orcadas (AR)
King Haakon VII Sea
Neumayer (DE)
Maitri (IN)
Novolazarevskaya (RU)
SOUTHERN OCEAN
60°
ARGENTINA
CHILE
South Shetland Islands (UK)
Bransfield Strait
Weddell Sea
Halley (UK)
Coats Land
Queen Maud Land
Syowa (JP)
Molodezhnaya (RU)
Enderby Land
Kemp Land
Palmer (US)
Larsen Ice Shelf
Belgrano II (AR)
Prime Meridian
Valkyrie Dome 3807 m
Mawson (AU)
Mac Robertson Land
Adelaide
Rothera (UK)
Ronne Ice Shelf
Berkner
Ronne Ice Shelf
Korff Ice Rise
Henry Ice Rise
ANTARCTICA
EAST ANTARCTICA
Amery Ice Shelf
Antarctic Circle
Alexander
Bellingshausen Sea
Peter I
Palmer Land
Mt Tyree 4852 m
Vinson Massif 4897 m
Polar Plateau
Dome Argus 4030 m
Princess Elizabeth Land
Zhongshan (CN)
South Pole
Amundsen-Scott (US)
Kaiser Wilhelm II Land
90°
90°
Thurston
Ellsworth Land
WEST ANTARCTICA
Hercules Dome
Geomagnetic South Pole
Mirny (RU)
Amundsen Sea
Marie Byrd Land
Mt Kirkpatrick 4528 m
Transantarctic Mountains
Vostok (RU)
Queen Mary Land
Amundsen Abyssal Plain
Ross Ice Shelf
Mt Markham 4351 m
Wilkes Land
Casey (AU)
Getz Ice Shelf
Roosevelt
Scott Base (NZ)
McMurdo (US)
Ross Sea
Adélie Land
International Date Line
George V Land
Australian-Antarctic Basin
Kerguelen Plateau
0   500   1000 Km
0   500 Miles
120°
135°
150°
165° West of Greenwich 180° East of Greenwich 165°
150°
135°
120°

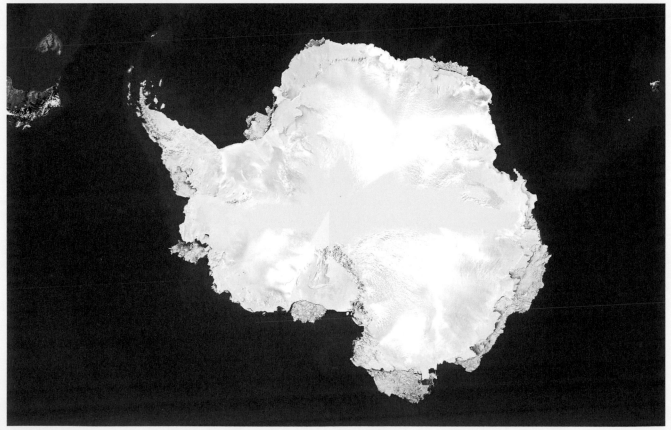

NORTH AMERICA

Comprised mainly of Canada and the USA, the second and third largest countries in the world, North America has mountains, deserts, swamps and permanantly frozen landscapes, with some of the the largest cities in the world and some of the least populated parts of the world.

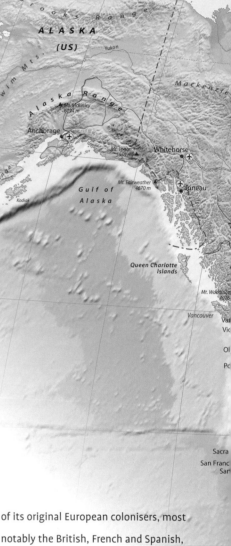

Extending from the Arctic Circle down into the Gulf of Mexico, Northern America covers an area of approximately 22 million square kilometres, 16 per cent of the Earth's total land mass, and has a population of around 337 million people.

The continent includes Canada, the USA, Greenland, which is a dependency of Denmark, the tiny islands of St Pierre and Miquelon off the Newfoundland coast, and the Bermuda archipelago, about 900 kilometres off the coast of North Carolina. Much of the continent lies on the North American plate which meets the Pacific Plate along the San Andreas Fault. So vast an extent produces great geographic and climatic diversity; in the north the sparsely inhabited territories of northern Canada and the detached US state of Alaska are covered by Arctic tundra, while in the much warmer south there are large swathes of desert in the south-west and tropical swamps and rainforests in the south-east. The Rocky Mountain range and its foothills dominate the west of the continent, running from the US state of Alaska south to the Mexican isthmus. The heart of the continent is dominated by the Great Plains and the plateau of the Canadian Shield, themselves punctured by the Hudson Bay and the Great Lakes. Drained by the great Mississippi-Missouri river system as well as the lakes, the plains, known as prairies, are now vast grain-growing farmlands. But their remoteness and the extremes of the continental climate make them relatively sparsely populated.

Owing to the extremes of terrain and climate and the pattern of predominantly European settlement, the greatest concentration of population is in the south and east of the continent, from southern Canada to the Gulf of Mexico and east of the Mississippi river, with further settlement along the west coast. Until the early sixteenth century, North America was home to thousands of Amerindian tribes, but with the arrival of European explorers and settlers, their way of life and culture was gradually, and in most cases brutally, expunged. North America's languages and culture are now derived mainly from those of its original European colonisers, most notably the British, French and Spanish, although the Spanish heritage is now influenced more by the recent large-scale immigration from Mexico and other Central American states that has produced a sizeable Latino minority. An additional element in the cultural mix is the equally large Afro-American population, particularly in the USA and the Caribbean islands, the result of four hundred years of importing African slaves to work on plantations. With its modern identity as a land of opportunity for millions of immigrants, North America is home to two of the most developed nations on earth, the USA and Canada.

GREENLAND
(Kalaallit Nunaat)
(DK)

Banks

Melville

Queen Elizabeth Islands

Devon

Baffin
Bay

McClure Strait

Viscount Melville Sound

Parry Channel

Somerset

Prince of Wales Strait

Hadley Bay

Victoria

Prince of Wales

M'Clintock Channel

Boothia Peninsula

Prince Regent Inlet

Brodeur Peninsula

Gulf of
Boothia

Baffin

Davis Strait

Mont Forel
3360 m

Arctic Circle

Ammassalik

Prince Albert Sound

Dolphin and Union Strait

Amundsen
Gulf

Coronation
Gulf

Victoria Strait

King William

Melville
Peninsula

Foxe
Basin

Nettilling
Lake

Godhavn

NUUK
(Godthåb)

Paamiut

Back

Southampton

Rae Welcome Sound

Coats

Mansel

Nanortalik

Yellowknife

Great
Slave Lake

Reindeer
Lake

Hudson
Bay

Belcher Islands

James
Bay

Ungava
Bay

Labrador
Sea

Northwest Atlantic Mid-Ocean Channel

Lac
Bienville

Smallwood
Reservoir

Peace

Lake
Athabasca

CANADA

NORTH

Severn

Winisk

Albany

Akimiski

Eastmain

Lac
Mistassini

Caniapiscau

Grand Banks of Newfoundland

Edmonton

N. Saskatchewan

Saskatoon

Cedar
Lake

Lake
Winnipeg

Lake
Manitoba

Winnipeg

Thunder Bay

Lake
Nipigon

Moose

Lake Superior

Laurentian Highlands

St. Lawrence

Anticosti

Québec

Gulf of
St. Lawrence

Charlottetown

Cabot Strait

Prince Edward
Island

Newfoundland

St. John's

Saint Pierre and
Miquelon (FR)

Calgary

Regina

AMERICA

Minneapolis

Missouri

Lake Michigan

Lake Huron

Toronto

OTTAWA

Ontario

Buffalo

Lake Erie

Rochester

Montreal

Boston

Cape Breton

Sable

Halifax

Nova Scotia

Bay of Fundy

Saint Pierre Bank

North

Great Salt Lake

Lake City

UNITED
STATES OF
AMERICA

Sioux Falls

Milwaukee

Mississippi

Chicago

Detroit

Cleveland

Pittsburgh

Columbus

Cincinnati

Gulf of
Maine

Providence

New York

Philadelphia

Baltimore

WASHINGTON DC

Virginia Beach

New England Seamounts

North

Denver

Lincoln

Des
Moines

Kansas City

St. Louis

Illinois

Appalachian Mountains

Atlantic

Ocean

Windom
Peak 4.293 m

Topeka

Santa Fe

Oklahoma City

Ozark
Plateau

Memphis

Tennessee

Arkansas

Atlanta

Alabama

Canadian

Colorado
Plateau

Grand Canyon

Colorado

Phoenix

Pecos

Edwards
Plateau

Austin

Dallas

Red

Baton
Rouge

Jacksonville

Bermuda (UK)

Bermuda Rise

El Paso

Ciudad
Juárez

Chihuahua

San
Antonio

Houston

New Orleans

Tampa

Orlando

Hatteras Abyssal Plain

Nares
Deep

Gulf of California

MEXICO

Monterrey

Gulf of
Mexico

Miami

Florida Strait

The Bahamas

Tropic of Cancer

La Paz

Middle America Trench

Sierra Madre Occidental

Mexico
Basin

Guadalajara

Bahía de
Campeche

Pico de Orizaba
5.610 m

Acapulco

NORTH AMERICA

CANADA

60° 00' N, 95° 00' W | 9,984,670 KM² | 3,855,103 MI² | UTC-5

Occupying 41 per cent of the North American continent, Canada is the world's second largest country, reaching across from the Pacific to the Atlantic and down from the Arctic in the north to its unfortified border with the United States.

Geography

Its vast size means that Canada covers an array of different regions. To the far north, where the country enters the Arctic Circle, the landscape is of snow and ice; its northernmost settlement on Ellesmere Island is just 824 kilometres from the North Pole. The arctic tundra and islands give way to boreal forests, lakes and rivers and then on to the geographical region known as the Canadian Shield, a vast rock base which incorporates many of the rivers and lakes which dominate the country. Part of the border with the United States consists of the five huge freshwater Great Lakes, along with hundreds of smaller lakes, rivers and islands. Lake Superior is the largest by surface area in the world. Lake Ontario is connected to the Atlantic via a great waterway, the

St Lawrence River, upon which the capital Ottawa sits. In 1959 the St Lawrence Seaway was inaugurated; it includes a number of artificial sections to enable shipping to bypass rapids in the river, and allows ocean-going vessels to navigate the Great Lakes. Canada has the longest coastline of any country in the world, 202,080 kilometres, including the huge scoop of Hudson Bay in its centre. To the west of the country lie the Rocky Mountains; the Yukon Territory to the north of this region contains a number of volcanoes. Towards the south and east are the more fertile lowland plains or prairies, the agricultural heart of the country. The less hospitable terrain to the north means that the majority of Canada's population lives in this southern region, and particularly around the St Lawrence lowlands; 90 per cent live within 160 kilometres of the US border.

History

The first European explorers to arrive on Canada's shores were Vikings, leaving remnants of the only Norse settlement in the Americas at L'Anse aux Meadows. In 1497, the Englishman John Cabot landed and was followed in 1534 by Jacques Cartier from France. The struggle between French and English settlers dominated the years between 1534 and 1867; a series of intercolonial wars involved not only the Europeans but also the newly independent Americans and the native Indian tribes. Territory along the St Lawrence River that had originally belonged to France was ceded to the British in 1763 after the French were defeated in the Seven Years War. Following the expansion of the country, the Constitution Act of 1867 established Canada as a single nation, divided into four original provinces, which would eventually become a federation of ten provinces and three

THE ROCKY MOUNTAINS
A view of the Valley of the Ten Peaks and Moraine Lake in Banff National Park.

territories. Canada became autonomous at this time, and full independence was granted in 1931. The country has retained ties with the United Kingdom as a member of the British Commonwealth and as a constitutional monarchy with Queen Elizabeth II as head of state. Divisions still exist between the Francophone population in Quebec, where a separatist movement is active, and the rest of the country. In 1999 Canada created Nunavut as an Inuit-governed territory; the largest but least populated of the territories, it was instituted in response to land claims made by the indigenous peoples. Although Canada shares a positive relationship with the US it carefully retains a separate identity; it fosters close ties with both the UK and France and sets itself apart from US foreign policy. Canada also has a liberal culture, with emphasis on welfare provision and environmental awareness.

Economy

With a wealth of natural resources, a skilled and well-educated labour force and sophisticated industrialization, Canada's economy is one of the most successful and affluent in the world. The export market provides one third of the annual GDP and the majority of trade occurs with the US, to whom Canada supplies oil, natural gas, uranium and electricity. Huge oil reserves, second only to that of Saudi Arabia, provide much of the wealth. Fishing is important, and major agricultural products include wheat, barley and timber. Canada is a member of the OECD, the G8, the United Nations and NATO and its currency is the Canadian Dollar.

TORONTO
The CN Tower, opened in 1976 and measuring 553 metres, is the symbol of Toronto. Situated on the north-western shore of Lake Ontario, Toronto is the largest city in Canada.

FACT FILE

LOCAL NAME Canada

CAPITAL CITY Ottawa

CURRENCY Canadian Dollar (CAD)

MEMBERSHIP AC, APEC, ASEAN (dialogue partner), C, CE (observer), EAPC, G8, G20, NATO, OAS, OECD, WTO

GOVERNMENT Parliamentary Democracy and Constitutional Monarchy

POPULATION 33,169,734

POP. DENSITY 3/km²; 9/mi²

GDP 1.266 Trillion US$

LANGUAGE(S) English, French, Chinese, Italian, German

ETHNICITY British Isles origin 28%, French origin 23%, Other European 15%, Amerindian 2%, Other (mostly Asian, African, Arab) 6%, Mixed background 26%

RELIGION Roman Catholic 43%, Protestant 23%, Other Christian 4%, Muslim 2%

CLIMATE Temperate, Subarctic and Arctic

REGIONAL DIVISIONS 10 Provinces and 3 Territories; second level administrative divisions differ in each province and territory

ECONOMIC ACTIVITIES Forestry, Agriculture, Fishery, Mining, Transportation Equipment, Chemicals, Processed and Unprocessed Minerals, Food Products, Wood and Paper Products, Petroleum and Natural Gas extraction, Automobile Manufacturing, Aerospace, Computer and Computer Equipment, Pharmaceuticals, Tourism

NATURAL RESOURCES Iron Ore, Nickel, Zinc, Copper, Gold, Lead, Molybdenum, Potash, Diamonds, Silver, Fish, Timber, Coal, Petroleum, Natural Gas, Hydropower

GREENLAND

72° 00' N, 40° 00' W | 2,166,086 KM² | 836,330 MI² | UTC-3

The world's largest island, Greenland is an autonomous Danish province and consequently European, despite being geographically part of the Americas and the Arctic.

This large landmass situated between the Arctic Ocean and the North Atlantic is almost permanently covered with ice; the weight of this icecap has depressed the centre of the island into a basin below sea level. The majority of the mixed European/Inuit population lives along the rocky Western coastline; the capital, Nuuk, is home to a quarter of Greenlanders. For many years a Danish colony, Greenland became more self-reliant during the Second World War when Denmark was occupied, and achieved Home Rule in 1979. The economy rests upon fishing, with traditional whaling and sealing being more controversial. Greenland also relies upon subsidies from Denmark, although it does have substantial mineral deposits, including uranium, iron, diamonds and gold.

FACT FILE

LOCAL NAME Greenland
SOVEREIGN Denmark
CAPITAL/MAIN CITY Nuuk (Godthab)
CURRENCY Danish Krone (DKK)
GOVERNMENT Parliamentary Democracy within a Constitutional Monarchy (self-governing overseas administrative division of Denmark)
POPULATION 57,564
POP. DENSITY 0.03/ km²; 0.09/mi²
GDP 1.1 Billion US$
LANGUAGE(S) Greenlandic (East Inuit), Danish, English
ETHNICITY Greenlander 88% (Inuit and Greenland-born whites), Danish and others 12%
RELIGION Protestant 69% (Evangelical Lutheran 64%, Pentecostal 3%), Other Christian 27%
CLIMATE Arctic and Subarctic

ST PIERRE AND MIQUELON

46° 50' N, 56° 20' W | 242 KM² | 93 MI² | UTC-3

This small archipelago in the North Atlantic Ocean is all that remains of the once vast American colonial empire of France.

Situated just 25 kilometres from the Burin Peninsula of Newfoundland, St Pierre and Miquelon are a collective of eight French-owned islands, only two of which are permanently inhabited, those from which the archipelago takes its name. St Pierre is separated from Miquelon by a 6-kilometre strait which is known as 'The Mouth of Hell' because of its treacherous currents; more than 600 ships have been wrecked there. The inhabitants rely upon fishing and subsidies from France; there is little opportunity for agriculture. Recent drilling for oil in the area may develop into an industry which will provide future wealth.

FACT FILE

LOCAL NAME Territorial Collectivity of Saint Pierre and Miquelon
SOVEREIGN STATE France
CAPITAL/MAIN CITY Saint-Pierre
CURRENCY Euro (EUR)
GOVERNMENT Self-governing Territorial Overseas Collectivity of France
POPULATION 6,360
POP. DENSITY 26/km²; 68/mi²
GDP 48.3 Million US$
LANGUAGE(S) French
ETHNICITY Basques and Bretons (French fishermen)
RELIGION Roman Catholic 99%
CLIMATE Maritime

ST PIERRE
Fishing boats on the beach at St Pierre.

NORTH AMERICA

UNITED STATES OF AMERICA

38° 00' N, 97° 00' W | 9,826,630 KM² | 3,794,083 MI² | UTC-5

The United States of America is the world's strongest economic power, with the most ethnically diverse population on the globe.

Geography

Covering a vast area, the forty-eight states of the mainland US are accompanied by the two states of Alaska and Hawaii; one arctic tundra, the other an archipelago of tropical islands. The contiguous US is dominated in

MANHATTAN ISLAND, NEW YORK
The Manhattan skyline is one of the most recognizable in the world. The island is bounded by the Hudson River to the west, the Harlem River to the north and East River to the east.

its centre by a vast central plain, through which flows the extensive Mississippi–Missouri river system. To the west the Great Plains are bordered by the Rocky Mountains, which run from north to south, with arid desert in the south-west. To the east of the Great Plains, the Appalachian Mountains run parallel to the Atlantic seaboard. The temperate north-east is forested mountains and rolling hills. Further south, towards Florida and the Gulf of Mexico, are lowlands and tropical swamps.

FACT FILE

LOCAL NAME United States of America

CAPITAL CITY Washington, D C

CURRENCY US Dollar (USD)

MEMBERSHIP APEC, AC, ASEAN (dialogue partner), BSEC (observer), CBSS (observer), CE (observer), CP, EAPC, G5, G8, G20, NATO, OAS, OECD, SAARC (observer), SPC, WTO

GOVERNMENT Constitutional Federal Presidential Republic

POPULATION 308,798,281

POP. DENSITY 31/km²; 81/mi²

GDP 13.84 Trillion US$

LANGUAGE(S) English, Spanish, French, Chinese, German

ETHNICITY White 80%, African American 13%, Asian 4%, Amerindian and Alaska native 1%, Native Hawaiian/other Pacific Islander 0.2%. Hispanic (of any of the above ethnic groups) 15%

RELIGION Protestant 51%, Roman Catholic 24%, Mormon 2%, Other Christian 2%, Jewish 2%, Buddhist 0.7%, Muslim 0.6%

CLIMATE Temperate, Tropical, Arctic, Semiarid, Arid

REGIONAL DIVISIONS 6 geographical and cultural regions are divided into 50 States and 1 District and further into 3142 counties

DEPENDENCIES America Samoa, Baker Island, Guam, Howland Island, Jarvis Island, Johnston Atoll, Kingman Reef, Midway Island, Navassa Island, Palmyra Atoll, U.S. Virgin Islands and Wake Island (Unincorporated Territories) Northern Mariana Islands and Puerto Rico (Freely Associated Commonwealth)

ECONOMIC ACTIVITIES Agriculture, Petroleum extraction, Steel, Motor Vehicles, Aviation, Aerospace & Defence, Telecommunication and Computing, Chemicals, Electric Goods, Food Processing, Consumer Goods, Lumber, Mining, Media and Entertainment, Commerce and Banking, Tourism

NATURAL RESOURCES Coal, Copper, Lead, Molybdenum, Phosphates, Uranium, Bauxite, Gold, Iron, Mercury, Nickel, Potash, Silver, Tungsten, Zinc, Petroleum, Natural Gas, Timber

History

The United States was proclaimed with the Declaration of Independence of 4th July, 1776, when the thirteen former British Colonies along the Atlantic coast united and instigated the American Revolution. Their victory was followed by a period of expansion westward, acquiring territory from the Native American Indian population. Civil war broke out in 1861 and lasted for four years; the victory of Abraham Lincoln over the South was crucial to the country as it exists now. Slavery was abolished, racial equality generally encouraged and the US became the destination for millions of immigrants. Victory in the Second World War confirmed the country's position as a military superpower, and the Cold War with the USSR led to a massive accumulation of nuclear weapons. However, with the collapse of the Soviet Union in 1991, the US became the world's foremost military power. Since the attacks on the World Trade Center in September 2001, the country has been engaged in a 'war on terror'.

Economy

The United States currently has the largest and most technologically advanced economy in the world, despite recent economic stagnation. Its strongest areas are its high-tech engineering and manufacturing sectors, with electrical machinery, cars and chemical products at the forefront. The majority of the economy however, is supported by the service sector and American culture can also be considered an export commodity. The US is also the world's largest importer, despite a wealth of natural resources. It is the fourth-largest oil-producing country yet also one of the largest importers of petroleum.

YOSEMITE, CALIFORNIA
Yosemite is a vast wilderness, over 2,500 square kilometres, of granite mountains, deep valleys and spectacular waterfalls.

USA: WEST

The Western United States covers a huge expanse of territory from the Pacific coast inland towards the Mississippi River system and is consequently geographically diverse.

The Rocky Mountains wind their way through Colorado, Wyoming and Montana while the Pacific coast states of Washington, Oregon and California are home to rainforests, deserts, giant redwood forests and snow-capped mountains. To the south are the desert states of Nevada and Arizona, which also boasts the spectacular Grand Canyon. The great expansion westwards during the nineteenth century has been shaped into folklore by the 'Western' of cinema and literature; however, during the 1840s and 1850s events such as the California gold rush encouraged thousands to migrate from the east and from Mexico to the south. Once considered a frontier land, the area is now home to the greatest concentration of Native American tribal reservations. During the twentieth century cities along the Pacific coast, such as Los Angeles and San Francisco, underwent massive expansion, and Silicon Valley in northern California eventually became the world's leading centre for high-tech engineering and the birthplace of the Internet. Los Angeles, while also a key centre for high-tech industries, is perhaps best known as the entertainment capital of the world and home to Hollywood.

ALASKA (AK)

N/E LOCATION 64° 30' N, 153° 00' W

STATE CAPITAL Juneau

LARGEST CITY Anchorage

AREA 1,717,854 km²; 663,267 mi² (1st)

POPULATION 683,478 (47th)

WASHINGTON (WA)

N/E LOCATION 47° 20' N, 120° 30' W

STATE CAPITAL Olympia

LARGEST CITY Seattle

AREA 184,665 km²; 71,299 mi² (18th)

POPULATION 6,468,424 (13th)

IDAHO (ID)

N/E LOCATION 44° 00' N, 114° 30' W

STATE CAPITAL Boise

LARGEST CITY Boise

AREA 216,446 km²; 83,570 mi² (14th)

POPULATION 1,499,402 (39th)

MONTANA (MT)

N/E LOCATION 47° 00' N, 110° 00' W

STATE CAPITAL Helena

LARGEST CITY Billings

AREA 380,838 km²; 147,042 mi² (4th)

POPULATION 957,861 (44th)

OREGON (OR)

N/E LOCATION 44° 30' N, 120° 30' W

STATE CAPITAL Salem

LARGEST CITY Portland

AREA 254,805 km²; 98,380 mi² (9th)

POPULATION 3,747,455 (27th)

WYOMING (WY)

N/E LOCATION 43° 00' N, 107° 30' W

STATE CAPITAL Cheyenne

LARGEST CITY Cheyenne

AREA 253,336 km²; 97,813 mi² (10th)

POPULATION 522,830 (51st)

CALIFORNIA (CA)

N/E LOCATION 37° 00' N, 119° 30' W

STATE CAPITAL Sacramento

LARGEST CITY Los Angeles

AREA 423,970 km²; 163,695 mi² (3rd)

POPULATION 36,553,215 (1st)

NEVADA (NV)

N/E LOCATION 39° 00' N, 116° 30' W

STATE CAPITAL Carson City

LARGEST CITY Las Vegas

AREA 286,351 km²; 110,560 mi² (7th)

POPULATION 2,565,382 (35th)

UTAH (UT)

N/E LOCATION 39° 00' N, 111° 30' W

STATE CAPITAL Salt Lake City

LARGEST CITY Salt Lake City

AREA 219,887 km²; 84,898 mi² (13th)

POPULATION 2,645,330 (34th)

COLORADO (CO)

N/E LOCATION 39° 00' N, 105° 30' W

STATE CAPITAL Denver

LARGEST CITY Denver

AREA 269,601 km²; 104,093 mi² (8th)

POPULATION 4,861,515 (22nd)

ARIZONA (AZ)

N/E LOCATION 34° 00' N, 112° 00' W

STATE CAPITAL Phoenix

LARGEST CITY Phoenix

AREA 295,254 km²; 113,998 mi² (6th)

POPULATION 6,338,755 (16th)

NEW MEXICO (NM)

N/E LOCATION 34° 30' N, 106° 00' W

STATE CAPITAL Santa Fe

LARGEST CITY Albuquerque

AREA 314,915 km²; 121,589 mi² (5th)

POPULATION 1,969,915 (36th)

HAWAII (HI)

N/E LOCATION 20° 00' N, 155° 40' W

STATE CAPITAL Honolulu

LARGEST CITY Honolulu

AREA 28,311 km²; 10,930 mi² (43rd)

POPULATION 1,283,388 (42nd)

Figures in brackets indicate the state's ranking within the USA. For example, Alaska is the largest state by area and is ranked 47th in terms of population size.

THE GRAND CANYON, ARIZONA
The Grand Canyon is the largest gorge on Earth, measuring 1,600 metres deep, 446 kilometres long and up to 30 kilometres wide. The canyon has extreme weather conditions. Summer temperatures can reach 40° C, while in winter -18°C is common.

NORTH AMERICA

USA: MIDWEST

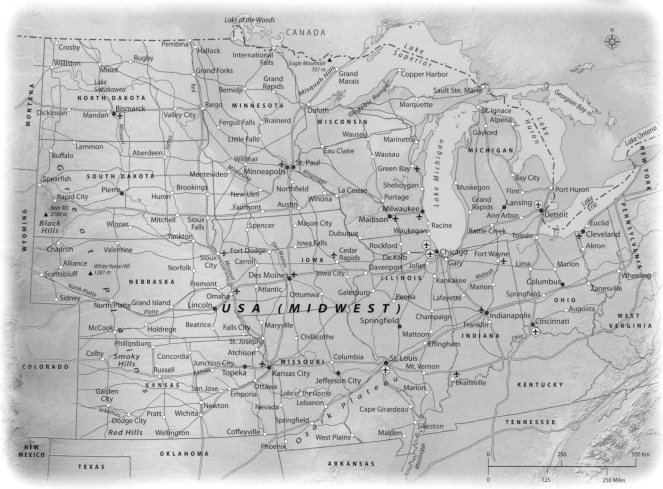

The heartland of the United States, the Midwest, consists of those states situated around the Great Lakes to the north and the states that mark the geographical centre of the country. The region, as defined by the US Census Bureau, comprises twelve states.

Settled by the French, it was not until 1803, with the enactment of the Louisiana Purchase, that these central states officially became part of the US. The landscape here is dominated by flat grasslands, known

as prairies; the states of North Dakota, South Dakota, Nebraska and Kansas are often referred to as the Great Plains States. Typically the economy of the Midwest is agrarian, and cereal crops have traditionally been the most important commodity. During the period leading up to the American Civil War, some of the southern states of the Midwest, particularly Ohio, provided assistance to slaves escaping from the plantations of the South; known as the 'underground railway', passage was provided to Lake Erie, the gateway to

Canada. Following the Civil War, during the early decades of the twentieth century, migration into the industrialized urban centres of the Midwest saw a massive population expansion. Cities such as Chicago, currently the third most populous city in the US, Detroit, which straddles the US–Canadian border and is the centre of the automobile industry, Indianapolis and Minneapolis developed rapidly, while rural communities of German, Dutch and Scandinavian immigrants were also established.

NORTH DAKOTA (ND)

N/E LOCATION 47° 30' N, 100° 30' W

STATE CAPITAL Bismarck

LARGEST CITY Fargo

AREA 183,112 km²; 70,699 mi² (19th)

POPULATION 639,715 (48th)

SOUTH DAKOTA (SD)

N/E LOCATION 44° 30' N, 100° 30' W

STATE CAPITAL Pierre

LARGEST CITY Sioux Falls

AREA 199,731 km²; 77,116 mi² (17th)

POPULATION 796,214 (46th)

MINNESOTA (MN)

N/E LOCATION 46° 00' N, 94° 30' W

STATE CAPITAL St. Paul

LARGEST CITY Minneapolis

AREA 225,171 km²; 86,939 mi² (12th)

POPULATION 5,197,621 (21st)

WISCONSIN (WI)

N/E LOCATION 44° 30' N, 89° 30' W

STATE CAPITAL Madison

LARGEST CITY Milwaukee

AREA 169,639 km²; 65,497 mi² (23rd)

POPULATION 5,601,640 (20th)

MICHIGAN (MI)

N/E LOCATION 44° 00' N, 85° 00' W

STATE CAPITAL Lansing

LARGEST CITY Detroit

AREA 250,494 km²; 96,716 mi² (11th)

POPULATION 10,071,822 (8th)

NEBRASKA (NE)

N/E LOCATION 41° 30' N, 100° 00' W

STATE CAPITAL Lincoln

LARGEST CITY Omaha

AREA 200,345 km²; 77,353 mi² (16th)

POPULATION 1,774,571 (38th)

IOWA (IA)

N/E LOCATION 42° 00' N, 93° 30' W

STATE CAPITAL Des Moines

LARGEST CITY Des Moines

AREA 145,743 km²; 56,271 mi² (26th)

POPULATION 2,988,046 (30th)

ILLINOIS (IL)

N/E LOCATION 40° 00' N, 89° 00' W

STATE CAPITAL Springfield

LARGEST CITY Chicago

AREA 149,998 km²; 57,914 mi² (25th)

POPULATION 12,852,548 (5th)

CHICAGO
Chicago, largest city in the state of Illinois.

INDIANA (IN)

N/E LOCATION 40° 00' N, 86° 00' W

STATE CAPITAL Indianapolis

LARGEST CITY Indianapolis

AREA 94,322 km²; 36,417 mi² (38th)

POPULATION 6,345,289 (15th)

OHIO (OH)

N/E LOCATION 40° 00' N, 83° 00' W

STATE CAPITAL Columbus

LARGEST CITY Columbus

AREA 116,096 km²; 44,824 mi² (34th)

POPULATION 11,466,917 (7th)

KANSAS (KS)

N/E LOCATION 38° 30' N, 98° 30' W

STATE CAPITAL Topeka

LARGEST CITY Wichita

AREA 213,096 km²; 82,276 mi² (15th)

POPULATION 2,775,997 (33rd)

MISSOURI (MO)

N/E LOCATION 38° 00' N, 92° 00' W

STATE CAPITAL Jefferson City

LARGEST CITY Kansas City

AREA 180,533 km²; 69,704 mi² (21st)

POPULATION 5,878,415 (18th)

AGRICULTURE
The income from cereal crops is a major contributor to the economy of the Midwest.

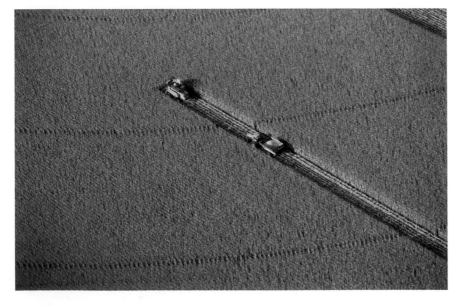

NORTH AMERICA

USA: NORTH-EAST

Home to the rugged states of New England and the great cities of New York, Philadelphia and Boston, the North-east has traditionally been considered the gateway to the United States for millions of European immigrants and visitors since the seventeenth century.

The Pilgrim colonies established along the Massachusetts coast during the first half of the seventeenth century saw the first wave of mass immigration. Since then the North-east has been at the forefront of change. It led the revolution against British rule, it was one of the first areas to become industrialized and one of the first to voice opposition to slavery. The region is also traditionally associated with education and many of the country's oldest and most highly regarded universities, such as Harvard and Yale, can be found there.

New York, the largest city in the North-east, is the most populous urban centre in the United States. It is home to around 8,300,000 inhabitants, although 36 per cent of that population was born outside the USA. Built across three islands, Manhattan, Staten Island and Long Island, the city has one of the most recognizable skylines in the world with features such as the Statue of Liberty, the Chrysler Building and the Empire State Building. The Empire State Building

was, from its completion in 1931, the tallest building in the world until the construction of the World Trade Center towers in the 1970s. These twin towers were infamously destroyed during the terrorist attacks on

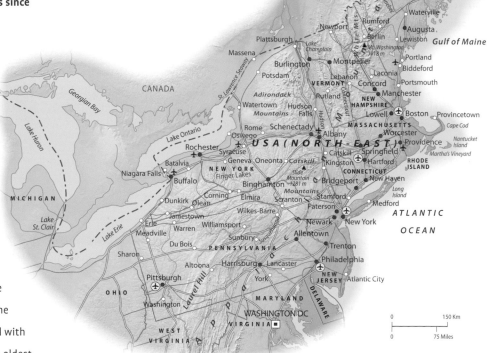

NEW YORK CITY
Times Square, one of the symbols of New York.

NEW YORK (NY)

N/E LOCATION 43º 00' N, 75º 00' W

STATE CAPITAL Albany

LARGEST CITY New York City

AREA 141,299 km²; 54,555 mi² (27th)

POPULATION 19,297,729 (3rd)

NEW HAMPSHIRE (NH)

N/E LOCATION 44º 00' N, 72º 44' W

STATE CAPITAL Concord

LARGEST CITY Manchester

AREA 24,216 km²; 9,349 mi² (46th)

POPULATION 1,315,828 (41st)

CONNECTICUT (CT)

N/E LOCATION 41º 40' N, 72º 40' W

STATE CAPITAL Hartford

LARGEST CITY Bridgeport

AREA 14,357 km²; 5,543 mi² (48th)

POPULATION 3,502,309 (29th)

NEW JERSEY (NJ)

N/E LOCATION 40º 00' N, 74º 30' W

STATE CAPITAL Trenton

LARGEST CITY Newark

AREA 22,588 km²; 8,721 mi² (47th)

POPULATION 8,685,920 (11th)

MAINE (ME)

N/E LOCATION 45º 30' N, 69º 00' W

STATE CAPITAL Augusta

LARGEST CITY Portland

AREA 91,646 km²; 35,384 mi² (39th)

POPULATION 1,317,207 (40th)

RHODE ISLAND (RI)

N/E LOCATION 41º 41' N, 71º 30' W

STATE CAPITAL Providence

LARGEST CITY Providence

AREA 4,002 km²; 1,545 mi² (50th)

POPULATION 1,057,832 (43rd)

VERMONT (VT)

N/E LOCATION 44º 00' N, 72º 00' W

STATE CAPITAL Montpelier

LARGEST CITY Burlington

AREA 24,901 km²; 9,614 mi² (45th)

POPULATION 621,254 (49th)

MASSACHUSETTS (MA)

N/E LOCATION 42º 20' N, 72º 00' W

STATE CAPITAL Boston

LARGEST CITY Boston

AREA 27,336 km²; 10,554 mi² (44th)

POPULATION 6,449,755 (14th)

PENNSYLVANIA (PA)

N/E LOCATION 41º 00' N, 78º 00' W

STATE CAPITAL Harrisburg

LARGEST CITY Philadelphia

AREA 119,283 km²; 46,055 mi² (33rd)

POPULATION 12,432,792 (6th)

the city on September 11th, 2001. The state of New York shares lake borders with the Canadian state of Ontario; between two of these Great Lakes are the Niagara Falls, which are a source of both tourist income and hydroelectric power.

The state of Pennsylvania is home to Philadelphia, birthplace of the Declaration of Independence and the US Constitution. This state is also one of the US's most economically productive, with large manufacturing and agricultural sectors, although on the whole the states of the North-east have a wealth that rests less upon manufacturing and more on post-industrial services and financial sectors.

NIAGARA FALLS
Niagara Falls consist of three separate waterfalls called Horseshoe Falls, American Falls and the smaller Bridal Veil Falls. At night most of the water is diverted into tunnels and used to turn turbines which produce electricity.

NORTH AMERICA

USA: SOUTH

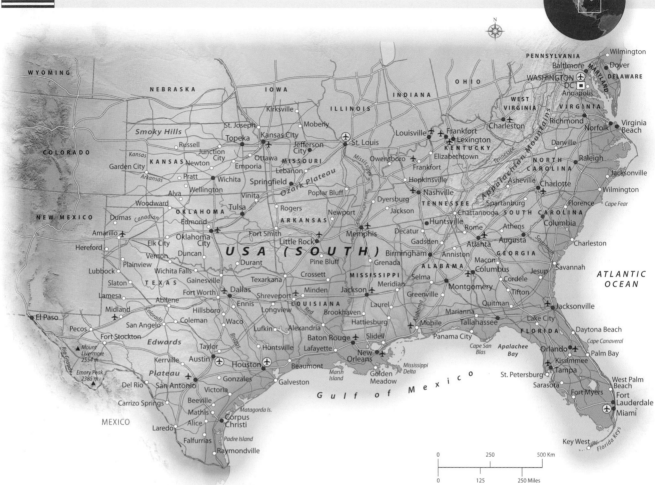

WYOMING

NEBRASKA

IOWA

ILLINOIS

INDIA

OHIO

PENNSYLVANIA

Wilmington

Baltimore · Dover

WASHINGTON DELAWARE

DC

Annapolis

WEST VIRGINIA

VIRGINIA

Richmond · Norfolk

Kirksville

Moberly

Louisville · Frankfort

Lexington

Charleston

Danville

Virginia Beach

Smoky Hills

St. Joseph

Topeka Kansas City

St. Louis

KENTUCKY

Raleigh

COLORADO

Russell

Junction City

Jefferson City

Owensboro

Elizabethtown

NORTH CAROLINA

Asheville Charlotte

Jacksonville

KANSAS

Newton

Ottawa

Springfield

MISSOURI

Lebanon

Frankfort

Hopkinsville

Nashville

Wilmington

Kansas

Garden City

Emporia

Poplar Bluff

Dyersburg

TENNESSEE

Spartanburg

Florence

Cape Fear

Arkansas

Pratt

Wichita

Ozark Plateau

Jackson

Chattanooga

SOUTH CAROLINA

Alva

Wellington

Vinita

Rogers

Newport

Huntsville

Rome

Athens

Columbia

Woodward

OKLAHOMA

Tulsa

ARKANSAS

Memphis

Decatur

Gadsden

Atlanta

Augusta

Charleston

NEW MEXICO

Dumas

Canadian

Edmond

Fort Smith

Little Rock

USA (SOUTH)

Birmingham

Anniston

GEORGIA

Savannah

Amarillo

Elk City

Oklahoma City

Durant

Pine Bluff

Grenada

ALABAMA

Macon

Columbus

Jesup

ATLANTIC OCEAN

Hereford

Vernon

Duncan

Crossett

MISSISSIPPI

Selma

Montgomery

Cordele

Tifton

Plainview

Wichita Falls

Gainesville

Texarkana

Minden

Jackson

Meridian

Quitman

Lubbock

Slaton

TEXAS

Fort Worth

Dallas

Shreveport

LOUISIANA

Greenville

Marianna

Jacksonville

Lamesa

Abilene

Ennis

Longview

Red

Laurel

Mobile

Tallahassee

Lake City

FLORIDA

Daytona Beach

Midland

Hillsboro

Waco

Lufkin

Alexandria

Hattiesburg

Panama City

Cape Canaveral

El Paso

Colorado

Coleman

Baton Rouge

Slidell

Cape San Blas

Apalachee Bay

Orlando

Palm Bay

Pecos

Fort Stockton

Edwards

Taylor

Huntsville

Lafayette

New Orleans

Kissimmee

Tampa

Mount Livermore 2554 m

Kerrville

Austin

Houston

Beaumont

Marsh Island

Golden Meadow

Mississippi Delta

St. Petersburg

West Palm Beach

Emory Peak 2385 m

Plateau

Gonzales

Galveston

Gulf of Mexico

Sarasota

Fort Myers

Fort Lauderdale

Del Rio

San Antonio

Victoria

Miami

Carrizo Springs

Beeville

Matagorda Is.

MEXICO

Mathis

Alice

Corpus Christi

Key West

Laredo

Padre Island

Florida Keys

Falfurrias

Raymondville

0   250   500 Km

0   125   250 Miles

The South is one of the Census Bureau's four regions of the US and is made up of sixteen states, including the eleven states which formed the Confederacy during the American Civil War, as well as the District of Colombia, home to the city of Washington, the federal capital of the United States.

This large and diverse region ranges from the temperate, agricultural, states to the north, including Kentucky, West Virginia and Maryland, to the arid states of Oklahoma and Texas and the more tropical Gulf states

MIAMI BEACH, FLORIDA
The Colony Hotel is one of a few dozen meticulously restored buildings in the Art Deco National Historic District in Miami Beach.

of Louisiana and Florida. The Appalachian Mountains stretch down through the northern states into Mississippi and Alabama and are generally associated with the timber and coal mining industries. In contrast, the Florida peninsula is home to the Everglades National Park with its swathes of swampland, river systems and saw-grass prairies. The largest river in the United States, the Mississippi, wends its way through the region; it is over 3,700 kilometres long from the source in Minnesota to its mouth in Louisiana. The river is the focal point of a number of important cities in the south including St Louis and New Orleans, and its alluvial plain provides a rich source of fertile land. To the north, Washington DC is the political heart of the US

and home of the White House and a number of memorials recognizing key figures or moments in US history.

Much of the South retains traditions and a culture which separates it from the rest of the country, with influences from a large Native American population, African-Americans and immigrants from the Caribbean and South America. It's antebellum history as an area rich in tobacco and cotton production with subsequent African slave ownership has defined it as a region. Following the Confederate defeat in the Civil war, African-Americans were freed and initially enfranchised, but the growth of the white supremacist movement led to increased inequality and

WASHINGTON DC
The White House has been the residence of every US president since John Adams.

disenfranchisement. This led in turn to massive migration north and, during the 1960s, to the Civil Rights movement, giving rise to prominent figures such as Malcolm X and Martin Luther King. Although today the South benefits from industrialization, it remains a generally agricultural region and pockets of poverty, particularly in some of the larger metropolitan areas still exist. The wealthier states include Texas with its rich oil reserves, Georgia, which is the centre for many multinational companies, and North Carolina, which is a centre for higher education and research.

NORTH AMERICA

WASHINGTON DC (DC)

N/E LOCATION 38° 54' N, 77° 00' W

AREA 177 km2 ; 68 mi2 (51st)

POPULATION 588292 (50th)

KENTUCKY (KY)

N/E LOCATION 37° 00' N, 85° 00' W

STATE CAPITAL Frankfort

LARGEST CITY Louisville

AREA 104,659 km²; 40,409 mi² (37th)

POPULATION 4,241,474 (26th)

WEST VIRGINIA (WV)

N/E LOCATION 38° 00' N, 80° 00' W

STATE CAPITAL Charleston

LARGEST CITY Charleston

AREA 62,755 km²; 24,229 mi² (41st)

POPULATION 1812035 (37th)

MARYLAND (MD)

N/E LOCATION 39° 00' N, 76° 36' W

STATE CAPITAL Annapolis

LARGEST CITY Baltimore

AREA 32,133 km2; 12,406 mi2 (42nd)

POPULATION 5,618,344 (19th)

DELAWARE (DE)

N/E LOCATION 39° 00' N, 75° 30' W

STATE CAPITAL Dover

LARGEST CITY Wilmington

AREA 6,447 km²; 2,489 mi² (49th)

POPULATION 864,764 (45th)

VIRGINIA (VA)

N/E LOCATION 37° 30' N, 79° 00' W

STATE CAPITAL Richmond

LARGEST CITY Virginia Beach

AREA 110,785 km²; 42,774 mi² (35th)

POPULATION 7,712,091 (12th)

OKLAHOMA (OK)

N/E LOCATION 35° 00' N, 97° 00' W

STATE CAPITAL Oklahoma City

LARGEST CITY Oklahoma City

AREA 181,036 km²; 69,898 mi² (20th)

POPULATION 3,617,316 (28th)

ARKANSAS (AR)

N/E LOCATION 35° 00' N, 92° 00' W

STATE CAPITAL Little Rock

LARGEST CITY Little Rock

AREA 137,732 km²; 53,178 mi² (29th)

POPULATION 2,834,797 (32nd)

TENNESSEE (TN)

N/E LOCATION 35° 45' N, 86° 00' W

STATE CAPITAL Nashville

LARGEST CITY Memphis

AREA 109,151 km²; 42,143 mi² (36th)

POPULATION 6,156,719 (17th)

NORTH CAROLINA (NC)

N/E LOCATION 35° 45' N, 79° 00' W

STATE CAPITAL Raleigh

LARGEST CITY Charlotte

AREA 139,389 km²; 53,818 mi² (28th)

POPULATION 9,061,032 (10th)

TEXAS (TX)

N/E LOCATION 32° 00' N, 100° 00' W

STATE CAPITAL Austin

LARGEST CITY Houston

AREA 695,621 km²; 268,580 mi² (2nd)

POPULATION 23,904,380 (2nd)

SOUTH CAROLINA (SC)

N/E LOCATION 34° 00' N, 81° 00' W

STATE CAPITAL Columbia

LARGEST CITY Columbia

AREA 82,932 km²; 32,020 mi² (40th)

POPULATION 4,407,709 (24th)

LOUISIANA (LA)

N/E LOCATION 31° 00' N, 92° 00' W

STATE CAPITAL Baton Rouge

LARGEST CITY New Orleans

AREA 134,264 km²; 51,839 mi² (31st)

POPULATION 4,293,204 (25th)

MISSISSIPPI (MS)

N/E LOCATION 32° 30' N, 89° 45' W

STATE CAPITAL Jackson

LARGEST CITY Jackson

AREA 125,434 km²; 48,430 mi² (32nd)

POPULATION 2,918,785 (31st)

FLORIDA EVERGLADES
A vast wilderness of swamp and marshland in southern Florida, the shallow waters and 10,000 islands of the Everglades are home to some rare and endangered species.

ALABAMA (AL)

N/E LOCATION 32º 30' N, 87º 00' W

STATE CAPITAL Montgomery

LARGEST CITY Birmingham

AREA 135,765 km²; 52,419 mi² (30th)

POPULATION 4,627,851 (23rd)

GEORGIA (GA)

N/E LOCATION 32º 30' N, 83º 00' W

STATE CAPITAL Atlanta

LARGEST CITY Atlanta

AREA 153,910 km²; 59,424 mi² (24th)

POPULATION 9,544,750 (9th)

FLORIDA (FL)

N/E LOCATION 28º 00' N, 81º 30' W

STATE CAPITAL Tallahassee

LARGEST CITY Jacksonville

AREA 170,304 km²; 65,754 mi² (22nd)

POPULATION 18,251,243 (4th)

BERMUDA

32º 20' N, 64º 45' W | 53.3 KM² | 21.6 MI² | UTC-4

Bermuda, or the Bermuda Islands, is a group of approximately 138 islands and islets in the North Atlantic Ocean about 1000 kilometres east of North Carolina.

Named after Juan Bermudez, a Spanish navigator who first sighted the uninhabited islands in 1503, they became the first colony of the British Empire when settled by some British emigrants, who were shipwrecked on their way to Virginia in 1609. Bermuda remains a self-governing territory of the United Kingdom. The islands are formed from volcanic rocks; the coral that caps them accounts for the famous pink sand beaches. Bermuda has the world's third-highest per capita income, derived mainly from financial services and tourism, the

vast majority of the islands' visitors coming from the USA. The proximity of the Gulf Stream gives Bermuda its subtropical climate but also makes the region vulnerable to hurricanes.

HAMILTON
A view of the waterfront at Hamilton.

FACT FILE

LOCAL	Bermuda
SOVEREIGN STATE	United Kingdom
CAPITAL/MAIN CITY	Hamilton
CURRENCY	Bermudian Dollar (BMD)
MEMBERSHIP	CARICOM (Associate)
GOVERNMENT	Parliamentary; Self-Governing Territory (British Overseas Territory)
POPULATION	66,536
POP. DENSITY	1,248/km²; 3,080/mi²
GDP	4.5 Billion US$
LANGUAGE(S)	English, Portuguese
ETHNICITY	Black 55%, White 34%, Mixed 6%,
RELIGION	Anglican 23%, Roman Catholic 15%, African Methodist Episcopal 11%, Other Protestant 18%
CLIMATE	Subtropical

NORTH AMERICA

CENTRAL AMERICA AND THE CARIBBEAN

Colonized by Europe since the fifteenth century, much of Central America remains poor and politically unstable, while many of the Caribbean islands have benefited from the income from tourists from Europe and North America.

Central America, also known as Meso-America, and the island territories of the Caribbean Sea lie geographically close together and they have experienced similar histories since Christopher Columbus' 'discovery' of the New World in 1492 led to invasion and settlement by the Spanish from the early decades of sixteenth century.

In the era before 1492, known as pre-Columbian, various advanced civilizations

with rich cultures thrived throughout Central America, culminating in the Aztec empire, which reached its peak in the fifteenth century. This was defenceless, however, against the Spanish soldiers and colonizers of the sixteenth century and was mercilessly exploited and destroyed. Though much of the pre-Columbian history was expunged during the subsequent centuries of Spanish colonial rule, archaeologists have steadily

uncovered more about the fascinating civilizations of the Maya and Aztec peoples. The astonishing architecture of their ancient cities remains a major tourist attraction.

For nearly two hundred years Central America and the Caribbean were a pivotal point in the economies of several European countries; the so-called 'Triangular Trade' transported slaves, sugar and rum, among other highly valued commodities, between

CENTRAL AMERICA

Africa, Central American and Caribbean plantations, and Europe.

Although Central America is considered geographically to be part of North America, culturally the region has a stronger connection with South America, also colonized largely by the Spanish. The Caribbean, however, has a more mixed heritage, with the islands all former colonies or present-day territories of a number of European countries or the USA; many changed hands several times as the fortunes of European empires waxed and waned. In post-colonial times, the decline of the sugar and banana industries has left many reliant economically on tourism and the provision of off-shore tax havens.

Although the two areas share a wildness and beauty attractive to tourists, another common factor is their vulnerability to natural disasters such as earthquakes, arising from their geophysical location on tectonic plates, and their exposure to tropical

TEOTIHUCAN
The pyramid of the Sun at Teotihucan in Mexico.

cyclones during the hurricane season. Human influence has increased the impact of natural disasters with the felling of forests and rainforests destabilizing the friable tropical soil.

Mexico, with its emergent economy, is the local giant but political and economic progress there, as elsewhere in the region, is compromised by increasing lawlessness as drug cartels undermine the structures of government.

Map labels: (UK), Virgin Is. (UK), JAN, JUAN, Virgin Is. (US), Anguilla (UK), ANTIGUA & BARBUDA, ST KITTS & NEVIS, Guadeloupe (FR), DOMINICA, Martinique (FR), ST. LUCIA, BARBADOS, ST VINCENT & THE GRENADINES, GRENADA, Leeward Islands, Windward Islands, Lesser Antilles, CAS, Cumaná, PORT OF SPAIN, TRINIDAD AND TOBAGO, Ciudad Guayana, Tucupita, GUYANA

MEXICO

23° 00' N, 102° 00' W | 1,972,550 KM² | 761,606 MI² | UTC-6

The fifth largest country in the Americas, Mexico is a swiftly developing industrial nation which is also the most populous Spanish-speaking country in the world.

Geography

Comprising the southernmost tip of North America as it reaches into the isthmus of Central America, Mexico is generally not considered to be part of Central America, but is instead Middle America or 'Mesoamerica'. The border with the United States stretches for 3,141 kilometres, much of which is defined by the course of the Rio Grande. Wide lowland plains border both the Atlantic and the Pacific coasts; the north-western coast is dominated by the Baja California peninsula. The interior of northern Mexico is mountainous, rising to a central plateau which is punctuated with a number of river valleys. These valleys are the location for several of the major cities, including the capital, Mexico City, and Guadalajara. The two main mountain ranges are the Sierra Madre Occidental (West) and Oriental (East), which are an extension of the Rocky Mountains of the southern US. Situated within a volcanic region, a number of peaks in Mexico are dormant, including the

MEXICO CITY
The Palacio del Belles Artes in Mexico City.

FACT FILE

LOCAL NAME United Mexican States

CAPITAL CITY Mexico City (Federal District)

CURRENCY Mexican Peso (MXN)

MEMBERSHIP APEC, CAN (observer), CARICOM (observer), CE (observer), G15, G24, LAIA (observer), SELA, OAS, OECD, RG, WTO

GOVERNMENT Federal Presidential Republic

POPULATION 107,801,063

POP. DENSITY 55/km²; 142/mi²

GDP 1.353 Trillion US$

LANGUAGE(S) Spanish, Mayan, Nahuatl

ETHNICITY Mestizo 60%, Amerindian or predominantly Amerindian 30%, White 9%

RELIGION Roman Catholic 77%, Protestant 6%

CLIMATE Tropical, Subtropical, Temperate, Arid, Semi-arid

REGIONAL DIVISIONS 31 States and 1 Federal District; these are grouped into 6 Tourist Regions

ECONOMIC ACTIVITIES Agriculture, Food and Beverages, Tobacco, Chemicals, Iron and Steel, Petroleum, Mining, Textiles, Clothing, Motor Vehicles, Consumer Durables, Tourism

NATURAL RESOURCES Petroleum, Silver, Copper, Gold, Lead, Zinc, Natural Gas, Timber

highest, Pico de Orizaba (5,700 metres). The Yucatán peninsula, which curves northward from the south-west is mainly flat landscape. Despite over 150 rivers, freshwater is unevenly distributed around the country; further north the landscape is more arid. Mexico City is the largest urban area and one of the most densely populated cities in the world, with over 8 million inhabitants.

History

Before the arrival of the Spanish in 1519, Mexico was the centre for a number of important civilizations; the Toltecs with their city states were followed by the Aztec peoples, whose capital Tenochtitlan was the Mesoamerican equivalent of Ancient Rome. In 1521 the Conquistadors, led by Hernan Cortes, laid siege to the city with the aid of a number of indigenous tribes, keen to reduce the power of the Aztecs. The Aztec capital became the administrative capital for the Spanish, who renamed it Mexico City. At least 60 per cent of Mexico's current population are mestizos, mixed-race descendants of the Spanish and the Amerindians; minority languages such as Mayan, Nahuatl and Zapotec are still spoken. Independence from Spain was achieved in 1836; however, civil strife followed and within just ten years war with the US broke out over their contested annexation of Texas. The early twentieth century saw political instability and civil unrest; one of the consequences is the current disparity in the distribution of wealth. Issues of massive emigration to the United States and the export of illegal narcotics manufactured in Mexico still raise tensions.

Economy

The Mexican economy is stable, with a mix of modern infrastructures and outdated industries. Agricultural cash crops include corn, wheat, beans and exotic fruits, while industrial exports are food, tobacco, chemicals, iron and steel. With good reserves of natural gas and oil, Mexico is largely energy-independent. In 1994 Mexico signed the North American Free Trade Agreement with the US and Canada; although a recession was initially triggered by the devaluation of the peso, the economy has since returned to growth.

CHICHEN ITZA, NORTHERN YUCATÁN PENINSULA
Kukulcan pyramid in the Mayan city of Chichen Itza.

CENTRAL AMERICA/CARIBBEAN

GUATEMALA

15° 30' N, 90° 15' W | 108,890 KM² | 42,043 MI² | UTC-6

Guatemala has shown signs in recent years of overcoming the legacy of its troubled past, when the later decades of the twentieth century endured thirty-six years of guerrilla war.

Geography

Bordering four countries and with two coastlines, Guatemala is the second largest country on the isthmus of Central America. The majority of the landscape is mountainous highlands, with two major ranges, the Sierra Madre and the Cuchumatanes. There are thirty-seven volcanoes in the Sierra Madre, four of which are active. The north of the country is the tropical lowland area of the Petén, once the centre of the ancient Mayan civilization. The capital, Guatemala City, is, like other major cities, located in the central highlands.

History

When the Mayan civilization collapsed in around AD 900, archaeological ruins remained which today provide the focus for tourism. In 1518 the Spanish brought diseases which decimated the Amerindian population. Guatemala won independence from Spain in 1821, initially as part of the Mexican Empire, but eventually as a separate state. During the twentieth century, a series of dictatorships and military coups resulted in almost continuous conflict, much of which was financed by the US. Paramilitary oppression led to a diaspora of over 1 million Guatemalans, most of whom fled to the United States.

Economy

Although still a developing country, with 30 per cent of the population living below the poverty line, Guatemala has a growing economy. Agriculture accounts for one-tenth of GDP; sugar, coffee, bananas and beans are major products. Other commodities include textiles, tourism and ethanol. High unemployment and a huge disparity in the distribution of wealth remain problematic.

FACT FILE

LOCAL NAME Republic of Guatemala

CAPITAL CITY Guatemala City

CURRENCY Quetzal (GTQ), US Dollar (USD)

MEMBERSHIP G24, G77, LAIA (observer), OAS, RG, SELA, WTO

GOVERNMENT Constitutional Republic

POPULATION 13,686,399

POP. DENSITY 126/km²; 326/mi²

GDP 64.76 Billion US$

LANGUAGE(S) Spanish, Amerindian languages

ETHNICITY Mestizo and European 59%, K'iche 9%, Kaqchikel 8%, Mam 7%, Q'eqchi 6%, Other Mayan 9%

RELIGION Roman Catholic 73%, Protestant 11%, Indigenous Christian 8%, Other Christian 4%,

CLIMATE Tropical

REGIONAL DIVISIONS 22 Departments are divided into 332 Municipalities; Department of Guatemala is the location of the capital and is the most populous Department

ECONOMIC ACTIVITIES Agriculture (including sugar, coffee, bananas and beans) Textiles and Clothing, Furniture, Chemicals, Petroleum, Metals, Rubber, Tourism

NATURAL RESOURCES Petroleum, Nickel, Rare Timbers, Fish, Chicle, Hydropower

TIKAL
Tikal in northen Guatemala is one of the most important Mayan sites in Central America.

BELIZE

17° 15′ N, 88° 45′ W | 22,966 KM² | 8,867 MI² | UTC-6

Once part of the British Empire, known as British Honduras until independence in 1981, Belize is the only officially English-speaking country in Central America.

To the north, Belize has mainly tropical forests; its Caribbean coastal plains are swampy and the landscape rises to low mountains in the south-eastern Maya range. Its barrier reef is the world's second-largest. Belize is vulnerable to the frequent hurricanes of the region as well as to flooding. Even with the lowest population density in Central America, the country has a highly diverse society, influenced by its history as a pawn in Spanish and British colonial disputes. Tourism and agriculture are economic mainstays, with sugar and banana exports being of particular importance. The discovery of oil in 2006 has boosted the economy; however, debt, poverty and high unemployment are persistent concerns.

FACT FILE

LOCAL NAME	Belize
CAPITAL CITY	Belmopan
CURRENCY	Belizean Dollar (BZD)
MEMBERSHIP	C, CARICOM, G77, OAS, SELA, WTO
GOVERNMENT	Parliamentary Democracy
POPULATION	293,717
POP. DENSITY	13/km²; 33/mi²
GDP	2.444 Billion US$
LANGUAGE(S)	Spanish, Creole, Mayan, English, Garifuna, German
ETHNICITY	Mestizo 49%, Creole 25%, Maya 11%, Garifuna 6%
RELIGION	Roman Catholic 50%, Protestant 27% (Pentecostal 7%, Anglican 5%, Seventh-day Adventist 5%, Mennonite 4%, Methodist 4%)
CLIMATE	Tropical

RAIN FOREST
The jaguar's range extends from Mexico down to the northern areas of South America.

HONDURAS

15° 00′ N, 86° 30′ W | 112,090 KM² | 43,278 MI² | UTC-6

Formerly distinguished from British Honduras (now Belize) as Spanish Honduras, this relatively large country in Central America belonged to the Spanish Empire until 1821.

FACT FILE

LOCAL NAME	Republic of Honduras
CAPITAL CITY	Tegucigalpa
CURRENCY	Lempira (HNL)
MEMBERSHIP	G77, LAIA (observer), SELA, OAS, RG, WTO
GOVERNMENT	Democratic Constitutional Republic
POPULATION	7,246,016
POP. DENSITY	65/km²; 167/mi²
GDP	32.26 Billion US$
LANGUAGE(S)	Spanish, Amerindian
ETHNICITY	Mestizo 90%, Amerindian 7%, Black 2%, White 1%
RELIGION	Roman Catholic 97%, Protestant 3%
CLIMATE	Tropical, Temperate in mountains

With the Caribbean coast to the north and a short stretch of Pacific coast in the south at the Gulf of Fonseca, Honduras straddles the Central American isthmus. It has a mountainous interior, with a number of river valleys which are home to the majority of the population, including the capital, Tegucigalpa. A tense relationship with neighbour El Salvador culminated in a brief war in 1969. Later decades saw the rule of military dictatorships, and Honduras became embroiled in the struggles between Marxist Nicaragua, left-wing guerrillas in El Salvador and the US. With an economy relying upon agriculture, Honduras is generally poor; social inequalities have resulted in instability and high levels of violent crime. The situation was exacerbated in 1998 by the devastation caused by Hurricane Mitch.

EL SALVADOR

13° 50' N, 88° 55' W | 21,040 KM² | 8,124 MI² | UTC-6

Bordering the Pacific Ocean, Guatemala and Honduras, El Salvador is Central America's smallest and most densely populated country.

The mountainous terrain of El Salvador contains over twenty volcanoes and the country has experienced regular, often destructive, earthquakes. The high central plateau between two mountain ranges is home to a number of inland lakes as well as major towns and cities. A Spanish colony from 1525 until 1821, El Salvador was reluctantly part of the United Provinces of Central America until 1839. The twentieth century saw the brutal suppression of the rural indigenous poor by a series of military dictatorships. Civil war (1980–92) led to 75,000 deaths. Since then, El Salvador has struggled with rising gang crime, high unemployment and rural poverty.

FACT FILE

LOCAL NAME	Republic of El Salvador
CAPITAL CITY	San Salvador
CURRENCY	US Dollar (USD)
MEMBERSHIP	G77, OAS, SELA, RG, WTO
GOVERNMENT	Presidential Republic
POPULATION	6,952,819
POP. DENSITY	331/km²; 856/mi²
GDP	41.63 Billion US$
LANGUAGE(S)	Spanish, Nahuat
ETHNICITY	Mestizo 90%, White 9%, Amerindian 1%
RELIGION	Roman Catholic 57%, Protestant 21%, Jehovah's Witness 2%
CLIMATE	Tropical

NICARAGUA

13° 00' N, 85° 00' W | 129,494 KM² | 49,998 MI² | GMT +/- | UTC-6

The largest county in Central America, Nicaragua has extensive coastlines along the Pacific Ocean and the Caribbean Sea.

Situated between Honduras and Costa Rica, Nicaragua has a varied landscape. To the east the large rain-forested lowlands border the Atlantic 'mosquito' coast, which is punctuated by lagoons and deltas. The central highlands are the most populated region, where the majority of the country's main export, coffee, is grown. This fertile area is also home to a number of active volcanoes. The Pacific lowlands are dominated by large freshwater lakes. A turbulent post-independence history included the Somoza dictatorship and the ensuing left-wing Sandinista revolution in 1978. Eleven years of civil war between the Sandinistas and the US-sponsored Contras ended in 1990. Still politically unstable, Nicaragua is now a presidential democracy, although beset by corruption and heavy international debt.

FACT FILE

LOCAL NAME	Republic of Nicaragua
CAPITAL CITY	Managua
CURRENCY	Gold Cordoba (NIO)
MEMBERSHIP	G77, LAIA (observer), SELA, OAS, RG, WTO
GOVERNMENT	Presidential Republic
POPULATION	5,676,067
POP. DENSITY	44/km²; 114/mi²
GDP	16.17 Billion US$
LANGUAGE(S)	Spanish, Miskito
ETHNICITY	Mestizo 69%, White 17%, Black 9%, Amerindian 5%
RELIGION	Roman Catholic 73%, Evangelical 15%
CLIMATE	Tropical

OMETEPE ISLAND
A smoking volcano on Ometepe Island in the centre of Lake Nicaragua. Nicaragua has a chain of volcanoes running from the north to the south of the country, a number of which are active.

COSTA RICA

10° 00' N, 84° 00' W | 51,100 KM² | 19,730 MI² | GMT +/- | UTC-6

Located in southern Central America, Costa Rica was, in 1949, the first ever country to abolish its army by constitutional means.

Running from north to south, to the west of the region is a mountain range that serves as a spine to this narrow country. The low coastal plains are given over to tropical forests and mangrove swamps. A rich diversity of wildlife makes Costa Rica a popular destination for tourists. The most stable of the Central American countries, it

maintains positive international relations. Agriculture, technology and tourism support the economy, with bananas, beef and coffee the main exports.

FACT FILE

LOCAL NAME Republic of Costa Rica
CAPITAL CITY San José
CURRENCY Costa Rican Colon (CRC)
MEMBERSHIP G77, LAIA (observer), OAS, RG, SELA, WTO
GOVERNMENT Democratic Republic
POPULATION 4,534,435
POP. DENSITY 89/km²; 230/mi²
GDP 45.77 Billion US$
LANGUAGE(S) Spanish, English
ETHNICITY White (including mestizo) 94%, Black 3%, Amerindian 1%
RELIGION Roman Catholic 76%, Evangelical 14%
CLIMATE Tropical

PANAMA

9° 00' N, 80° 00' W | 78,200 KM² | 30,193 MI² | UTC-5

Connecting the two continents of the Americas, post-colonial Panama belonged to a union with Columbia until the United States enabled their secession in 1903.

Panama has a coastline of 2,490 kilometres; the two coastal plains are separated by rolling hills and a mountainous interior. The canal is situated on the saddle of the country. Opened in 1914, it had been one of the most complex and costly engineering projects in history; it is estimated 27,000 workers died during its construction. Formerly owned by the US, the canal and the surrounding territory were returned to Panama in 1999 following the removal of the dictator Manuel Noriega by US forces ten years earlier. Panama's strategic location results in an economy that relies upon the service industries, particularly commerce, trading, banking and tourism.

PANAMA CANAL
The canal is 81.6 kilometres long and connects the Pacific Ocean with the Caribbean Sea.

FACT FILE

LOCAL NAME Republic of Panama
CAPITAL CITY Panama City
CURRENCY Balboa (PAB); US Dollar (USD)
MEMBERSHIP CAN (observer), G77, LAIA (observer), SELA, OAS, RG, WTO
GOVERNMENT Constitutional Democracy
POPULATION 3,398,912
POP. DENSITY 44/km²; 113/mi²
GDP 34.81 Billion US$
LANGUAGE(S) Spanish, English
ETHNICITY Mestizo 70%, Amerindian and mixed (West Indian) 14%, White 10%, Amerindian 6%
RELIGION Roman Catholic 85%, Protestant 15%
CLIMATE Tropical

CUBA

21º 30' N, 80º 00' W | 110,860 KM² | 42,803 MI² | UTC-5

The Republic of Cuba consists of the largest island in the Caribbean along with several smaller, adjacent islands.

Geography

Cuba has a landscape that is mainly flat plains and rolling hills. There are three mountain ranges on the island: to the north-west, south-east and centre. The largest, the Sierra Maestra, is in the south-east. Cuba has 3,735 kilometres of coastline, with the Caribbean Sea to the south and the North Atlantic Ocean on its northern shores. Although the island was once covered in tropical forests, much of the land has been cleared for agriculture, particularly for sugarcane and, to a lesser extent, tobacco. Cuba's capital Havana is the largest city.

History

After Columbus discovered Cuba in 1492, in 1511 the Spanish built their first Cuban settlement at Baracoa. The indigenous population was gradually killed off, mainly by European diseases. The island was valued by the Spanish for its strategic position on the trade route; their rule was overthrown in 1898, with support from the United States. Concerns over Cuban annexation into the US kept it loyal to Spain for far longer than other Spanish colonies. Relations with the US soured during the twentieth century following the revolution against military dictator Batista. Cuba has since been a communist state, led for five decades by Fidel Castro, who resigned as prime minister in 2008.

Economy

The state-controlled economy suffered a downturn during the 1990s when Russian economic support was withdrawn. Special trading deals exist with Venezuela, which provides oil in return for medical personnel, and with Japan, which supplies cars and computers for sugar. Cuba also exports nickel and cobalt.

HAVANA
Havana Cathedral and the Plaza de la Catedral.

FACT FILE

LOCAL NAME Republic of Cuba

CAPITAL CITY Havana

CURRENCY Cuban Peso (CUP) and Convertible Peso (CUC)

MEMBERSHIP G77, LAIA, not IMF Member, not WB Member, OAS (suspended), SELA, WTO

GOVERNMENT Socialist Republic

POPULATION 11,265,216

POP. DENSITY 102/km²; 263/mi²

GDP 125.5 Billion US$

LANGUAGE(S) Spanish

ETHNICITY White 65%, Mulatto and Mestizo 25%, Black 10%

RELIGION Nominally 85% Roman Catholic prior to Castro assuming power; Protestants, Jehovah's Witnesses, Jews and Santeria are also represented

CLIMATE Tropical

REGIONAL DIVISIONS 14 Provinces and 1 Special Municipality; Ciudad de La Habana (national capital province) has the highest and most dense population

ECONOMIC ACTIVITIES Agriculture, Sugar, Petroleum, Tobacco, Rum, Construction, Nickel Mining, Steel, Cement, Agricultural Machinery, Pharmaceuticals, Biotechnology

NATURAL RESOURCES Cobalt, Nickel, Iron Ore, Chromium, Copper, Salt, Timber, Silica, Petroleum

THE BAHAMAS

24° 15' N, 76° 00' W | 13,940 KM² | 5,382 MI² | UTC-5

Situated just off the Florida Coast, the Bahamas is a popular tourist destination, and as a result it is one of the wealthiest of the Caribbean countries.

The Commonwealth of the Bahamas is an archipelago of over 2,000 cays and 700 islands, only thirty of which are inhabited.

The largest is Andros Island; the capital city Nassau is found on New Providence. San Salvador was the site of Columbus' first landing in the Americas. All the islands and cays are the surface projections of three great ocean banks, formed from fossilized coral and limestone. Their landscape is either rocky or mangrove swamp, with some islands being thickly forested. The first

island to be settled by European pilgrims was Eleuthera; the country eventually became a pirate haven. A British colony between 1783 and 1973, this prosperous country still struggles with drug-smuggling and people-trafficking.

FACT FILE

LOCAL NAME	Commonwealth of the Bahamas
CAPITAL CITY	Nassau
CURRENCY	Bahamian Dollar (BSD)
MEMBERSHIP	C, CARICOM, G77, OAS, SELA, WTO (observer)
GOVERNMENT	Parliamentary Democracy and Constitutional Monarchy
POPULATION	335,286
POP. DENSITY	24/km²; 62/mi²
GDP	8.55 Billion US$
LANGUAGE(S)	English, Creole (Haitian immigrants)
ETHNICITY	Black 85%, White 12%, Asian and Hispanic 3%
RELIGION	Baptist 35%, Anglican 15%, Roman Catholic 16%, Pentecostal 8%, Church of God 5%, Methodist 4%, Other Christian 15%
CLIMATE	Tropical Maritime

ATLANTIS RESORT
The Atlantis resort illuminated. Tourism is an important part of the economy of the island.

TURKS AND CAICOS ISLANDS

21° 45' N, 71° 35' W | 430 KM² | 166 MI² | UTC-5

A British overseas territory, the Turks and Caicos are two island groups that are separated by the Turk Island Passage.

Geographically, the Turks and Caicos are a continuation of the Bahamas Islands, but they are politically distinct. The fossilized coral and limestone islands are low and flat; many are covered with marshes and mangrove swamps. The most densely populated island is Providenciales in the Caicos. The island of Grand Turk is home to the capital, Cockburn Town. Surrounded by

coral reefs, the islands attract diving tourists, the main industry along with a strong

FACT FILE

LOCAL NAME	Turks and Caicos Islands
SOVEREIGN STATE	United Kingdom
CAPITAL/MAIN CITY	Grand Turk (Cockburn Town)
CURRENCY	US Dollar (USD)
MEMBERSHIP	CARICOM (associate)
GOVERNMENT	British Overseas Territory
POPULATION	22,352
POP. DENSITY	52/km²; 135/mi²
GDP	216 Million US$
LANGUAGE(S)	English
ETHNICITY	Black 90%, Mixed, European or North American 10%
RELIGION	Baptist 40%, Anglican 18%, Methodist 16%, Church of God 12%
CLIMATE	Tropical

financial services sector. Agricultural goods produced by the Turks and Caicos are mainly corn, cassava, beans and fish.

CENTRAL AMERICA/CARIBBEAN

JAMAICA
18° 15' N, 77° 30' W | 10,991 KM² | 4,244 MI² | UTC-5

Jamaica is part of the Greater Antilles group and is a lush and fertile mountainous island.

In 1655, the British forcibly evicted the Spanish from Santiago and turned Jamaica into a productive agricultural centre. The numerous sugar, cocoa and coffee plantations were worked by thousands of African slaves; Jamaica became the most slave-dependent nation in the world. With the abolition of slavery in 1834, most of the 750,000 freed men and women became small farmers. Independence from Britain was achieved in 1962 and the economy now relies upon the extraction of bauxite and tourism in addition to agriculture. Cultural exports include reggae music, the late Bob Marley being the most prominent musician. Violent crime and gang culture are persistent problems.

FACT FILE

LOCAL NAME	Jamaica
CAPITAL CITY	Kingston
CURRENCY	Jamaican Dollar (JMD)
MEMBERSHIP	C, CARICOM, G15, G77, OAS, SELA, WTO
GOVERNMENT	Parliamentary Democracy and Constitutional Monarchy
POPULATION	2,728,196
POP. DENSITY	248/km²; 643/mi²
GDP	20.48 Billion US$
LANGUAGE(S)	English, English patois
ETHNICITY	Black 91%, Mixed 6%
RELIGION	Protestant 63%, Roman Catholic 3%
CLIMATE	Tropical, Temperate interior

DEVON HOUSE, KINGSTON
Built in the 1880s by George Stiebel, one of the first black millionaires in the Caribbean, Devon House is now one of the main tourist attractions in Kingston.

CENTRAL AMERICA/CARIBBEAN

CAYMAN ISLANDS
19° 30' N, 80° 30' W | 262 KM² | 101 MI² | UTC-5

This group of three islands is actually formed by the peaks of a massive underwater ridge bordering the Cayman Trench.

Consisting of Grand Cayman and the sister islands of Cayman Brac and Little Cayman, this British Overseas Territory was once governed as a single colony with Jamaica. Separate since 1959, the Caymans are a prosperous tax haven and offshore finance centre with one of the world's highest standards of living. The islands' geographical location makes them susceptible to the numerous hurricanes in the area; nonetheless they remain a popular tourist destination.

FACT FILE

LOCAL NAME	Cayman Islands
SOVEREIGN STATE	United Kingdom
CAPITAL/MAIN CITY	George Town
CURRENCY	Caymanian Dollar (KYD)
MEMBERSHIP	CARICOM (associate)
GOVERNMENT	British Overseas Territory
POPULATION	47,919
POP. DENSITY	183/km²; 475/mi²
GDP	1.94 Billion US$
LANGUAGE(S)	English, Spanish
ETHNICITY	Mixed 40%, White 20%, Black 20%
RELIGION	Church of God 26%, United Church 12%, Roman Catholic 11%, Baptist 9%, Seventh-day Adventist 8%, Anglican 6%, Pentecostal 5%, Other Christian 3%
CLIMATE	Tropical Maritime

HAITI

19° 00' N, 72° 25' W | 27,750 KM² | 10,714 MI² | UTC-5

Occupying the western corner of the Greater Antillean island of Hispaniola, Haiti is a former French colony which became the first independent black republic in 1804.

With a mountainous terrain, fertile plains and forests, Haiti was once valued for its agricultural potential. French settlers acquired the Haitian portion of Hispaniola from the Spanish in 1697 and soon established a large number of slave-worked sugar and tobacco plantations. Independence from France came in 1804, as a result of the only successful slave rebellion to ever result in a separate nation being formed. Having once been the richest of the Caribbean islands, Haiti is now the poorest,

with 70 per cent unemployment and over 80 per cent of the population living below the poverty line. Political violence continued into 2004 with armed rebellion against President Aristide. Extensive deforestation and soil erosion has led to frequent severe flooding, regularly destroying crops.

FACT FILE

LOCAL NAME	Republic of Haiti
CAPITAL CITY	Port-au-Prince
CURRENCY	Gourde (HTG)
MEMBERSHIP	CARICOM, G77, OAS, SELA, WTO
GOVERNMENT	Presidential Republic
POPULATION	9,751,432
POP. DENSITY	351/km²; 910/mi²
GDP	11.38 Billion US$
LANGUAGE(S)	French, Creole
ETHNICITY	Black 95%, Mulatto and White 5%
RELIGION	Roman Catholic 80%, Protestant 16% (Baptist 10%, Pentecostal 4%)
CLIMATE	Tropical, Semi-arid in east

Haiti is the home of the *Vodou* (Voodoo) religion; the legendary Isle of Tortuga (Ila de la Tortue), centre of piracy in the sixteenth century, was a filming location for *Pirates of the Caribbean*. Carnival in Port-au-Prince is a boisterous annual spectacle that draws many thousands of people.

DOMINICAN REPUBLIC

19° 00' N, 70° 40' W | 48,730 KM² | 18,815 MI² | UTC-4

Covering eastern Hispaniola, the Dominican Republic was the first settlement of the Spanish New World, having been 'discovered' by Columbus on his first voyage.

Formerly inhabited by the Arawak peoples who had populated most of the Caribbean islands, Hispaniola is mountainous, forested and fertile. In 1697 the eastern portion of the island was ceded to the French and Spain kept control of Santo Domingo, building the first roads, fortresses, Christian churches and university. Independence from Spain came in 1821, but twenty-two years of Haitian rule

followed, until the republic was created in 1844. The majority of Dominicans today are descendants of African slaves, although a unique community of indigenous peoples

FACT FILE

LOCAL NAME	Dominican Republic
CAPITAL CITY	Santo Domingo
CURRENCY	Dominican Peso (DOP)
MEMBERSHIP	CARICOM (observer), G77, LAIA (observer), OAS, SELA, RG, WTO
GOVERNMENT	Presidential Republic
POPULATION	9,904,327
POP. DENSITY	203/km²; 526/mi²
GDP	61.67 Billion US$
LANGUAGE(S)	Spanish
ETHNICITY	Mixed 73%, White 16%, Black 11%
RELIGION	Roman Catholic 95%
CLIMATE	Tropical Maritime

populates the north-east of the island. A generally stable society, the Dominican Republic has experienced economic growth in recent years. The export of sugar, bananas and coffee has been supplemented by income from the service industry and tourism.

CENTRAL AMERICA/CARIBBEAN

PUERTO RICO

18° 15' N, 66° 30' W | 13,790 KM² | 5,324 MI² | UTC–4

Claimed by the Spanish crown following its discovery by Columbus in 1493, Puerto Rico was ceded to the United States in 1898 following the Spanish–American War.

It is now a semi-autonomous US common-wealth territory; Puerto Ricans have the right to claim US citizenship, but cannot vote in US elections. Instead they are entitled

to elect their own governors. The island itself is mainly mountainous, with fertile coastal plains to the north and south. Its position on the shipping lane to the Panama Canal provides Puerto Rico with strategic importance. The economy is boosted by US investment; the service industries and tourism are now more productive than the agricultural sector, which relies upon dairy and livestock farming in addition to sugar.

Despite this, many Puerto Ricans continue to emigrate to the United States.

SAN JUAN
The lighthouse and rampart at El Morro Fort.

FACT FILE

LOCAL NAME Commonwealth of Puerto Rico
SOVEREIGN STATE United States
CAPITAL/MAIN CITY San Juan
CURRENCY US Dollar (USD)
MEMBERSHIP CARICOM (observer)
GOVERNMENT Commonwealth
POPULATION 4,012,389
POP. DENSITY 291/km²; 754/mi²
GDP 72.61 Billion US$
LANGUAGE(S) Spanish, English
ETHNICITY White (mostly Spanish origin) 81%, Black 8%, Amerindian 0.4%
RELIGION Roman Catholic 85%, Protestant and other 15%
CLIMATE Tropical Maritime

US IN THE CARIBBEAN

The United States has a variety of interests in the Caribbean, from their possession of several small unihabited islands to their use of Guantanamo Bay, situated at the western edge of Cuba.

The most notorious US interest in the Caribbean is Guantanamo Bay, situated on Cuba's south-east coast. Assumed as a US territory in 1903 following the Cuban-American Treaty, the natural harbour is home to a US

Naval Base. Its infamy grew in 2002 when the base was used to detain suspected terrorists.

During the nineteenth century, guano (the droppings of marine birds) became prized for use as fertilizer and the 1865 Guano Islands Act stipulated that any uninhabited and unclaimed territory which held phosphate guano was open for possession by the US. As a result the US now holds Navassa Island, a coral limestone island off the Haitian coast, the atoll Seranilla Bank off the coast of Nicaragua

and the Baja Neuvo Bank or Petrel Islands in the Western Caribbean. These and other islands have been the subject of dispute with claims of sovereignty made by nations within closer proximity of the islands, for instance Haiti's claims over Navassa. Mona Island had been a Spanish territory until 1898, when Guano deposits ensured its addition to the US territory, Puerto Rico. Now prized for its flora and fauna, Mona Island is a popular nature reserve.

UNITED STATES VIRGIN ISLANDS

18° 20' N, 64° 50' W | 1,910 KM² | 737 MI² | UTC-4

Shared between the United States and the United Kingdom since 1917, the archipelago of the Virgin Islands is part of the Lesser Antilles island group.

The three major islands of St Croix, St John and St Thomas, along with a number of smaller islands, are overseas territories of the US. Denmark first settled them during the seventeenth and eighteenth centuries then sold them to the US in 1917. The abolition of slavery in 1848 led to their economic decline but their strategic location and the onset of World War I increased their value. Rolling hills with some low mountains, long stretches of shallow beaches and coral reefs provide an attractive landscape and tourism is now the most profitable industry. St Croix is home to a large petroleum refinery.

FACT FILE

LOCAL NAME	United States Virgin Islands
SOVEREIGN STATE	United States
CAPITAL/MAIN CITY	Charlotte Amalie
CURRENCY	US Dollar (USD)
GOVERNMENT	Unincorporated Territory of the US
POPULATION	111,390
POP. DENSITY	58/km²; 151/mi²
GDP	1.577 Billion US$
LANGUAGE(S)	English, Spanish/Spanish Creole, French/French Creole
ETHNICITY	Black 76%, White 13%, Mixed 6%
RELIGION	Baptist 42%, Roman Catholic 34%, Episcopalian 17%
CLIMATE	Subtropical

BRITISH VIRGIN ISLANDS

18° 30' N, 64° 30' W | 153 KM² | 59 MI² | UTC-4

Consisting of nearly sixty islands and cays, the British Virgin Islands were acquired from the Dutch in 1672.

A combination of flat coral islands and others more mountainous and volcanic, the British Virgin Islands are home to around 24,000 people, the majority of whom live on Tortola. As with many other Caribbean islands, the colony was populated by African slaves who worked the sugar plantations, and many of the inhabitants today are their descendants. Since autonomy was granted in 1967, the islands have benefited from tourism as opposed to agriculture. Strong economic ties with neighbouring Puerto Rico and the US Virgin Islands have also been beneficial.

FACT FILE

LOCAL NAME	British Virgin Islands
SOVEREIGN STATE	United Kingdom
CAPITAL/MAIN CITY	Road Town
CURRENCY	US Dollar (USD)
MEMBERSHIP	CARICOM (associate), OECS
GOVERNMENT	British Overseas Territory
POPULATION	24,041
POP. DENSITY	157/km²; 408/mi²
GDP	853.4 Million US$
LANGUAGE(S)	English
ETHNICITY	Black 83%, White 7%, Mixed 5%, Indian 3%
RELIGION	Protestant 86%, Roman Catholic 10%
CLIMATE	Subtropical

TORTOLA
The beautiful Lambert Bay on the island of Tortola.

CENTRAL AMERICA/CARIBBEAN

LEEWARD ISLANDS

The northern islands of the Lesser Antilles group, the Leewards, are so called because of their position, sheltered from the prevailing trade winds from the east.

There are over twenty-five islands that constitute the Leewards, some of which are autonomous states. Others are overseas territories or former colonies of some of the major colonial nations: France, the United States, Great Britain and the Netherlands. Major Leeward islands are listed below; however, significant smaller islands include Saint Martin, which is the smallest land-mass in the world to be divided between two countries, the Netherlands and France.

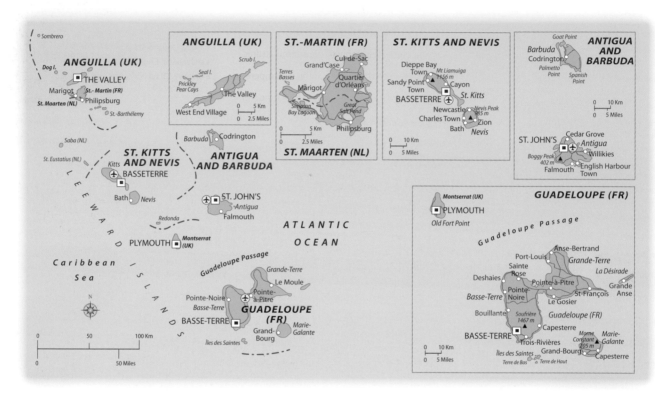

ANGUILLA

18° 15' N, 63° 10' W | 102 KM² | 39 MI² | UTC-4

The northernmost of the Leeward Islands, Anguilla's distinctive shape probably led to its being named, in both French and Spanish, after an eel.

Consisting of the main island of Anguilla itself and a number of largely uninhabited smaller islands and cays, this overseas territory of the UK is mainly flat coral limestone. The highest point on Anguilla is Crocus Hill, standing at 65 metres. With poor soil, there are few natural resources to be found; the economy currently depends upon luxury tourism and lobster fishing. During the seventeenth and eighteenth centuries the British settlers failed to establish any successful plantations. With the abolition of slavery, African subsistence farmers and fishermen were left to inhabit the island, which was largely abandoned by the white settlers. An enforced incorporation into Saint Kitts and Nevis was abandoned in 1971, when Anguilla became a separate British dependency.

FACT FILE

LOCAL NAME Anguilla
SOVEREIGN STATE United Kingdom
CAPITAL/MAIN CITY The Valley
CURRENCY East Caribbean Dollar (XCD)
MEMBERSHIP CARICOM (associate), OECS
GOVERNMENT British Overseas Territory
POPULATION 14,108
POP. DENSITY 138/km²; 362/mi²
GDP 108.9 Million US$
LANGUAGE(S) English
ETHNICITY Black 90%, Mulatto 5%, White 4%
RELIGION Anglican 29%, Methodist 24%, Other Protestant 30%, Roman Catholic 6%
CLIMATE Tropical

SAINT KITTS AND NEVIS

17° 20' N, 62° 45' W | 261 KM² | 101 MI² | UTC-4

The two-island federal nation of Saint Kitts and Nevis is the smallest in the Americas.

Home to the first British colony in the Caribbean, Saint Kitts and Nevis were first settled in 1623 and achieved independence in 1983. Both islands are mountainous and volcanic, with their central peaks covered in thick rain forest and providing a number of freshwater rivers. The main agricultural crop had historically been sugar; tourism and financial services are now of greater economic importance and the ailing sugar industry was shut down in 2005. Saint Kitts and Nevis are also the Caribbean's most successful electrical goods exporter, having developed an industry based on the assembly of pre-manufactured parts. Despite this the economy is hampered by soaring international debt and the poorer island of Nevis is keen to secede from the union.

FACT FILE

LOCAL NAME Federation of Saint Kitts and Nevis
CAPITAL CITY Basseterre
CURRENCY East Caribbean Dollar (XCD)
MEMBERSHIP C, CARICOM, G77, OAS, OECS, WTO
GOVERNMENT Parliamentary Democracy
POPULATION 39,817
POP. DENSITY 153/km²; 394/mi²
GDP 721 Million US$
LANGUAGE(S) English
ETHNICITY Black 90%, Mulatto 5%, Indo-Pakistani 3%
RELIGION Protestant 84%, Roman Catholic 7%
CLIMATE Tropical

ANTIGUA AND BARBUDA

17° 03' N, 61° 48' W | 443 KM² | 171 MI² | UTC-4

The two islands of Antigua and Barbuda lie within the middle of the Leeward Islands and consist of the two main islands and a number of smaller islets and cays.

The larger of these two tropical islands is Antigua, which is home to a number of small towns as well as the capital, Saint John's. Generally low-lying limestone coral islands, there are some volcanic mountains, but the lack of freshwater supplies on Antigua has historically been problematic and the islands are as susceptible to drought as to hurricanes. In 1981, the islands became independent of the United Kingdom and are now members of the British Commonwealth. The relatively stable economy is reliant on tourism, with the majority of visitors coming from the United States.

SAINT JOHN'S
Brightly-painted houses in the town of Saint John's, which has been the administrative centre of Antigua since it was colonized by the British in 1632.

FACT FILE

LOCAL NAME Antigua and Barbuda
CAPITAL CITY Saint John's
CURRENCY East Caribbean Dollar (XCD)
MEMBERSHIP C, CARICOM, G77, OAS, OECS, WTO
GOVERNMENT Parliamentary Democracy and Federal Constitutional Monarchy
POPULATION 84,522
POP. DENSITY 191/km²; 494/mi²
GDP 1.526 Billion US$
LANGUAGE(S) English, Creole
ETHNICITY Black 91%, Mixed 4%, White 2%
RELIGION Anglican 25.%, Seventh-day Adventist 12%, Pentecostal 11%, Moravian 11%, Roman Catholic 10%, Methodist 8%, Baptist 5%, Church of God 5%, Other Christian 5%
CLIMATE Tropical Maritime

CENTRAL AMERICA/CARIBBEAN

MONTSERRAT

16° 45' N, 62° 12' W | 102 KM² | 39 MI² | UTC-4

The devastating eruption of the Soufrière Hills Volcano in 1995 reduced the population of Montserrat from 13,000 to 5,000, most people having abandoned the island.

This tropical volcanic island was first settled in 1632 by the British who imported African slaves to aid with the exporting of sugar, rum and arrowroot. Large numbers of Irish settlers on Montserrat during the seventeenth century has led to its being often referred to as the Caribbean Emerald Isle. The majority of today's population is of mixed black African and Irish descent. In 1989 Hurricane Hugo destroyed much of the island's infrastructure. The eruption of the previously dormant Soufrière Hills began in 1995 and slowly continues to this day. The main city, Plymouth, was evacuated before it was covered by pyroclastic debris and the island's main airport was destroyed. Once a popular tourist destination, this British overseas territory now depends upon aid, particularly from the UK, and much of the island remains uninhabitable.

SOUFRIÈRE HILLS VOLCANO
A view of the volcano during the 1997 eruption. There is now an exclusion zone around the mountain.

FACT FILE

LOCAL NAME Montserrat
SOVEREIGN STATE United Kingdom
CAPITAL/MAIN CITY Plymouth
CURRENCY East Caribbean Dollar (XCD)
MEMBERSHIP CAICOM, OECS
GOVERNMENT British Overseas Territory
POPULATION 5,079
POP. DENSITY 50/km²; 130/mi²
GDP 29 Million US$
LANGUAGE(S) English
ETHNICITY Black 93%, White 3%
RELIGION Anglican 30%, Methodist 23%, Roman Catholic 10%
CLIMATE Tropical

GUADELOUPE

16° 15' N, 61° 35' W | 1,630 KM² | 629 MI² | UTC-4

The southernmost of the Leeward Islands, the archipelago of Guadeloupe is an overseas department of France.

Taken as a possession by France in 1635, Guadeloupe was for a while the focus of attacks by the British, who wished to control a profitable island. The major commodity was sugar, so valued by the French that in 1763 they agreed to abandon claims to Canada in exchange for a formal withdrawal of British interest. Today's population consists mainly of descendants of African slaves, although it was much reduced in 2007 when the island communes of Saint Martin and Saint Barthélemy separated into independent French territories. As an integral region of France, Guadeloupe is a member of the European Union and its currency is the euro. The island is heavily dependent on financial support from France, although tourism is a major source of revenue.

FACT FILE

LOCAL NAME Department of Guadeloupe
SOVEREIGN STATE France
CAPITAL/MAIN CITY Basse-Terre
CURRENCY Euro (EUR)
GOVERNMENT Overseas Department of France
POPULATION 447,927
POP. DENSITY 275/km²; 712/mi²
GDP 3.51 Billion US$
LANGUAGE(S) French, Creole patois
ETHNICITY Creole (mulatto) 77%, Black 10%, Guadeloupe Mestizo (French-East Asian) 10%, White 2%
RELIGION Roman Catholic 81%, Jehovah's Witness 5%, Protestant 5%
CLIMATE Tropical

CENTRAL AMERICA/CARIBBEAN

WINDWARD ISLES

The name of these islands in the south-east of the Lesser Antilles group, the Windwards, refers to their position in the path of the prevailing trade winds, which blow from east to west.

The Windward Islands were the first to be encountered by the trading ships that had been brought across the North Atlantic by prevailing winds and currents. During the seventeenth and eighteenth centuries, the majority of these vessels would have been transporting slaves captured from the African Gold Coast, who were destined for North, Central and South America. The main Windward Islands are covered below.

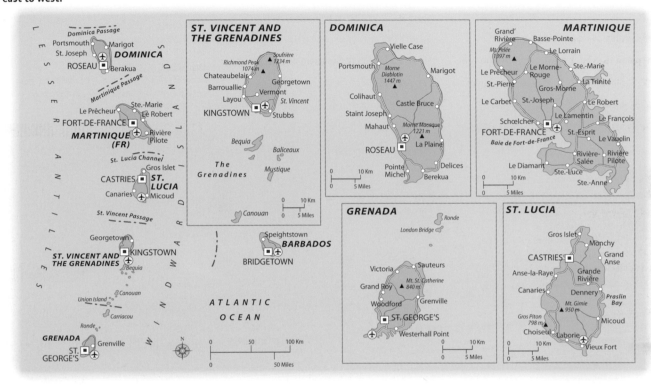

DOMINICA

15° 25' N, 61° 20' W | 754 KM² | 291 MI² | UTC–4

This rugged volcanic island is thickly covered in rain forest, rivers and waterfalls, and much of it is protected national parkland.

With only two major towns, Roseau and Portsmouth, Dominica is renowned for its status as an unspoiled natural environment, home to several endangered species of flora and fauna. It has the world's second largest boiling lake, a flooded crater located within the Morne Trois Pitons National Park, a World Heritage Site. Initially valued for its timber, the inhospitable landscape was problematic for rival French and English settlers, who encountered fierce resistance from the indigenous Carib Indians. In 1763, the island became a British colony, achieving independence as a Commonwealth state in 1978. Two years of political instability ended with the election of Mary Eugenia Charles, the Caribbean's first female prime minister. The economy rests upon agriculture, particularly the export of bananas, although the eco-tourism industry is growing.

FACT FILE

LOCAL NAME Commonwealth of Dominica

CAPITAL CITY Roseau

CURRENCY East Caribbean Dollar (XCD)

MEMBERSHIP C, CARICOM, G77, OAS, OECS, WTO

GOVERNMENT Parliamentary Republic

POPULATION 72,514

POP. DENSITY 96/km²; 249/mi²

GDP 648 Million US$

LANGUAGE(S) English, French patois

ETHNICITY Black 87%, Mixed 9%, Carib Amerindian 3%

RELIGION Roman Catholic 61%, Seventh-day Adventist 6%, Pentecostal 6%, Baptist 4%, Methodist 4%, Rastafarian 1%

CLIMATE Tropical

MARTINIQUE

14º 40' N, 61º 00' W | 1,100 KM² | 436 MI² | UTC-4

An overseas department of France, Martinique is a member of the EU and appears on the reverse of every euro banknote.

Lush, rainforested volcanic mountains dominate the north of the island. The volcanic peaks include the now dormant Mount Pelée, whose eruption in 1902 killed over 30,000 people. Vulnerable to hurricanes and tornadoes, Martinique experiences regular natural disasters. French settlers from Saint Kitts arrived in 1635 and exterminated the native Carib population. Sugar-exporting made the island prosperous and, as with Guadeloupe, the 1763 Treaty of Paris which ended the seven-year Anglo-French wars saw France relinquish Canada rather than the profitable Martinique. Although the official language is French, the majority of the black population speak Antillean Creole, a blending of French and African.

FACT FILE

LOCAL NAME	Department of Martinique
SOVEREIGN STATE	France
CAPITAL/MAIN CITY	Fort-de-France
CURRENCY	Euro (EUR)
GOVERNMENT	Overseas Department of France
POPULATION	399,747
POP. DENSITY	363/km²; 917/mi²
GDP	6.12 Billion US$
LANGUAGE(S)	French, Creole patois
ETHNICITY	Mixed race (Black/White/Asian) 93%, French white 3%, East Indian 2%
RELIGION	Roman Catholic 86%, Protestant 6%, Other Christian 5%
CLIMATE	Tropical

SAINT LUCIA

13º 53' N, 60º 58' W | 616 KM² | 238 MI² | UTC-4

During its colonial period, Saint Lucia passed between British and French possession fourteen times before being ceded to the UK in 1814.

One of the most mountainous islands in the Caribbean, Saint Lucia's highest peak is Mount Gimie at 950 metres. The Pitons are a famous landmark, two conical peaks which are in fact volcanic plugs. The interior of the island is covered in tropical rain forest and the Atlantic coast has numerous natural harbours and coves. An independent commonwealth nation since 1979, it enjoys a relatively stable economy; tourism is the most profitable sector, although this is becoming increasingly unpopular with locals. Agriculture, particularly the export of bananas, and financial services are also important.

CUL DE SAC
A worker in a banana plantation. Much of the mountainous landscape in the background is covered in dense rain forest.

FACT FILE

LOCAL NAME	Saint Lucia
CAPITAL CITY	Castries
CURRENCY	East Caribbean Dollar (XCD)
MEMBERSHIP	C, CARICOM, G77, OAS, OECS, WTO
GOVERNMENT	Parliamentary Democracy and Constitutional Monarchy
POPULATION	166,789
POP. DENSITY	271/km²; 701/mi²
GDP	1.794 Billion US$
LANGUAGE(S)	English, French patois
ETHNICITY	Black 83%, Mixed 12%, East Indian 2%
RELIGION	Roman Catholic 67%, Seventh-day Adventist 9%, Pentecostal 6%, Anglican 2%, Other Christian 7%, Rastafarian 2%,
CLIMATE	Tropical

SAINT VINCENT AND THE GRENADINES
13° 15' N, 61° 12' W | 389 KM² | 150 MI² | UTC-4

An island nation in the Windward Isles, Saint Vincent and the Grenadines is an arc-shaped archipelago.

Saint Vincent is home to the administrative capital Kingstown and is itself a rugged volcanic isle, with the highest active peak, Soufrière, standing at 1,234 metres. The Grenadines are a chain of much smaller islands and cays, one-third of which belong to Grenada. The major Grenadine islands include Mustique, Union Island and the former Carib prison island, Baliceaux. Resistance from Carib tribes meant that the islands were not colonized until 1719; they then became the focus of disputes between France and the UK. A British colony from 1783 to 1979, they are now members of the British Commonwealth and the Caribbean Commonwealth. They are a destination for cruise liners and also cater for the luxury tourist market. Agriculture and offshore financial services are also important to the economy.

FACT FILE
LOCAL NAME Saint Vincent and the Grenadines
CAPITAL CITY Kingstown
CURRENCY East Caribbean Dollar (XCD)
MEMBERSHIP C, CARICOM, G77, OAS, OECS, WTO
GOVERNMENT Parliamentary Democracy and Constitutional Monarchy
POPULATION 121,010
POP. DENSITY 311/km²; 807/mi²
GDP 1.04 Billion US$
LANGUAGE(S) English, French patois
ETHNICITY Black 66%, Mixed 19%, East Indian 6%, European 4%, Carib Amerindian 2%
RELIGION Anglican 47%, Methodist 28%, Roman Catholic 13%, other (includes Hindu, Seventh-day Adventist, other Protestant) 12%
CLIMATE Tropical

GRENADA
12° 07' N, 61° 40' W | 344 KM² | 133 MI² | UTC-4

First settled in the seventeenth century by the French, who established profitable, slave-driven sugar plantations, Grenada was acquired by the British under the 1763 Treaty of Paris.

Comprising the larger Grenada and a number of smaller Grenadine islands to the north, the nation belongs to the Windward Isles. Grenada itself is a mountainous, volcanic island with a densely forested interior and is vulnerable to hurricanes and tornadoes. The largest of the Grenadines is Carriacou, which is home to people of mixed Scottish, Irish and African descent. Grenada became independent from the UK in 1974, but political instability ensued. This culminated in 1983 in a Marxist military coup, which then resulted in the controversial invasion of the island by US forces, who suppressed the revolution. Despite this and the destruction caused by Hurricane Ivan in 2004, the agriculture-led economy is recovering.

SAINT GEORGE'S
A view across the bay at Saint George's.

FACT FILE
LOCAL NAME Grenada
CAPITAL CITY Saint George's
CURRENCY East Caribbean Dollar (XCD)
MEMBERSHIP C, CARICOM, G77, OAS, OECS, WTO
GOVERNMENT Parliamentary Democracy and Constitutional Monarchy
POPULATION 105,552
POP. DENSITY 307/km²; 794/mi²
GDP 1.11 Billion US$
LANGUAGE(S) English, French patois
ETHNICITY Black 82%, Mixed Black and European 13%, European and East Indian 5%
RELIGION Roman Catholic 53%, Anglican 14%, Other Protestant 33%
CLIMATE Tropical

CENTRAL AMERICA/CARIBBEAN

BARBADOS

13º 10' N, 59º 32' W | 431 KM² | 166 MI² | UTC-4

Situated in the Atlantic Ocean, just east of the Caribbean Sea, Barbados is considered part of the Lesser Antilles group.

With its relatively flat landscape, Barbados is much drier than its more mountainous neighbours. The island is surrounded by coral reefs and is formed of limestone coral. There are a number of mangrove swamps. Much of the fertile land was given over to sugar plantations worked by African slaves, and sugar, rum and molasses production were economic mainstays well into the twentieth century. Independent from the UK since 1966, Barbados still functions as a constitutional monarchy, modelled upon Westminster, with Queen Elizabeth II as head of state. Light industry and tourism have now replaced sugar as the most profitable economic sectors.

FACT FILE

LOCAL NAME Barbados

CAPITAL CITY Bridgetown

CURRENCY Barbadian Dollar (BBD)

MEMBERSHIP C, CARICOM, G77, OAS, SELA, WTO

GOVERNMENT Parliamentary Democracy and Constitutional Monarchy

POPULATION 294,826

POP. DENSITY 684/km²; 1776/mi²

GDP 5.31 Billion US$

LANGUAGE(S) English, Bajan dialect

ETHNICITY Black 90%, White 4%, Asian and mixed 6%

RELIGION Protestant 63% (Anglican 28%, Pentecostal 19%, Methodist 5%, other 11%), Roman Catholic 4%, other Christian 7%

CLIMATE Tropical

SUGAR CANE
There are still more than 1,000 small sugar plantations on Barbados but yield is relatively low in comparison with islands such as Cuba.

TRINADAD AND TOBAGO

11º 00' N, 61º 00' W | 5,128 KM² | 1,980 MI² | UTC-4

The most southerly of the Windward Islands, Trinidad and Tobago is a two-island state surrounded by a number of smaller, uninhabited islands.

The landscape of both islands is rolling, with some low mountains found to the north of the larger island, Trinidad. Both islands are wooded and fertile; however the major export is no longer sugar but oil and oil-related products. One of the most prosperous of the Caribbean Islands, Trinidad and Tobago has developed petroleum and natural gas industries. A UK colony from 1797, following

FACT FILE

LOCAL NAME Republic of Trinidad and Tobago

CAPITAL CITY Port-of-Spain

CURRENCY Trinidad and Tobago Dollar (TTD)

MEMBERSHIP C, CARICOM, G24, G77, OAS, SELA, WTO

GOVERNMENT Parliamentary Republic

POPULATION 1,338,225

POP. DENSITY 24/km²; 62/mi²

GDP 26.79 Billion US$

LANGUAGE(S) English, Caribbean Hindustani, French, Spanish, Chinese

ETHNICITY Indian (South Asian) 40%, African 38%, Mixed 21%

RELIGION Roman Catholic 26%, Hindu 22%, Anglican 8%, Baptist 7%, Pentecostal 7%, Muslim 6%, Seventh-day Adventist 4%, Other Christian 6%

CLIMATE Tropical

the abolition of slavery the British imported Hindu Indians as a workforce; today Trinidad and Tobago has a proportionally large Hindu and Muslim population.

NETHERLANDS ANTILLES

12° 15' N, 68° 45' W | 960 KM² | 371 MI² | UTC-4

The islands owned by the Dutch consist of two groups, one just north of Venezuela and the other in the Leeward Islands, east of the US Virgin Islands.

The three Leeward Islands, Sint Maarten, Saba, and Sint Eustatius, are of mixed volcanic and coral formation. Saba contains Mount Scenery, which at 862 metres is the highest point in the Kingdom of the Netherlands. Sint Maarten is the Dutch portion of Saint Martin Island, which is shared with France. The two southerly Dutch Antilles, Curaçao and Bonaire, are volcanic islands geographically linked to South America but politically considered Caribbean. Curaçao is the larger and was historically the centre of the Dutch slave trade. During the twentieth century, both prospered through the petroleum industry, serving the Venezuelan oilfields. Despite the prosperity of Curaçao and Bonaire, the Antilles still rely upon financial aid from the Netherlands.

FACT FILE

LOCAL NAME Netherlands Antilles
SOVEREIGN STATE Netherlands
CAPITAL/MAIN CITY Willemstad
CURRENCY Netherlands Antillean Guilder (ANG)
MEMBERSHIP CARICOM (observer)
GOVERNMENT Parliamentary
POPULATION 194,381
POP. DENSITY 203/km²; 524/mi²
GDP 2.8 Billion US$
LANGUAGE(S) Papiamento, English, Dutch, Spanish, Creole
ETHNICITY Mixed Black 85%, other 15% (includes Carib Amerindian, White, East Asian)
RELIGION Roman Catholic 72%, Pentecostal 5%, Protestant 4%, Seventh-day Adventist 3%, Methodist 3%, Other Christian 6%,
CLIMATE Tropical

CURACAO
A brightly painted Dutch style building in the Punda district of Willemstad on Curaçao.

ARUBA

12° 30' N, 69° 58' W | 193 KM² | 75 MI² | UTC-4

An autonomous region of the Netherlands, Aruba was acquired by the Dutch from the Spanish in 1636; it seceded from the Netherlands Antilles in 1986.

Just 27 kilometres north of the Paraguaná peninsula of Venezuela, Aruba is a flat, dry, riverless island which lies just outside the hurricane belt. First inhabited by Arawak Indians, it was initially strategically useful to the Dutch; poor soil kept the island relatively free of plantations. During the nineteenth century a gold rush brought temporary

FACT FILE

LOCAL NAME Aruba
SOVEREIGN STATE Netherlands
CAPITAL/MAIN CITY Oranjestad
CURRENCY Aruban Guilder/Florin (AWG)
MEMBERSHIP CARICOM (observer)
GOVERNMENT Parliamentary Democracy (member of Kingdom of Netherlands)
POPULATION 103,530
POP. DENSITY 536/km²; 1,380/mi²
GDP 2.26 Billion US$
LANGUAGE(S) Papiamento, Spanish, English, Dutch
ETHNICITY Mixed White/Caribbean Amerindian 80%
RELIGION Roman Catholic 82%, Protestant 8%, Other (includes Hindu, Muslim, Confucian, Jewish) 10%
CLIMATE Tropical Maritime

prosperity. In 1924 the petroleum industry used Aruba, first to set up an oil shipment facility, then a refinery, which eventually closed in 1985. Tourism has since boosted the economy; oil storage and financial services are also important.

Caribbean Sea

N O R T H

A T L A N T I C

O C E A N

Barranquilla Maracaibo CARACAS

Valencia

VENEZUELA GEORGETOWN

Orinoco PARAMARIBO

Medellín BOGOTÁ **GUYANA** CAYENNE

SURINAME French Guiana (FR)

COLOMBIA

Guiana Highlands

Quito Macapa

ECUADOR *Negro* *Amazon* Belém

Chimborazo
6310 m

*Galapagos
Islands (EC)*

*Gulf of
Panama*

Cocos Ridge

*Gulf of
Guayaquil*

Putumayo *A m a z o n* *Amazon* Manaus

Marañón *Represa de
Balbina*

PERU *B a s i n* Fortalez

Nevado de
Huascarán
6768 m *Purus* *Madeira* *Tapajós* *Xingu* Teresina

Chimbote *Ucayali* *Represa de
Sobradinho*

Feira de
Santana

*Peru
Basin* LIMA **B R A Z I L** Ara

Lake
Titicaca Mato Grosso *São Francisco* Salvad

BOLIVIA

Nazca Ridge BRASÍLIA

Arica LA PAZ Cuiabá *Brazilian Highlands*

Atacama Desert SUCRE Goiânia

Peru-Chile Ridge Campo
Grande São José do
Rio Preto Belo
Horizonte Vitória

PARAGUAY *Paraná*

Antofagasta *CHILE Trench* Ourinhos São
Paulo Rio de Janeiro

*Chile
Basin* ASUNCIÓN Curitiba Paranaguá

Santos

Pilcomayo *Paraguay* *Gran Chaco*

ARGENTINA Santa
Maria Porto Alegre

Uruguay

Cerro Aconcagua
6959 m Mendoza San
Luis Río Cuarto **URUGUAY** Río Grande

Argentine Rise

SANTIAGO San Rafael

S O U T H *Juan Fernández
Islands
(CL)* MONTEVIDEO *S O U T H*

P A C I F I C Talcahuano Santa Rosa BUENOS
AIRES *Río de la Plata* *A T L A N T I*

Concepción Mar del Plata

O C E A N Neuquen *Colorado* Bahía Blanca *O C E A N*

Río Negro

Puerto Montt *Península
Valdés*

Isla de Chiloé *Argentine*

*Península
de Taitao* Gulf of San Jorge
Comodoro Rivadavia *Basin*

Chile Rise *Golfo de Penas* *Patagonia*

*Bahía
Grande* *Falkland Islands
(UK)*

Stanley

Strait of Magellan *Scotia Ridg*

Punta Arenas

Monte Darwin
2438 m *Cape Horn*

SOUTH AMERICA

Measuring 7,500 kilometres from north to south and 4,800 kilometres from east to west at its widest point, South America is home to just over 300 million people, more than half of whom live in Brazil.

The continent of South America is physically separated from the rest of the northern part of the Americas by the Panama canal but its political boundary ends at the border between Panama and Columbia. The Caribbean Sea washes its northern coast, while to the west is the Pacific Ocean and to the east the Atlantic Ocean; its southernmost tip, in Tierra del Fuego, lies close to the Antarctic Circle and provided a terrifying obstacle to the earliest sailors circumnavigating the world.

The elongated shape of South America owes much to the American Cordillera of which the dramatic Andes mountain range forms a part. The Andes provide a backbone running the length of the continent, and the range continues under the Southern Ocean as the South Georgian Ridge, emerging as the mountains of the Antarctic Peninsula.

Geographically complex, South America has dramatic terrain, immense river systems, and possibly the most notable ecosystems on Earth in the Amazon rainforest and the Galapagos Islands. Its peoples vary from secretive jungle tribes to the large mestizo population, and include enduring micro-populations such as the Welsh of Patagonia. Despite great ethnic variety, the dominant languages are Spanish and Portuguese, reflecting the colonial powers that shaped this continent's modern culture.

South America's seemingly boundless natural resources drew European settlers from sixteenth century onwards, and are the current foundation of the growing economic might of Brazil. Colonists also established the plantations and farming practices that produce the trading commodities of coffee, sugar and beef in Brazil and Argentina. Exploitation of their petroleum reserves has boosted the economies of Venezuela, Brazil, Argentina, Colombia and Ecuador, taking South America to the top of world league tables of crude oil and natural gas production. Growing global demand has also stimulated production of essential minerals and coal.

In the modern era South America became synonymous with dictatorship and abuse of human rights, with political struggle often leading to ideology-driven guerrilla warfare that became intertwined with drug trafficking. The complex play between state and religion, politics and organized crime, combined with recent memories of the repression of authoritarian governments, continue to challenge and affect the development of this fascinating continent.

THE ANDES
The Andes is the longest mountain range in the world.

SOUTH AMERICA

COLOMBIA

4° 00' N, 72° 00' W | 1,138,910 KM² | 439,736 MI² | UTC-5

The fourth largest country in South America, Colombia occupies the north-western corner of the South American continent.

Geography

Colombia has a distinctively diverse landscape. To the north-west, the Andes mountain chain extends towards the Caribbean Sea, the fertile highlands lend themselves to intense agriculture, and torrential rivers provide hydro-electricity. The Caribbean coastal plain is home to several large cities and towns whereas the Pacific plains to the west are dominated by tropical swamps and jungle. East of the Andes are the more sparsely populated lowland plains, which reach south to the Amazon basin and the border with Peru. The capital city, Bogotá, is Colombia's largest.

History

Colombia was originally populated by indigenous Chibcha tribes including the Muisca and Quimbaya civilizations. The arrival of the Spanish in 1499 led to the eventual colonization of an area consisting of modern Colombia, Venezuela, Ecuador and Panama. Known as New Granada, it remained a Spanish colony until 1819; following a long period of territorial shifting, the Republic of Colombia was finally established in 1886. The twentieth century was dominated by an internal conflict lasting over four decades between government forces and anti-government insurgents and paramilitary groups. Despite the continued presence and funding of the cocaine trade, the violence has been decreasing since 2002.

ARMENIA, CENTRAL COLUMBIA
Coffee is one of Colombia's principal exports.

Economy

Improved internal security and government-led economic reforms have stimulated increased growth in recent years. Agriculture provides 11 per cent of the GDP and key products include coffee, bananas and plantains, cocoa and tobacco. Textiles and clothing, in addition to minerals, gold and emeralds, are all exported, although the illegal exporting of cocaine remains problematic.

FACT FILE

LOCAL NAME Republic of Colombia

CAPITAL CITY Bogotá

CURRENCY Colombian Peso (COP)

MEMBERSHIP CAN, CARICOM (observer), G24, G77, SELA, LAIA, OAS, RG, WTO

GOVERNMENT Presidential Republic

POPULATION 46,741,098

POP. DENSITY 41/km²; 106/mi²

GDP 319.5 Billion US$

LANGUAGE(S) Spanish, Wayuu, Paez, Embera, Romani

ETHNICITY Mestizo 58%, White 20%, Mulatto 14%, Black 4%, Mixed Black-Amerindian 3%, Amerindian 1%

RELIGION Roman Catholic 90%

CLIMATE Tropical along the coast and eastern plains, Temperate in plateaux

REGIONAL DIVISIONS 32 Departments and 1 Capital District; the departments are divided into 1,119 municipalities

ECONOMIC ACTIVITIES Agriculture, Textiles, Food Processing, Oil, Clothing and Footwear, Beverages, Chemicals, Pharmaceuticals, Metalworking, Iron and Steel Products, Wood Products, Machinery, Electrical Equipment, Cement, Mining, Construction

NATURAL RESOURCES Petroleum, Natural Gas, Coal, Iron Ore, Nickel, Gold, Copper, Emeralds, Hydropower

VENEZUELA

8° 00' N, 66° 00' W | 912,050 KM² | 352,144 MI² | UTC-4:30

This former Spanish colony is one of the most urbanized countries in South America, with a number of large cities situated on its northern coast.

Geography

Bisected by the Orinoco River, Venezuela has a richly varied landscape. To the north-west is the Andean region, which reaches the Caribbean coast. This 2,800-kilometre maritime border is studded by numerous islands and inlets. Vast plains and swampland stretch from the Caribbean to the Colombian border, north of the Orinoco. To the south and east of the river basin, the Guyana Plateau is believed to be one of the oldest land formations on earth. In this region is found Angel Falls, the world's highest waterfall.

History

First colonized by Spain in 1522, Venezuela finally achieved independence in 1811 under the leadership of Simón Bolívar. The Republic of Venezuela was established in 1830 following the collapse of the Gran Colombia alliance founded by Bolívar. During the twentieth century, the country was a military state until democratic elections were introduced in 1959. Since 1999 leadership of the country has become more left-wing, which has soured international relations, particularly with the US, and drug trafficking and violence on the border with Colombia have raised concerns.

Economy

The majority of Venezuela's economic wealth rests on the oil industry; there are massive oil reserves and exports account for around 30 per cent of the GDP. The country is also rich in other minerals, including coal and gold, but inefficient mining is both uneconomic and endangering the environment. With high inflation, many Venezuelans still live in poverty.

FACT FILE

LOCAL NAME Bolivarian Republic of Venezuela

CAPITAL CITY Caracas

CURRENCY Bolívar (VEB)

MEMBERSHIP CARICOM (observer), G15, G24, G77, SELA, LAIA, LAS (observer), OAS, OPEC, RG, WTO

GOVERNMENT Federal Presidential Republic

POPULATION 28,121,688

POP. DENSITY 31/km²; 80/mi²

GDP 334.6 Billion US$

LANGUAGE(S) Spanish, Indigenous dialects

ETHNICITY Spanish 45%, Catalán 28%, Galacian 8%, Basque 6%, Aragonese 5%, Rom (Gypsy) 2%

RELIGION Roman Catholic 96%, Protestant 2%

CLIMATE Tropical

REGIONAL DIVISIONS 23 States, 1 Capital District and 1 Special Territory; Federal Dependencies are grouped into 10 Administrative Regions

ECONOMIC ACTIVITIES Petroleum Refining, Petrochemicals, Construction Materials, Food Processing, Textiles, Iron Ore Mining, Steel, Aluminium, Motor Vehicle Assembly, Paper Products, Consumer Products

NATURAL RESOURCES Petroleum, Natural Gas, Iron Ore, Coal, Gold, Bauxite, Other Minerals, Hydropower, Diamonds

ANGEL FALLS
Angel Falls, the world's highest waterfall at a height of 979 metres, was named after the aviator Jimmie Angel who first flew over the falls in 1933.

GUYANA

5° 00' N, 59° 00' W | 214,970 KM² | 83,000 MI² | UTC-4

One of only four non-Spanish-speaking countries in South America, Guyana was once a British colony and now maintains strong ties with the Anglophone Caribbean islands.

Geography

Occupying the north-eastern corner of the continent, Guyana's coastline stretches along the Atlantic Ocean. Its low coastal plains are home to most of the country's major cities, and much of the land here is reclaimed from swamp and tidal marshes. The interior landscape is dense rain forest and mountains with grass savannahs in the far south of the country. Tropical and humid, much of the interior is uninhabited; the capital city, Georgetown, is found on the coast.

History

Originally a Dutch colony, control was ceded to the British in the eighteenth century and British Guiana was established. The indigenous population of Amerindians was joined by large numbers of African slaves; upon the abolition of slavery in 1834 many former slaves settled in the expanding urban areas. The British imported Indian labourers to work the sugar plantations, creating tense cultural divisions which persist today. Independence came in 1966, and although Guyana remains a member of the Commonwealth it is now a semi-presidential republic.

Economy

A generally stable economy, Guyana has experienced growth since 2000, with the expansion of the agriculture and mining sectors. Around a quarter of the population is employed in agriculture. Exported goods include rice, sugar, tobacco, spices, gold, bauxite and timber. Problems include a shortage of skilled labour and industrial inefficiency, although Guyana's large international debt was recently cancelled by the Inter-American Development Bank.

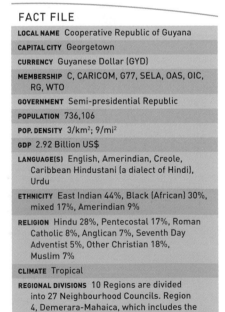

FACT FILE

LOCAL NAME Cooperative Republic of Guyana

CAPITAL CITY Georgetown

CURRENCY Guyanese Dollar (GYD)

MEMBERSHIP C, CARICOM, G77, SELA, OAS, OIC, RG, WTO

GOVERNMENT Semi-presidential Republic

POPULATION 736,106

POP. DENSITY 3/km²; 9/mi²

GDP 2.92 Billion US$

LANGUAGE(S) English, Amerindian, Creole, Caribbean Hindustani (a dialect of Hindi), Urdu

ETHNICITY East Indian 44%, Black (African) 30%, mixed 17%, Amerindian 9%

RELIGION Hindu 28%, Pentecostal 17%, Roman Catholic 8%, Anglican 7%, Seventh Day Adventist 5%, Other Christian 18%, Muslim 7%

CLIMATE Tropical

REGIONAL DIVISIONS 10 Regions are divided into 27 Neighbourhood Councils. Region 4, Demerara-Mahaica, which includes the capital, is the most densely populated region

ECONOMIC ACTIVITIES Agriculture, Mining (Bauxite, Gold, Diamonds), Textiles, Forestry, Fisheries, Manufacturing (Beverages, Foodstuff Processing, Apparel, Footwear, Pharmaceuticals), Construction, Services

NATURAL RESOURCES Bauxite, Gold, Diamonds, Hardwood Timber, Shrimp, Fish

POTARO RIVER
Guyana has one of the largest areas of unspoiled rainforest in South America. More than 80 per cent of the interior of the country is covered by rain forest.

SURINAME

4° 00' N, 56° 00' W | 163,270 KM² | 63,039 MI² | UTC-3

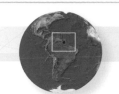

The smallest state in South America, this former Dutch colony is also the only fully independent Dutch-speaking country in the Western Hemisphere.

First settled by the Dutch in 1667, Suriname is a hot tropical country with cultivated lowlands to the north and thick rain forest dominating the interior. Further south towards the Brazilian border is generally uninhabited savannah. An artificial reservoir, the Brokopondomeer, is one of the largest in the world and was constructed to provide hydro-electricity to power the bauxite and aluminium plants that support Suriname's economy. The reservoir also supplies power to the capital city, Paramaribo. Independent

from the Netherlands since 1975, the socialist military regime that had thereafter held power was finally replaced by a democratic elected government in 1991.

FACT FILE

LOCAL NAME	Republic of Suriname
CAPITAL CITY	Paramaribo
CURRENCY	Surinam Dollar (SRD)
MEMBERSHIP	CARICOM, G77, SELA, OAS, OIC, WTO
GOVERNMENT	Constitutional Democracy
POPULATION	460,530
POP. DENSITY	3/km²; 7/mi²
GDP	4.07 Billion US$
LANGUAGE(S)	Dutch, English, Sranang Tongo, Caribbean Hindustani (a dialect of Hindi), Javanese
ETHNICITY	Hindustani 37%, Creole 31%, Javanese 15%, Maroons 10%, Amerindian 2%, Chinese 2%
RELIGION	Hindu 27%, Protestant 25%, Roman Catholic 23%, Muslim 20%, Indigenous Beliefs 5%
CLIMATE	Tropical

FRENCH GUIANA

4° 00' N, 53° 00' W | 83,534 KM² | 32,253 MI² | UTC-3

An overseas department of the Republic of France, French Guiana has experienced agitation for increased autonomy which has led to violent protest in recent years.

Situated along the northern Atlantic coast of South America, French Guiana is dominated by its tropical rain forest interior. The majority of the population lives along the coastal strip, and the administrative centre, Cayenne, is also the largest city in the department. Having been the first French settlement, the city was once surrounded by plantations and cayenne pepper farms, all of which were abandoned with the abolition of slavery in 1834. With very little agriculture and an economy that relies upon fishing, gold and timber, the colony is now highly dependent upon France for its trade and for subsidies. Its currency is the euro. First settled by the French in the seventeenth

century, it was until 1951 the home of the 'Devil's Island' penal colonies. The European Space Agency is based on the coast near Kourou.

FACT FILE

LOCAL NAME	Département de la Guyane française
SOVEREIGN STATE	France
CAPITAL/MAIN CITY	Cayenne
CURRENCY	Euro (EUR)
MEMBERSHIP	None (French overseas territory)
GOVERNMENT	French Overseas Territory
POPULATION	206,972
POP. DENSITY	3/km²; 6/mi²
GDP	4.1 Billion US$
LANGUAGE(S)	French, Creole
ETHNICITY	Guianese mulatto 38%, French 8%, Haitian 8%, Surinamese 6%, Antillean 5%, Chinese 5%, Brazilian 5%, East Indian 4%
RELIGION	Christian 85% (Roman Catholic 80%), Chinese folk-religionist 4%, Spiritist 4%, Indigenous Beliefs 2%
CLIMATE	Tropical

SOUTH AMERICA

ECUADOR

2° 00' S, 77° 30' W | 283,560 KM² | 109,483 MI² | UTC-5

The Republic of Equador sits directly on the central latitudinal line and its territory includes the Galapagos Islands some 1,000 kilometres to the west.

Geography

Occupying the north-western Pacific coast of the continent, Ecuador has large coastal plains, much of them natural mangrove swamps. These rise into the Andes, which sweep from north to south. To the west of the mountains the landscape is given over to the dense rain forest of the Amazon Basin. The majority of the population lives in the cities located in the highlands, although Ecuador's largest city is the port of Guayaquil. The slightly smaller capital Quito is within reach of Ecuador's second highest peak, the active volcano Cotopaxi.

History

Pre-Columbian Ecuador was part of the Inca Empire with Quito serving as its northern capital during the early sixteenth century. Following the Spanish conquest the city remained an administrative centre until independence in 1822. In 1835, Charles Darwin's visits to the biodiverse Galapagos Islands contributed to his theory of evolution by natural selection. Mainland Ecuador engaged in a series of border disputes with neighbouring Peru during the first decades of the twentieth century and tensions erupted again in 1996, leading to a war lasting four years. The country remains politically unstable.

Economy

Although the economy was stabilized by the adoption of the US dollar as currency in 2000, Ecuador remains a relatively poor nation, with around 35 per cent of the population living in extreme poverty. The main export is petroleum; it also relies upon the export of bananas and on fishing, all goods with fluctuating market prices.

FACT FILE

LOCAL NAME Republic of Ecuador

CAPITAL CITY Quito

CURRENCY US Dollar (USD)

MEMBERSHIP CAN, G77, SELA, LAIA, OAS, OPEC, RG, WTO

GOVERNMENT Presidential Republic

POPULATION 13,481,180

POP. DENSITY 48/km²; 123/mi²

GDP 98.79 Billion US$

LANGUAGE(S) Spanish, Amerindian languages (especially Quechua)

ETHNICITY Mestizo 65%, Amerindian 25%, Spanish and others 7%

RELIGION Roman Catholic 95%

CLIMATE Tropical; Temperate in highlands

REGIONAL DIVISIONS 4 geographical Regions are divided into 22 Provinces.

ECONOMIC ACTIVITIES Agriculture, Petroleum Extraction, Food Processing, Textiles, Wood Products, Chemicals, Pharmaceuticals

NATURAL RESOURCES Petroleum, Fish, Timber, Hydropower, Gold

QUITO
Quito, the capital city, with the volcano Mount Cotopaxi in the background.

PERU

10° 00' S, 76° 00' W | 1,285,220 KM² | 496,226 MI² | UTC-5

Once the heart of the Inca Empire, Peru has a long history as the seat of ancient Andean civilizations; it remained loyal to the Spanish conquistadors until 1821.

Geography

Occupying the mid-western coast of the continent, Peru has 2,414 kilometres of coastline. Running parallel to the generally arid coastal plains are the Andes Mountains, whose highest Peruvian peak at 6,768 metres is Huascarán. Titicaca is the world's highest lake. To the east is the lowland jungle basin of the Amazon; two of Peru's major rivers, the Marañón and the Ucayali, are key tributaries of the Amazon, which passes through Peru and Colombia into Brazil.

History

The arrival of the Spanish conquistador Francisco Pizarro in 1532 signalled the end of the Inca civilization, the largest of the pre-Columbian empires. The Amerindians became a semi-enslaved workforce for the Spanish, many being used to mine silver, a key natural resource. Fears of indigenous rebellion kept Peru loyal; however, the campaigns of Simón Bolívar and José de San Martín led to independence. The War of the Pacific (1879–83) between Peru and Chile saw the loss of substantial mineral-rich territory in the south. Economic and political instability led to military junta rule in the 1970s. Democracy was reintroduced in 1980, but violence and instability persisted until the late 1990s.

Economy

Although recognized as a developing country, despite recent economic growth 40 per cent of the population remains poor. Abundant supplies of minerals such as copper and gold and a strong fishing industry are economic mainstays. Peru signed a free-trade agreement with the United States which has strengthened the export market.

MACHU PICCHU
Machu Picchu, the 'lost city of the Incas'.

FACT FILE

LOCAL NAME Republic of Peru

CAPITAL CITY Lima

CURRENCY Nuevo Sol (PEN)

MEMBERSHIP APEC, CAN, G15, G24, G77, SELA, LAIA, OAS, RG, WTO

GOVERNMENT Constitutional Republic

POPULATION 28,221,492

POP. DENSITY 22/km²; 57/mi²

GDP 219 Billion US$

LANGUAGE(S) Spanish, Quechua, Aymara, Campa, Aguaruno

ETHNICITY Amerindian 45%, Mestizo 37%, White 15%

RELIGION Roman Catholic 81%

CLIMATE Tropical in east, Arid and Semi-arid in west, Temperate

REGIONAL DIVISIONS 3 geographical Regions are divided into 25 Administrative Regions and 1 Province

ECONOMIC ACTIVITIES Agriculture, Mining and Refining of Minerals, Steel, Metal Fabrication, Petroleum (Extraction and Refining), Natural Gas, Fishery, Textiles, Clothing, Food Processing and Beverages, Paper, Chemicals, Iron and Steel

NATURAL RESOURCES Copper, Silver, Gold, Petroleum, Timber, Fish, Iron Ore, Coal, Phosphate, Potash, Hydropower, Natural Gas

BOLIVIA

17° 00' S, 65° 00' W | 1,098,580 KM² | 424,164 MI² | UTC-4

Once part of northern Peru, this landlocked country was formed following independence from Spain in 1825.

Geography

The west of Bolivia's territory belongs to the highlands of the Andes, with the windswept plains of the altiplano lying between the cordillera mountain ranges. One of the main features on the altiplano is Lake Titicaca, on the border with Peru, the world's highest navigable lake and the largest in South America. The more sparsely populated east of the country is dominated by dry savannah, while to the north-east is tropical rain forest. Bolivia's administrative centre La Paz is also the world's highest capital city.

History

Conquered by the Spanish in 1524, Bolivia was valued for its rich silver deposits and provided an important source of revenue for the Empire. Although independence was claimed in 1809, sixteen years of war against the Spanish ensued before the republic was fully established. This was followed by decades of instability, exacerbated by a series of wars against Chile and Argentina. Democracy was established in 1982, but the persistent problems of poverty and racial tensions between Amerindians and Spanish descendants have undermined development.

Economy

Despite abundant resources of minerals and natural gas, Bolivia's economic growth is hampered by outdated infrastructures and overbearing state control which deters investment. Agricultural production includes coca, controversial because of its contribution to the illegal cocaine trade. Despite anti-narcotics intervention by the US the Bolivian government refuses to prevent its cultivation.

SALAR DE UYUNI
Salar de Uyuni, the world's largest salt flat, is the breeding ground of several species of flamingo.

FACT FILE

LOCAL NAME Republic of Bolivia

CAPITAL CITY La Paz (administrative), Sucre (constitutional, judicial)

CURRENCY Boliviano (BOB)

MEMBERSHIP CAN, G77, SELA, LAIA, OAS, RG, WTO

GOVERNMENT Presidential Republic

POPULATION 9,694,231

POP. DENSITY 9/km²; 23/mi²

GDP 39.44 Billion US$

LANGUAGE(S) Spanish, Quechua, Aymara

ETHNICITY Quechua 30%, Mestizo 30%, Aymara 25%, White 15%

RELIGION Roman Catholic 95%, Protestant (Evangelical Methodist) 5%

CLIMATE Tropical, Subtropical, Arid, Semi-arid

REGIONAL DIVISIONS 3 geographical Regions are divided into 9 Departments subdivided into 100 Provinces

ECONOMIC ACTIVITIES Agriculture, Mining, Smelting, Petroleum, Manufacturing, Commerce, Food and Beverages, Tobacco, Handicrafts, Clothing

NATURAL RESOURCES Tin, Natural Gas, Petroleum, Zinc, Tungsten, Antimony, Silver, Iron, Lead, Gold, Timber, Hydropower

BRAZIL

10° 00' S, 55° 00' W | 8,511,965 KM² | 3,286,488 MI² | UTC-2 TO -5

The largest and most economically powerful of the South American countries, Brazil is also the fifth largest country in the world and the fifth most populous.

Geography

Covering almost half of the South American continent, Brazil is home to a richly diverse geological and ecological landscape. It has 7,491 kilometres of Atlantic coastline and shares borders with ten countries: every South American country apart from Chile and Ecuador. The north of the country is dominated by the Amazon River, the world's largest river by volume and, at almost 7,000 kilometres in length, it is the second-longest after the Nile. The Amazon basin is covered by rain forest; undeniably the world's most ecologically important, it constitutes half of all rainforest on the planet, an area of over 3 million square kilometres. The Amazonian rain forest is home to more plant and animal species than any other habitat on Earth. One hectare of forest may contain up to 1,500 different plant species. More than 3,000 species of fish have been found in the river and thousands of different animals, birds, reptiles and insects live in the forest. New species of flora and fauna are still regularly discovered by scientists working in the Amazon basin. However,

FACT FILE

LOCAL NAME Federative Republic of Brazil

CAPITAL CITY Brasília

CURRENCY Real (BRL)

MEMBERSHIP CAN (associate), G15, G24, G77, SELA, LAIA, OAS, RG, WTO

GOVERNMENT Presidential Federal Republic

POPULATION 194,227,984

POP. DENSITY 23/km²; 59/mi²

GDP 1.836 Trillion US$

LANGUAGE(S) Portuguese, Spanish, English, Japanese, Creole

ETHNICITY White 54% (Portuguese being the largest European ethnic group), Mulatto (Pardo) 39%, Black 6%

RELIGION Roman Catholic 74%, Protestant 15%

CLIMATE Tropical, Temperate in south

REGIONAL DIVISIONS 5 Regions are divided into 26 States and 1 Federal District, consisting of the capital city Brasília

ECONOMIC ACTIVITIES Agriculture, Mining, Textiles, Footwear, Chemicals and Petrochemicals, Cement, Lumber, Iron Ore, Tin, Steel, Aircraft, Motor Vehicles, Auto Parts, Consumer Durables, Machinery and Equipment

NATURAL RESOURCES Bauxite, Gold, Iron Ore, Manganese, Nickel, Phosphates, Platinum, Tin, Uranium, Petroleum, Hydropower, Timber

despite international recognition of the importance of the Amazon rain forest, both as a rich habitat and as an important factor in preventing global warming, large areas of the forest are destroyed each year by loggers and those who wish to farm the land. To the south of the rain forest, the River Paraná forms the border with Paraguay and Argentina. Most of the rest of the country is the Brazilian Highlands, with several mountain regions and a central plateau of rolling terrain. The coastal strip is generally the most populous, although much is given over to mangroves and swamps. Brazil's largest city is São Paulo, which is situated in the south of the country. With a population of over ten million, it is also Brazil's wealthiest city. The capital, however, is Brasília; situated inland and

THE AMAZON
An aerial view of the Amazon River surrounded by thousands of hectares of rain forest.

created in the late 1950s, it became the administrative and political centre in 1960, replacing the coastal city of Rio de Janeiro which is famous for its beautiful setting and spectacular carnival.

History

Originally home to thousands of indigenous tribes, Brazil was discovered by the Portuguese in 1500. By the late twentieth century, an estimated 300,000 Amerindians remained in Brazil; before European colonization their population is thought to have exceeded four million. Initially undervalued as a colony, it soon had a thriving sugar industry established by the Portuguese around the southern coastal region. During the Napoleonic Wars, the Portuguese royal family escaped from Europe to set up court in Rio de Janeiro, returning to Lisbon in 1821. The following year, Brazil achieved independence from Portugal, although the Portuguese nobility retained their hold on power and the country temporarily became an empire. By 1889, Brazil had become a republic and despite the loss of the slave trade, which had been abolished the previous year, a period of rapid growth

RIO DE JANEIRO
Sandwiched between the coast and the mountains, Rio de Janeiro is the third largest city in South America, behind São Paulo and Buenos Aires.

began. The early half of the twentieth century saw a series of military dictatorships, then in 1985 democracy returned. Now an ethnically diverse mix of white Europeans, blacks, mixed-race and Amerindians, the population is mainly Roman Catholic and many are direct ancestors of the first Portuguese settlers and the three million black slaves that were imported from Africa. This diversity is apparent in Brazil's culture which demonstrates a blending of European and African traditions, perhaps the most potent symbol of which is Brazil's carnival, the forty-day festival period which marks Lent.

Economy

Brazil's agriculture, manufacturing and service industries benefit from a large labour pool, an abundance of natural resources and high commodity prices. Exports include goods such as coffee, cocoa, sugar, beef, textiles and cement and the manufacturing industry is bolstered by large natural reserves of iron and manganese, as well as bauxite, gold, tin, copper and uranium. Yet despite this the distribution of wealth in Brazil is extremely unequal and some 30 per cent of the population exist below the poverty line, many living in large shanty towns.

CHILE

30° 00' S, 71° 00' W | 756,950 KM² | 292,260 MI² | UTC-4

With its distinctive long, narrow shape, on average 175 kilometres wide, Chile's coastline runs for 6,435 kilometres from the border with Peru to the southernmost tip of the South American continent.

Geography

Despite its narrowness, Chile's length ensures an extreme variety of landscapes and climate. In the far north it is home to the Atacama, the world's driest desert, which annually receives just 0.1 mm of rainfall. The Central Valley is the most populated area and contains the capital city Santiago. Further south, forests and fertile grassland are punctuated by lakes and volcanoes and, to the extreme Antarctic south, the coastline is dominated by thousands of islands, peninsulas and fjords. Territory includes the Polynesian island of Rapa Nui, or Easter Island, which lies 3,600 kilometres west of Chile. The island is a world heritage site famous for the almost 900 huge stone statues which were carved by the islanders using stone chisels.

History

Chile was part of the Spanish Viceroyalty of Peru following the arrival of gold-seeking Spaniards in 1535, and the native tribes maintained a strong resistance to their European rivals until the nineteenth century. Proclaimed an autonomous Spanish republic in 1810, Chile then underwent an eight-year struggle for full independence. During the late nineteenth century Chile won a territorial victory over Peru in the War of the Pacific (1879–83). In 1973, the military general Augusto Pinochet overthrew the Marxist government of Salvador Allende to establish a brutal dictatorship which lasted for twenty-seven years.

Economy

Now a democratic republic, Chile has a strong, market-led capitalist economy where foreign investment is encouraged. Chile claims 57 international free-trade agreements. Copper is a major export and the government has reserved copper revenues to maintain income during periods of lowered prices. Other exports include wine and fruit, which are produced in the central area of the country, and salmon.

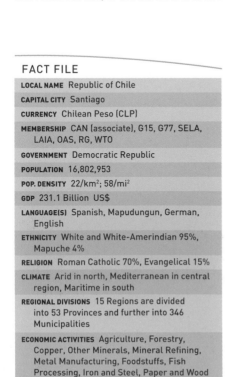

FACT FILE

LOCAL NAME Republic of Chile

CAPITAL CITY Santiago

CURRENCY Chilean Peso (CLP)

MEMBERSHIP CAN (associate), G15, G77, SELA, LAIA, OAS, RG, WTO

GOVERNMENT Democratic Republic

POPULATION 16,802,953

POP. DENSITY 22/km²; 58/mi²

GDP 231.1 Billion US$

LANGUAGE(S) Spanish, Mapudungun, German, English

ETHNICITY White and White-Amerindian 95%, Mapuche 4%

RELIGION Roman Catholic 70%, Evangelical 15%

CLIMATE Arid in north, Mediterranean in central region, Maritime in south

REGIONAL DIVISIONS 15 Regions are divided into 53 Provinces and further into 346 Municipalities

ECONOMIC ACTIVITIES Agriculture, Forestry, Copper, Other Minerals, Mineral Refining, Metal Manufacturing, Foodstuffs, Fish Processing, Iron and Steel, Paper and Wood Products, Transport Equipment, Cement, Textiles

NATURAL RESOURCES Copper, Timber, Iron Ore, Nitrates, Precious Metals, Molybdenum, Hydropower

PARAGUAY

23° 00′ S, 58° 00′ W | 406,750 KM² | 157,047 MI² | UTC-4

One of only two landlocked countries in South America, Paraguay's position in the centre of the continent earns it the nickname 'Heart of America'.

Geography

Paraguay is divided into two distinct regions by the Río Paraguay, which runs from north to south. The occidental (western) region is known as the Chaco, a vast semi-desert alluvial plain which is sparsely populated. The eastern region, the Paraneña, is a mixture of lowlands, forest and hills and is home to the majority of Paraguay's urban populace. The capital city Asunción lies on the Paraguay River.

History

During the mid-sixteenth century, Asunción became the centre for the Jesuit population in Spanish South America. Paraguay achieved its independence from Spain in 1811, but its post-colonial history became a long struggle for stability amid a series of destructive wars with its neighbours. In the War of the Triple Alliance (1865–70) with Brazil, Argentina and Uruguay, over two-thirds of the adult male population were lost, along with territory. The Chaco War (1932–5) against Bolivia saw Paraguay gain the Chaco region. The twentieth century was marked by the thirty-five-year dictatorship of Alfredo Stroessner. Intermarriage between the native Indians and Spanish settlers has resulted in an ethnically homogenous population.

Economy

Paraguay remains generally poor, despite the income generated by exporting the hydro-electricity produced in massive dams. There is a large informal sector in the market economy, with thousands of small business and street vendors, and corruption and inefficiency contribute to the stagnation of the economy. The main agricultural commodity is soya beans.

ITA PUA PROVINCE, SOUTH PARAGUAY
The remains of one of the Jesuit missions which were established in the seventeenth and eighteenth centuries.

FACT FILE

LOCAL NAME Republic of Paraguay

CAPITAL CITY Asunción

CURRENCY Guarani (PYG)

MEMBERSHIP CAN (associate), G77, SELA, LAIA, OAS, RG, WTO

GOVERNMENT Constitutional Presidential Republic

POPULATION 6,238,376

POP. DENSITY 15/km²; 40/mi²

GDP 27.08 Billion US$

LANGUAGE(S) Spanish, Guarani

ETHNICITY Mestizo 95%

RELIGION Roman Catholic 90%, Protestant 6%

CLIMATE Tropical, Subtropical

REGIONAL DIVISIONS 2 Regions, Eastern and Western, are divided into 17 Departments and 1 Capital District

ECONOMIC ACTIVITIES Agriculture, Sugar, Cement, Textiles, Beverages, Wood Products, Steel, Metallurgic, Electric Power

NATURAL RESOURCES Hydropower, Timber, Iron Ore, Manganese, Limestone

URUGUAY

36° 00' S, 56° 00' W | 176,220 KM² | 68,039 MI² | UTC-3

Uruguay is situated in the south-east of the continent; one-third of the population lives in or around its capital, Montevideo.

Geography

Sharing borders with Brazil to the north and Argentina to the south and east, Uruguay's landscape is that of low, rolling grassland. Rich fertile plains along the Atlantic coast are studded with lagoons; the largest, Laguna Merín, marks the Brazilian border. Much of the territory is dominated by rivers: the border with Argentina is formed by the River Uruguay in the west and the River Plate (Río de la Plata) to the south, which feeds into the Atlantic and upon which the capital, Montevideo, is situated. The most prominent river is the Río Negro; dams here form the largest artificial reservoirs in South America.

History

During the seventeenth century, Uruguay became a centre for cattle grazing and a source of contention between the Spanish and Portuguese, and was the focus of a series of struggles between Brazil and Argentina; however, in 1828 Uruguay managed to secure its independence. Many Uruguayans today are descended from Spanish and Italian settlers who arrived at the end of the nineteenth century. A Marxist military dictatorship ended in 1985 after thirteen years, and since then Uruguay has become one of South America's most progressive nations, with a strong welfare system, a high rate of literacy and, powerful middle class.

Economy

Relying upon foreign investment and trade, much of Uruguay's agriculture and industry is geared towards the export market; products include rice, wheat, soya beans, livestock, fish, electrical machinery and transport equipment. Despite a recession in 1999–2002, the economy is buoyant.

MONTEVIDEO
The sumptuous interior of the Legislative Palace in Montevideo, the home of Uruguay's General Assembly. The architecture and culture in Uruguay's main cities has been heavily influenced by European migrants.

FACT FILE

LOCAL NAME Oriental Republic of Uruguay

CAPITAL CITY Montevideo

CURRENCY Uruguayan Peso (UYU)

MEMBERSHIP CAN (associate), G77, SELA, LAIA, OAS, RG, WTO

GOVERNMENT Socialist Presidential Republic

POPULATION 3,350,454

POP. DENSITY 19/km²; 49/mi²

GDP 37.19 Billion US$

LANGUAGE(S) Spanish, Portunol or Brazilero (Portuguese-Spanish mix on the Brazilian frontier)

ETHNICITY White 88%, Mestizo 8%, Black 4%

RELIGION Roman Catholic 66%, Protestant 2%

CLIMATE Temperate

REGIONAL DIVISIONS 19 Departments; Montevideo department, the smallest in area, is the most populous

ECONOMIC ACTIVITIES Agriculture, Food Processing, Electrical Machinery, Transportation Equipment, Petroleum Products, Textiles, Chemicals, Beverages and Tobacco, Wool, Leather Apparel, Cement

NATURAL RESOURCES Hydropower, Minor Minerals, Fisheries

SOUTH AMERICA

ARGENTINA

34° 00' S, 64° 00' W | 2,766,890 KM² | 1,068,302 MI² | UTC-3

The second largest of the South American countries, Argentina occupies most of the southern portion of the continent.

Geography

Even without its territorial claims over parts of Antarctica, Argentina is a large and varied country. Its border with Chile in the west is marked by the spine of South America, the Andes mountain chain. The highest peak in the Andes, Aconcagua, is found in the Argentine province of Mendoza; at 6,959 metres it is also the highest point in

PATAGONIAN ANDES
Mount (Cerro) Fitz Roy was called Chaltén, which means 'smoking mountain', in the local dialect.

the Southern and Western Hemispheres. In the north, the hot, semi-arid lowland plains of the Gran Chaco provide a sparsely populated border with Brazil, Paraguay and Bolivia. The central region is the Pampas,

fertile grasslands which are the source of Argentina's agricultural wealth and which include the capital city of Buenos Aires at the mouth of the River Plate (Río de la Plata). To the far south is Patagonia, a generally arid and cold region, with some forests and several large lakes. Argentina's coastline stretches 4,655 kilometres along the Atlantic. Of the population of over 40 million people, 13 million live within the conurbation of Buenos Aires.

SOUTH AMERICA

PERITO MORENO GLACIER
The Perito Moreno glacier in the Patagonian Andes is 32 kilometres long and more than seventy-five metres thick.

FACT FILE

LOCAL NAME Argentine Republic

CAPITAL CITY Buenos Aires

CURRENCY Argentine Peso (ARS)

MEMBERSHIP CAN (associate), G15, G24, G77, SELA, LAIA, OAS, RG, WTO

GOVERNMENT Federal Presidential Republic

POPULATION 39,934,109

POP. DENSITY 14/km^2; 37/mi^2

GDP 523.7 Billion US$

LANGUAGE(S) Spanish, Italian, English, German, French

ETHNICITY White (mostly Spanish and Italian) 97%, Mestizo, Amerindian, or other non-white 3%

RELIGION Roman Catholic 92%, Protestant 2%, Jewish 2%

CLIMATE Temperate, Arid in south-east, Subarctic in south-west

REGIONAL DIVISIONS 6 geographical Regions are divided into 23 Provinces and 1 Autonomous City. Provinces are further divided into 376 Departments; Buenos Aires has 134 similar divisions, known as partidos

DEPENDENCIES Claims Falkland Islands

ECONOMIC ACTIVITIES Agriculture, Mining, Fishing, Food Processing, Motor Vehicles, Consumer Durables, Textiles, Chemicals and Petrochemicals, Electrical Machinery, Metallurgy, Steel, Wine, Oil Refining

NATURAL RESOURCES Fertile plains of the Pampas, Lead, Zinc, Tin, Copper, Iron Ore, Manganese, Petroleum, Uranium

History

When the first European explorers arrived in 1516, the area now known as Argentina was populated by nomadic tribes and, to the far north, Inca colonizers. By the end of the seventeenth century the Viceroyalty of the River Plate was inhabited by Spanish immigrants and the descendants of African slaves, most of whom settled in the Buenos Aires area. In 1816, the United Provinces of the Río Plata declared independence from Spain and separated into the distinct states of Bolivia, Paraguay, Uruguay and Argentina. Popular with Spanish and Italian settlers, 90 per cent of Argentina's current population is of European descent, the native Amerindian minority having remained in the Andean and Gran Chaco regions. Despite enjoying prosperity during the first decades of the twentieth century, the country's later history was marked by internal political and military conflicts. The authoritarian post-war presidencies of Juan Perón were followed by a decade of military junta rule which ended in 1983. Despite the economic crisis of 2001–2, democracy has held firm. Much of Argentina's culture has been influenced by Europe, although many gaucho traditions, such as the tango, are particularly associated with Latin America.

Economy

Having once been one of the world's richest nations, Argentina saw its economy suffered from a series of crises during the twentieth century. The severe decline at the start of the twenty-first century saw more than 60

per cent of Argentinians reduced to living below the poverty line. Since 2002, growth has resumed, although international debt and inflation remain problematic. Rich agricultural resources bolster the economy, with the farming sector geared towards the export market. Products include livestock, tobacco, wheat, soya beans, tea and corn. Industry has also benefited from greater diversification and contributes 34 per cent to the GDP. Although a non-NATO ally and a member of the World Trade Organization,

BUENOS AIRES
The port city of Buenos Aires is situated on the western bank of the River Plate (Río de la Plata). People from the city are called 'porteños', meaning 'people of the port'.

Argentina considers its relationship to its South American allies to be paramount.

FALKLAND ISLANDS

51° 45' S, 59° 00' W | 12,173 KM² | 4,700 MI² | UTC-4

Located in the South Atlantic, just 483 kilometres east of the coast of Argentina, the British Overseas Territory of the Falklands remains the subject of international dispute.

First claimed by the British in 1833 when they established a naval garrison on the islands, the Falklands have been at the centre of conflicting territorial claims by the French, Spanish, British and Argentines. Consisting of two large islands, East and West Falkland,

and a further 200 smaller islands, and with an economy that depends mainly upon sheep

FACT FILE

LOCAL NAME	Falkland Islands
SOVEREIGN STATE	United Kingdom
CAPITAL/MAIN CITY	Stanley
CURRENCY	Falkland Pound (FKP)
MEMBERSHIP	None
GOVERNMENT	British Overseas Territory
POPULATION	3,140
POP. DENSITY	0.3/km²; 0.7/mi²
GDP	75 Billion US$
LANGUAGE(S)	English
ETHNICITY	British 96%
RELIGION	Christian 67%
CLIMATE	Cold Maritime

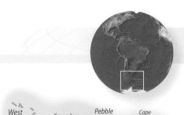

farming and fishing, the Falklands is home to a population of 3,140. The British–Argentine conflict of 1982 resulted in the islanders receiving full British citizenship.

SOUTH AMERICA

EUROPE AND THE RUSSIAN FEDERATION

1. LIECHTENSTEIN
2. KOSOVO
3. LUXEMBOURG

COUNTRY	PAGE
Albania	147
Andorra	140
Austria	133
Azores (PT)	137
Belarus	158
Belgium	124
Bosnia and Herzegovina	145
Bulgaria	156
Croatia	144

Europe is a grouping of countries rather than a discrete continent landmass; it merges into Asia to form the supercontinent of Eurasia. The vast Russian Federation spans the Ural Mountains, traditionally regarded as dividing Europe from Asia. The huge size of this continental region encompasses wide geographic variations, and its dense population and ethnic diversity have given it the world's richest historical and cultural heritage.

EUROPE AND THE RUSSIAN FEDERATION

NORTHERN EUROPE

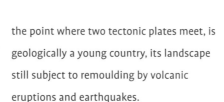

Shaped by surrounding seas, this region extends from Arctic territory in the north to the temperate Scilly Isles in the south. In between are great historic ports and cities, ancient mountains and deep fjords.

Arctic Circle

ICELAN

REYKJAVÍK

The countries of this region are united geographically and culturally by their strong connections with the sea. This provided not only convenient trading routes but also the means of conquest, initially within the region but later around the globe. The Vikings from Scandinavia extended their reach throughout medieval Europe, becoming established in many parts of Europe (including distant Greenland) and even briefly on the North American continent. Colonial expansion reached its zenith with the British Empire, which achieved a global extent on which 'the sun never set'.

The topography of Northern Europe is complex, owing to volcanic activity and the movements of the Earth's tectonic plates. These movements, forcing one area of land over or under another, resulted in folds and faults that created the high mountains and deep fjords of Scandanavia, while the erosion caused by glaciers during numerous ice ages carved out dramatic valleys. Changes in sea levels repeatedly redefined the extent of land masses; the United Kingdom, once physically part of mainland Europe, was cut off by the inundation that formed the English Channel between 450,000 and 200,000 years ago. Although these events occurred thousands of years ago, Iceland, straddling

the point where two tectonic plates meet, is geologically a young country, its landscape still subject to remoulding by volcanic eruptions and earthquakes.

Despite the northern latitude of the region, many of the countries benefit from the Gulf Stream, which carries warm water from the Gulf of Mexico across the North Atlantic to the western shores of Northern Europe. Climatically the western part of region is generally temperate maritime with prevailing weather systems from the Atlantic alternating from time to time with arctic extremes. The eastern part experiences a

more continental climate, with more marked extremes of temperature in summer and winter.

The peoples of Northern Europe still exhibit many of the characteristics of their ancestors. Those of Nordic extraction are characterised by their height, fair skin, blonde hair and blue eyes, while those of Celtic decent are generally shorter and darker haired. Migration has created ethnic and linguistic links between the various

SWEDEN
The Rapa Valley in Sweden's Sarek National Park.

Iceland's attempts to protect its fishing industry, on which it is economically dependent, led to 'Cod Wars' with the UK in the 1950s and 1970s, although Norway and the UK reached a negotiated agreement in the 1970s which has enabled the two countries to successfully exploit oil and gas reserves in the North Sea. Since 2004 all the North European countries have been members of the European Union, except Norway, which has rejected membership twice. The strong independence of the countries in this region reflects their relative economic strength and high standard of living.

nations. Swedish, Norwegian, Danish and Icelandic are based on a common language but the languages of Finland and the Baltic states, like their peoples, are quite separate and distinct. In the UK the influence of Scandinavian settlers is evident in certain words and many place names.

Despite their many historical and cultural points of contact, regional economic collaboration between Northern European states has been limited until recent times.

NORTHERN EUROPE

NORWAY

62° 00' N, 10° 00' E | 323,802 KM² | 125,021 MI² | UTC+1

From the early Norse explorers to the exploitation of natural resources, Norway has always made the most of its close relationship with the sea.

Geography

Norway occupies the western part of the Scandinavian peninsula, its lengthy coastline studded with numerous islands and fjords, huge inlets carved out during the last ice age. It is home to glaciers and waterfalls set within a landscape of mountainous terrain. Territories include the northerly island archipelago of Svalbard, which is mainly Arctic tundra. Because of its high latitude, reaching north of the Arctic Circle, during the summer Norway experiences almost twenty hours of daylight; in the far north, the sun never sinks below the horizon. Conversely, the sun hardly rises during the winter.

History

Norway's history was closely intertwined with that of its Scandinavian neighbours from the Middle Ages. It was ruled by Denmark from the fourteenth century and was under Swedish rule after 1814. Growing nationalism in the nineteenth century influenced artists such as Henrik Ibsen, Edvard Munch and Edvard Grieg. Union with Sweden ended in 1905, when Norway became an independent country and a constitutional monarchy under its own king.

Economy

Much of Norway's wealth comes from its state-owned petroleum and gas industries and its fisheries and forests. Engineering, shipping, mining and hydroelectricity all contribute to an economy with low unemployment and high standards of living. Although Norway has twice declined to join the European Union, its membership of the European Free Trade Association enables it to participate freely in key European markets.

GEIRANGER FJORD
Geiranger, near Ålesund, is one of Norway's most spectacular fjords.

FACT FILE

LOCAL NAME Kingdom of Norway

CAPITAL CITY Oslo

CURRENCY Norwegian Krone (NOK)

MEMBERSHIP AC, CBSS, CE, EAPC, NATO, OAS (observer), OECD, WTO

GOVERNMENT Constitutional Monarchy

POPULATION 4,727,260

POP. DENSITY 15/km²; 38/mi²

GDP 247.4 Billion US$

LANGUAGE(S) Bokmal Norwegian, Nynorsk Norwegian, Sami, Finnish

ETHNICITY Norwegian 94%, European 4%

RELIGION Church of Norway (Lutheran) 86%, Other Christian 4%, Muslim 2%

CLIMATE Subarctic, Temperate, Tundra

REGIONAL DIVISIONS 19 Counties and 430 Municipalities; Oslo has both municipality and county status

DEPENDENCIES Bouvet Island, Jan Mayen, Svalbard

ECONOMIC ACTIVITIES Petroleum and Natural Gas Extraction, Fisheries, Forestry, Food Processing, Mining, Timber Products (including Pulp and Paper), Machinery and Transport, Textiles, Shipbuilding and Shipping, Chemicals

NATURAL RESOURCES Petroleum, Natural gas, Iron Ore, Copper, Lead, Zinc, Titanium, Pyrites, Nickel, Fish, Timber, Hydropower

SWEDEN

62° 00' N, 15° 00' E | 449,964 KM² | 173,732 MI² | UTC+1

The largest country by area in Scandinavia, Sweden occupies the eastern part of the Scandinavian peninsula.

Geography

Sweden shares borders with Norway and Finland to the west and north, while the Baltic Sea provides an extensive coastline to the south and east. The more densely populated south is mainly flat and agricultural, while in the north the mountainous terrain is thickly forested. It is divided from Norway by the Skanderna mountain chain. The three 'lands' of Götaland, Svealand and Norrland are further divided into provinces and counties.

History

Sweden was formed in the tenth century with the union of Svealand and Götaland under Erik the Victorious, during a Viking age which saw the nation expand in the east towards Russia. After 150 years of Danish rule, independence was reasserted in 1521 and Sweden dominated north-eastern Europe in the seventeenth century. But constant warfare depleted the economy and it gradually lost its influence to a resurgent Russian Empire. Sweden remained neutral in both world wars. Modern Sweden is known for its egalitarianism and social permissiveness.

Economy

The economy is based mainly on exploitation and export of natural resources and the large general engineering industry, which produces machinery, motor vehicles, telecommunications and pharmaceuticals. Although a member of the European Union, which it joined in 1995, Sweden has retained the krona as its currency.

STOCKHOLM
One-fifth of Sweden's population lives in metropolitan Stockholm.

FACT FILE

LOCAL NAME Kingdom of Sweden

CAPITAL CITY Stockholm

CURRENCY Swedish Krona (SEK)

MEMBERSHIP AC, CBSS, CE, EAPC, EU, OAS (observer), OECD, WTO

GOVERNMENT Parliamentary Democracy and Constitutional Monarchy

POPULATION 9,159,978

POP. DENSITY 20/km²; 53/mi²

GDP 334.6 Billion US$

LANGUAGE(S) Swedish, Sami languages, Finnish

ETHNICITY Swedish 89%, European 7%, Asian 3%

RELIGION Church of Sweden (Lutheran) 87%, Muslim 4%

CLIMATE Continental: warm summer in south, sub-Arctic in north

REGIONAL DIVISIONS 21 Counties further divided into 290 Municipalities; Stockholm is the most densely populated county

ECONOMIC ACTIVITIES Agriculture, Mining, Machinery and Metal Products (Iron and Steel), Engineering and High Tech Manufacturing, Processed Food, Wood Pulp and Paper Products, Telecommunication, Automotive Manufacturing, Aviation, Pharmaceuticals, Armaments

NATURAL RESOURCES Timber, Iron Ore, Copper, Lead, Zinc, Gold, Silver, Tungsten, Uranium, Feldspar, Arsenic, Hydropower

FINLAND
64° 00' N, 26° 00' E | 338,145 KM² | 130,559 MI² | UTC+2

Although its capital Helsinki is vibrant, Finland is one of the most sparsely populated countries in Europe.

Geography

Finland lies between the Gulf of Finland to the south, the Gulf of Bothnia to the west and Russia to the east. The terrain is flat and low-lying, with thousands of lakes in the south-east and hundreds of small islands off the south coast. Further north the land is thickly forested. Over a quarter of the country lies north of the Arctic Circle and this area, Lappland, is home to the indigenous Sami peoples. Northern Finland has long, cold winters, with snow lying between mid-October and late April or mid-May. Average winter temperatures dip to -18°C but in summer reach almost 20°C .

History

A deeply ingrained national identity, rooted in folk art and its national poem, the *Kalevala*, has been engendered by Finland's historical domination by its neighbours, Sweden and Russia. Under Swedish rule from the twelfth century, the Finns found themselves subsumed in Swedish language and culture. In the early nineteenth century, Finland became a grand duchy within the Russian Empire until the Russian Revolution in 1917, when Finland declared itself independent. Under Soviet occupation in the Second World War, post-war Finland struggled to resist Soviet influence until the Soviet Union collapsed in 1991.

Economy

The thriving economy relies upon cutting-edge telecommunications and electronics (especially the manufacture of mobile phones) as well as the traditional timber and metal industries. Finland joined the European Union in 1995, and is the only Nordic member to have adopted the euro.

FACT FILE

LOCAL NAME Republic of Finland
CAPITAL CITY Helsinki
CURRENCY Euro (EUR)
MEMBERSHIP AC, CBSS, CE, EAPC, EU, OAS (observer), OECD, WTO
GOVERNMENT Parliamentary Republic
POPULATION 5,292,617
POP. DENSITY 16/km²; 41/mi²
GDP 185.5 Billion US$
LANGUAGE(S) Finnish, Swedish, Sami languages
ETHNICITY Finn 93%, Swede 6%, Sami 0.1%
RELIGION Lutheran Church of Finland 83%, Other Christian 2%
CLIMATE Subarctic, Temperate
REGIONAL DIVISIONS 6 Provinces, further divided into 415 Municipalities. The province of Åland Islands is autonomous, with Swedish the official language
ECONOMIC ACTIVITIES Agriculture, Forestry, Petroleum Products, Metals and Metal Products, Electronics, Machinery and Scientific Instruments, Shipbuilding, Wood Products (including Pulp and Paper), Food Products, Chemicals, Textiles, Clothing , IT, Telecommunications
NATURAL RESOURCES Timber, Iron Ore, Copper, Lead, Zinc, Chromite, Nickel, Gold, Silver, Limestone

LAKE INARI
Lake Inari is the third largest lake in Finland.

DENMARK

56° 00' N, 10° 00' E | 43,094 KM² | 16,639 MI² | UTC+1

The most southerly of the Scandinavian countries, Denmark is both typically Nordic and very European in character.

Geography

The country is made up of the Jylland (Jutland) Peninsula and over a thousand islands in the Baltic Sea. The larger islands, Fyn (Funen) and Sjaelland (Zealand), are connected to each other and to Jylland (Jutland) and Sweden by bridges, and the 7,845-metre-long Oresund Bridge links the Danish capital Copenhagen with the Swedish city of Malmö. There are over 7,000 kilometres of coastline and nowhere is further than 52 kilometres from the sea. The temperate climate and a low-lying landscape lend themselves to agriculture, which is intensive.

History

Denmark was part of the Viking kingdoms that raided much of northern Europe in the eighth to tenth centuries, and Danes settled Iceland, the Faroe Islands and Greenland; the latter two remain Danish territory. The dominant Scandinavian power in the Middle Ages, Danish influence declined from the sixteenth century and territory was lost to Sweden and Germany in the nineteenth century. Denmark was neutral in the First World War but was occupied by Germany in the Second World War. It is now one of the most socially progressive countries in Europe.

Economy

Agriculture, fishing and the export of manufactured goods such as wind turbines and processed foods are the mainstay of the economy, supporting a high standard of living. Although Denmark was the first Scandinavian member of the European Union, it has retained the krone as its currency.

COPENHAGEN
Boats line the harbour at Nyhavn.

FACT FILE

LOCAL NAME Kingdom of Denmark

CAPITAL CITY Copenhagen

CURRENCY Danish Krone (DKK)

MEMBERSHIP AC, CBSS, CE, EAPC, EU, NATO, OAS (observer), OECD, WTO

GOVERNMENT Parliamentary Democracy and Constitutional Monarchy

POPULATION 5,453,204

POP. DENSITY 127/km²; 328/mi²

GDP 203.7 Billion US$

LANGUAGE(S) Danish, Faroese, Greenlandic, German, English (predominant second language)

ETHNICITY Danish 95%, Asian 1%

RELIGION Church of Denmark (Lutheran) 95%

CLIMATE Temperate Maritime

REGIONAL DIVISIONS 5 Regions, further divided into 98 Municipalities. Hovedstaden is the most populous region

DEPENDENCIES Autonomous Territories: Faroe Islands, Greenland

ECONOMIC ACTIVITIES Agriculture, Fishery, Food Processing, Iron and Steel, Textiles, Electronics, Machinery and Transportation Equipment, Construction, Pharmaceuticals, Chemicals, Wood Products, Shipbuilding, Medical Equipment, Dairy Export, Beer Brewing

NATURAL RESOURCES Petroleum, Natural Gas, Fish, Salt, Limestone, Chalk, Stone, Gravel and Sand

ICELAND

65° 00' N, 18° 00' W | 103,000 KM² | 39,769 MI² | UTC

Situated on the Mid-Atlantic Ridge between the continents of Europe and America, Iceland is the second largest and the most westerly island of Europe.

Geography

Located just south of the Arctic Circle, with a climate tempered by the Gulf Stream, the dramatic landscape is home to numerous active volcanoes, geysers, lava deserts and glaciers. The coastline is heavily indented by fjords, while 80 per cent of the interior consists of a central plateau of glaciers, lakes and lava fields fringed by mountains. Subterranean hot water provides geothermal power, and rivers and waterfalls generate hydroelectricity. The few areas of grassland, found on the coastal plains, are given over to agriculture, mainly as grazing for livestock. Today very little remains of the birch forests that once covered much of the south of the island.

History

First settled in the ninth century by Norse explorers, Iceland became the seat of the world's oldest parliament, the Althing, in AD 930. The island united with Norway in the thirteenth century, and with Norway came under Danish rule in 1397. It became an independent kingdom under the Danish sovereign in 1918, declaring itself an independent republic in 1944. Since then it has become one of Europe's most prosperous and egalitarian societies, with a rich culture and heritage.

Economy

Despite having few natural resources, Iceland has low levels of unemployment and a high standard of living. Nearly two-thirds of the population live in and around the capital city of Reykjavik, situated on the west coast of the island. The economy is dominated by fishing and processing fish products, although it is diversifying into tourism, mineral production, information technology and bio-genetics.

STROKKUR GEYSER
Strokker erupts every five to ten minutes, throwing water and steam up to 20 metres in the air.

FACT FILE

LOCAL NAME Republic of Iceland

CAPITAL CITY Reykjavik

CURRENCY Euro (EUR)

MEMBERSHIP AC, CBSS, CE, EAPC, NATO, OECD, WTO

GOVERNMENT Constitutional Republic

POPULATION 303,495

POP. DENSITY 3/km²; 8/mi²

GDP 12.14 Billion US$

LANGUAGE(S) Icelandic, English, Nordic languages, German

ETHNICITY Icelandic 96%, European 3%, Asian 1%,

RELIGION Lutheran Church of Iceland 82%, Other Christian 9%

CLIMATE Subarctic, Continental Subarctic and Tundra

REGIONAL DIVISIONS 8 Regions and 79 Municipalities; the capital region is the most populous

ECONOMIC ACTIVITIES Agriculture, Fishing and Fish processing, Mining, Aluminium Smelting, Ferrosilicon Production, Tourism, IT, Construction

NATURAL RESOURCES Fish, Hydroelectric and Geothermal Power, Diatomite

FAROE ISLANDS

62° 00′ N, 7° 00′ W | 1,399 KM² | 540 MI² | UTC

Situated halfway between Norway and Iceland, where the Norwegian Sea meets the North Atlantic, the Faroe Islands are a self-governing territory of Denmark.

First settled by Viking explorers, this archipelago of eighteen rugged and rocky islands has a population of just over 48,000. All but one of the islands are inhabited, with the majority of villages being built on the coastal lowlands. With an economy dependent upon fishing, the Faroese are vulnerable to variations in the market and in stock levels, although recent discoveries of oil nearby offer the possibility of greater stability in the future. Many younger Faroese emigrate from the islands to Denmark, while most immigrants are Danish.

FACT FILE

LOCAL NAME Foroyar

SOVEREIGN STATE Denmark

CAPITAL/MAIN CITY Tórshavn

CURRENCY Danish Krone (DKK)

MEMBERSHIP Arctic Council, IMO (associate), NC, NIB, UPU

GOVERNMENT Self-governing overseas administrative division of Denmark

POPULATION 48,668

POPULATION DENSITY 35/km²; 90/mi²

GDP 1.87 Billion US$

LANGUAGE(S) Faroese, Danish

ETHNICITY Faroese 97%, Danish 3%

RELIGION Evangelical Lutheran 84%

CLIMATE Maritime, Subarctic

TÓRSHAVN
Tinganes, historic location of the parliament.

ESTONIA

59° 00′ N, 26° 00′ E | 45,226 KM² | 17,462 MI² | UTC+2

Estonia has been subject to rule by the Danes, Swedes, Poles, Germans and Russians, but is now successfully asserting itself as the most developed and westernized of the Baltic states.

Although under Russian or Soviet rule almost continuously from the eighteenth century until the 1990s, Estonia has a closer affinity with Finland, with which it shares linguistic and ethnic roots. A flat, wet and forested landscape, Estonia has a resurgent tourism industry, particularly popular with Finnish holidaymakers and visitors to its capital city Tallinn. Independence from the Soviet Union came in 1991 and it has since established strong links with Western Europe, joining NATO and the European Union in 2004.

FACT FILE

LOCAL NAME Republic of Estonia

CAPITAL CITY Tallinn

CURRENCY Estonian Kroon (EEK)

MEMBERSHIP CBSS, CE, EAPC, EU, NATO, OAS (observer), WTO

GOVERNMENT Parliamentary Republic

POPULATION 1,330,510

POP. DENSITY 29/km²; 76/mi²

GDP 29.35 Billion US$

LANGUAGE(S) Estonian, Russian

ETHNICITY Estonian 68%, Russian 26%

RELIGION Estonian Evangelical Lutheran Church 14%, Orthodox and other Christian 14%,

CLIMATE Temperate

NORTHERN EUROPE

LITHUANIA

56° 00' N, 24° 00' E | 65,300 KM² | 25,212 MI² | UTC+2

The largest and most populous of the Baltic states, Lithuania has a long history of struggle against Russian and Soviet dominance in the modern era.

Geography

Lithuania borders Poland, Russia, Belarus and Latvia, with the Baltic Sea to the west. It shares the Curonian Lagoon (Kurskiy Zaliv), formed by a lengthy sand peninsula, which protects about half its coast, with the Russian enclave around Kaliningrad. The terrain is mainly flat and low-lying, with numerous lakes, wetlands and forests. The River Nemunas is an important trade route for internal shipping.

History

During the thirteenth century, Lithuania formed a grand duchy in central and eastern Europe that covered parts of present-day Poland and Russia and extended to the Black Sea. It was confederated with Poland from the sixteenth century until 1795, when it was annexed by the Russian Empire. Despite declaring independence in 1918, Lithuania was occupied by the Soviet Union in 1940 and remained under Soviet rule until 1991, when the country became the first to rebel against the doomed Soviet state. Since independence, Lithuania has adopted a pro-Western stance, joining NATO and the European Union in 2004. Unlike many of its neighbours, Lithuania has experienced little internal strife since independence despite its varied ethnic population, which is made up of Poles, Russians, Belarusians and Lithuanians.

Economy

Since its entry into the European Union in 2004, Lithuania has seen a rapid growth in its economy, but the standard of living is not high and there remains a disproportion in the share of wealth. Its prosperity is based on high-technology industries, engineering, shipbuilding, food processing and agriculture.

FACT FILE

LOCAL NAME Republic of Lithuania

CAPITAL CITY Vilnius

CURRENCY Litas (LTL)

MEMBERSHIP CBSS, CE, EAPC, EU, NATO, WTO

GOVERNMENT Parliamentary Republic

POPULATION 3,371,128

POP. DENSITY 52/km²; 134/mi²

GDP 59.64 Billion US$

LANGUAGE(S) Lithuanian, Russian, Polish

ETHNICITY Lithuanian 83%, Polish 7%, Russian 6%

RELIGION Roman Catholic 79%, Russian Orthodox 4%, Protestant (including Lutheran and Evangelical Christian Baptist) 2%

CLIMATE Temperate

REGIONAL DIVISIONS 10 Counties divided into 60 Municipalities; the most densely populated county is Vilnius

ECONOMIC ACTIVITIES Machine Tools, Electrical Goods, Petroleum Refining, Shipbuilding, Furniture Making, Textiles, Food Processing, Fertilizers, Agricultural Machinery, Optical Equipment, Electronic Components, Computers, Amber jewellery

NATURAL RESOURCES Peat, Arable Land, Amber

VILNIUS
View of the new town from Gediminas Hill.

LATVIA

57° 00′ N, 25° 00′ E | 64,589 KM² | 24,938 MI² | UTC+2

With its large Russian population, this former Soviet republic has continuing intercommunal tensions despite achieving independence in 1991.

A large country on the shores of the Baltic Sea, Latvia has a landscape that is mainly flat, and with its moderate, wet climate, the poorly draining land is often too boggy for agriculture. Consequently, over 70 per cent of the populace lives in urban areas and its economy is more dependent upon industry and services, such as banking and transit services. Although independent of Soviet rule since 1991, Latvia retains many political and economic ties with its former master, despite being ethnically closer to neighbouring Lithuania. It joined the World Trade Organization in 1999 and the European Union in 2004.

RIGA
The centre of Riga has been designated a World Heritage Site.

FACT FILE

LOCAL NAME Republic of Latvia
CAPITAL CITY Riga
CURRENCY Lat (LVL)
MEMBERSHIP CBSS, CE, EAPC, EU, NATO, OAS (observer), WTO
GOVERNMENT Parliamentary Republic
POPULATION 2,265,485
POP. DENSITY 35/km²; 91/mi²
GDP 39.73 Billion US$
LANGUAGE(S) Latvian, Russian, Lithuanian
ETHNICITY Latvian 58%, Russian 30%, Belorussian 4%, Ukrainian 3%
RELIGION Lutheran 20%, Latvian Orthodox 15%
CLIMATE Temperate

ISLE OF MAN

54° 15′ N, 4° 30′ W | 572 KM² | 221 MI² | UTC

FACT FILE

LOCAL NAME Isle of Man
SOVEREIGN STATE United Kingdom
CAPITAL/MAIN CITY Douglas
CURRENCY Isle of Man Pound (Manx Pound) (IMP)
GOVERNMENT British Crown Dependency
POPULATION 76,220
POP. DENSITY 133/km²; 345/mi²
GDP 2.719 Billion US$
LANGUAGE(S) English, Manx Gaelic
ETHNICITY Manx (Norse-Celtic descent) 48%, English 38%, Scottish 4%, Northern Irish 2%, Irish 2%
RELIGION Christian 64% (including Anglican 41%, Methodist 10%, Roman Catholic 8%)
CLIMATE Temperate

Despite its proximity to the UK mainland, the Isle of Man is a self-governing Crown Dependency that receives British protection.

Located in the Irish Sea, midway between Northern Ireland and the north of England, the Isle of Man has over the centuries been ruled by the Vikings, the Scots and the English. Now self-governing, its parliament, the Tynwald, is responsible for a population of over 76,000. Agriculture and fishing were traditionally the mainstays of the economy, until the island's status as a tax haven and the investment incentives offered by the Manx government made it a thriving centre for offshore banking, financial and professional services and information technology manufacturing.

NORTHERN EUROPE

UNITED KINGDOM

54° 00' N, 2° 00' W | 244,820 KM² | 94,526 MI² | UTC

Although separated from mainland Europe by only a few miles of water, the United Kingdom is defined by a strong sense of cultural difference from its neighbours.

Geography

Consisting of the larger island Great Britain and the north-eastern corner of Ireland, the United Kingdom encompasses the distinct regions of England, Scotland, Wales and Northern Ireland. The entire archipelago, including a number of Scottish islands, lies between the North Atlantic Ocean and the North Sea and is separated from France by a channel only 27 kilometres at its narrowest. The landscape to the north and west, in Scotland, northern England and Wales, is generally rugged uplands, with the highest mountain ranges in the Scottish Highlands and northern Wales. Further south and east, rolling hills and moorlands give way to chalk and limestone downs and flat fenland. Northern Ireland is the only part with a land border, shared with the Republic of Ireland. Its landscape is also rugged and hilly, punctuated with inland lakes, Lough Neagh being the largest. The Lake District on the mainland is in north-west England. Major rivers include the Severn and the Thames, beside which the capital city London has grown since Roman times. London now boasts a population of over 7 million; indeed, the entire United Kingdom is densely populated, with over 61 million inhabitants, the vast majority residing in England.

LONDON
The recently completed Swiss Re Tower, known as the Gherkin building, has quickly become one of the City of London's most famous landmarks.

History

Formed by the Treaties of Union of 1707 and 1800, the United Kingdom has a history that stretches back to mainly Celtic origins in pre-Roman times. The early centuries of the islands' history saw repeated invasions from mainland Europe by the Romans, the Angles and Saxons, and the Vikings. The last significant conquest came in 1066, when William, Duke of Normandy, invaded and conquered England. The Middle Ages saw attempts by England to conquer its island neighbours, and Wales was absorbed in the sixteenth century. This century also saw the establishment of a powerful naval fleet, a key element in the subsequent creation of an overseas empire. Although the American colonies were lost in the eighteenth century, by the mid-nineteenth century the British Empire covered a quarter of the globe, a breadth of extent that is reflected in the multi-cultural nature of Britain today. Despite being the first nation to industrialize, two world wars and decolonialization in the twentieth century brought about a decline, until the economic resurgence of the 1990s. A rich tradition of intellectual and artistic endeavour was created by such notable Britons as Shakespeare, Sir Isaac Newton and Charles Darwin. Most Britons remain proud of their unique heritage, even if this is often expressed as regionalism rather than nationalism. The close of the twentieth century saw the devolution of self-governing powers to Scotland, Wales and Northern Ireland, which now have their own legislatures.

Economy

With one of the most powerful economies in the world, the United Kingdom is a centre for financial markets, banking, insurance and business. It has a highly efficient agricultural sector, and the twentieth-century decline in manufacturing and heavy industries has been offset by growth in biotechnology, communications and engineering. It also has reserves of oil, natural gas and coal. Although it remains reluctant to adopt the euro, the United Kingdom retains a global outlook; it is one of the five permanent members on the UN Security Council, a founder of NATO, and a member of the European Union.

FACT FILE

LOCAL NAME United Kingdom of Great Britain and Northern Ireland

CAPITAL CITY London

CURRENCY British Pound (GBP)

MEMBERSHIP AC (observer), CBSS (observer), CE, C, EAPC, EU, G5, G8, G20, NATO, OAS (observer), OECD, WTO

GOVERNMENT Parliamentary Democracy and Constitutional Monarchy

POPULATION 61,018,648

POP. DENSITY 249/km²; 646/mi²

GDP 2.137 Trillion US$

LANGUAGE(S) English, Welsh, Scottish Gaelic

ETHNICITY White (of which English 84%, Scottish 9%, Welsh 5%, Northern Irish 3%) 92%, black 2%, Indian 2%, Pakistani 1%

RELIGION Christian (Anglican, Roman Catholic, Presbyterian, Methodist) 72%, Muslim 3%, Hindu 1%

CLIMATE Temperate Maritime

REGIONAL DIVISIONS England: 34 Non-metropolitan Counties, 32 London Boroughs, 1 City of London, 36 Metropolitan Counties, 46 Unitary Authorities; Northern Ireland: 26 District Councils; Scotland: 32 Unitary Authorities; Wales: 22 Unitary Authorities

DEPENDENCIES Overseas Territories: Anguilla, Bermuda, British Indian Ocean Territory, British Virgin Islands, Cayman Islands, Gibraltar, Montserrat, Pitcairn Islands, St Helena, South Georgia and the South Sandwich Islands, Turks and Caicos Islands; Autonomous Territories: Falkland Islands; Crown Dependencies: Guernsey, Jersey, Isle of Man

ECONOMIC ACTIVITIES Agriculture, Steel, Machine Tools, Heavy Engineering, Metal Manufacturing, Aircraft, Motor Vehicles and Parts, Electronics and Communications Equipment, Chemicals, Textiles, Clothing, Consumer Goods, Pulp and Paper, Food Processing, Coal and Petroleum, Construction, Finance and Business Services, Tourism

NATURAL RESOURCES Coal, Petroleum, Natural Gas, Iron Ore, Lead, Zinc, Gold, Tin, Limestone, Salt, Clay, Chalk, Gypsum, Potash, Silica Sand, Slate

EDINBURGH
Edinburgh castle is perched on the remains of an extinct volcano in the centre of the historic area of the town. Edinburgh is Scotland's capital city and is the seat of the Scottish parliament, which was established in 1999.

JERSEY

49° 15' N, 2° 10' W | 116 KM² | 45 MI² | UTC

With its rolling hills and rugged coastline, Jersey is popular both as a tourist destination and as a tax haven for financial institutions and wealthy British expatriates.

Like the rest of the Channel Islands, Jersey was originally part of the medieval Duchy of Normandy and so is neither French, despite its location, nor part of the UK; it is a Crown Dependency that receives British protection. Although not a member of the European Union, Jersey is able to trade freely with EU member states. Its principal products are agricultural and horticultural crops such as potatoes, milk and flowers, although its prosperity rests on financial services.

JERSEY BEACHES
Jersey's beautiful coastline attracts tourists.

FACT FILE

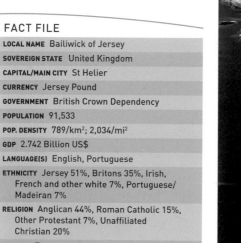

LOCAL NAME	Bailiwick of Jersey
SOVEREIGN STATE	United Kingdom
CAPITAL/MAIN CITY	St Helier
CURRENCY	Jersey Pound
GOVERNMENT	British Crown Dependency
POPULATION	91,533
POP. DENSITY	789/km²; 2,034/mi²
GDP	2.742 Billion US$
LANGUAGE(S)	English, Portuguese
ETHNICITY	Jersey 51%, Britons 35%, Irish, French and other white 7%, Portuguese/Madeiran 7%
RELIGION	Anglican 44%, Roman Catholic 15%, Other Protestant 7%, Unaffiliated Christian 20%
CLIMATE	Temperate

GUERNSEY

49° 28' N, 2° 35' W | 78 KM² | 30 MI² | UTC

A British Crown Dependency, Guernsey is part of the Channel Islands group, which lies in the English Channel close to the French coast.

Guernsey and the neighbouring minor islands of Alderney, Sark and Herm have a combined population of over 65,000 people. With a level, rolling terrain and moderate, if wet, climate, Guernsey has a thriving agriculture sector. Economic growth has been boosted

FACT FILE

LOCAL NAME	Bailiwick of Guernsey
SOVEREIGN STATE	United Kingdom
CAPITAL/MAIN CITY	St Peter Port
CURRENCY	Guernsey Pound
GOVERNMENT	British Crown Dependency
POPULATION	65,726
POP. DENSITY	843/km²; 2,191/mi²
GDP	2.742 Billion US$
LANGUAGE(S)	English, French
ETHNICITY	Guernsey 64%, United Kingdom 27%, Alderney 0.2%, Sark 0.1%
RELIGION	Protestant 51%, Unaffiliated Christian 20%, Roman Catholic 15%
CLIMATE	Temperate

by manufacturing and financial services. Although the majority of the population speak English, some speakers remain of the Norman French dialect, a remnant of Guernsey's past as part of the medieval Duchy of Normandy.

REPUBLIC OF IRELAND

53° 00' N, 8° 00' W | 70,282 KM² | 27,136 MI² | UTC

The Irish Republic is a sovereign state covering five sixths of the island of Ireland, which is part of the British Isles and lies to the west of Great Britain.

Geography

The centre of Ireland is dominated by low, flat plains and peat-rich bogs. Much of the country is given over to intense agriculture. Towards the coast, the terrain becomes more rugged, with coastal mountains forming a ring from the south-west across to the east. Major rivers include the Shannon, which is the longest river in the British Isles. Around 40 per cent of the republic's total population live in or within a 100-kilometre radius of Dublin, the capital city.

FACT FILE

LOCAL NAME Republic of Ireland

CAPITAL CITY Dublin

CURRENCY Euro (EUR)

MEMBERSHIP CE, EAPC, EU, OAS (observer), OECD, WTO

GOVERNMENT Republic and Parliamentary Democracy

POPULATION 4,380,073

POP. DENSITY 62/km²; 161/mi²

GDP 186.2 Billion US$

LANGUAGE(S) English, Irish (Gaelic or Gaeilge) (spoken in western seaboard areas)

ETHNICITY Irish 95%, Other (mainly British) 5%

RELIGION Roman Catholic 87%, Church of Ireland 3%

CLIMATE Temperate Maritime

REGIONAL DIVISIONS 26 Counties; traditionally Ireland was divided into 4 Provinces

ECONOMIC ACTIVITIES Agriculture, Mining Processing (Steel, Lead, Zinc, Silver, Aluminium, Barite, Gypsum), Food Processing, Brewing, Machinery, Computer Equipment, Information Technology, Pharmaceuticals, Chemicals, Tourism, Construction, Textiles, Clothing, Rail Transportation Equipment, Ship Construction and Refurbishment, Glass and Crystal, Software

NATURAL RESOURCES Natural Gas, Peat, Copper, Lead, Zinc, Barite, Gypsum, Limestone, Dolomite

History

Originally settled by Celtic tribes, since the first English invasions of the twelfth century Anglo-Irish relations were a series of repressions and rebellions until modern times. Desperate poverty and the great famine of 1845–9 led to massive emigration to the USA. In 1921 Ireland was granted independence, except for six predominantly Protestant counties in the north, which remain British. This partition caused political, religious and civil strife throughout the twentieth century, until the implementation of a peace settlement begun in 1998. Irish culture is rich in literary, artistic and musical achievements.

DUNMORE HEAD
An ancient stone at Dunmore Head on the Dingle peninsula, in the west of Ireland.

Economy

Ireland's traditionally agrarian economy has been transformed since the country joined the European Union into one based on services and industry; agriculture now contributes only 5 per cent of GDP. Ireland joined the Economic Union in 1973, and is also a member of the OECD and the UN, but its policy of neutrality has kept it out of NATO.

WESTERN EUROPE

Heartland of continental Europe with historic cities, rolling plains, great rivers and dramatic mountains: its history, once seething with unrest and conflict, has now entered a lasting peaceful phase under the EU.

The geography of Western Europe reflects the large-scale earth movements of nearly 25 million years ago, when the geological upheavals that built the Alpine and other mountain ranges in the south and east of the region reached their peak. The subsequent ice ages gouged out deep river valleys, and flattened the plains of the north and west. The lowlands of Flanders and the rolling plains of northern France are the breadbaskets of the region, with the mountain peaks and valleys of southern France, Switzerland, Austria and southern Germany just as intensively farmed for livestock and their products. The valleys of the great rivers, such as the Rhine and Rhône, and the region's extensive coastline provided the trading routes that led to the growth of commerce and of the major commercial cities of medieval and modern Europe.

The maritime tradition encouraged exploration and trade. In medieval times, this was dominated on the North Sea coast and in the Baltic by the German merchants of the Hanseatic League. The Dutch and the

FRANKFURT
A view of the Frankfurt skyline and the River Main.

French vied with Britain in naval strength and commercial and colonial ambitions in the seventeenth and eighteenth centuries, while Germany became the leading industrial power of Europe in the early twentieth century.

Although on the periphery of the Roman Empire, the region became the centre of political power in Christendom after the fall of Rome in the fifth century. Despite wars and internal upheavals as nation states emerged here, this part of Europe was the most powerful region in the world for centuries, owing to its military, commercial, colonial and industrial power, and the most culturally influential. But the era in which the 'Old World' occupied centre-stage in world affairs effectively ended with the emergence of the twentieth century's superpowers.

In the aftermath of the Second World War, the shared vision of the countries of Western Europe led to the establishment of the European Union. The Union, which has secured political peace and economic prosperity throughout Europe, has its heart in Western Europe, with its parliaments and its judiciary based in Brussels and Strasbourg. Today, Western Europe is an ethnic and cultural melting pot, as its economic opportunities and the relaxation of border controls have attracted migrants from poorer countries to the east and south.

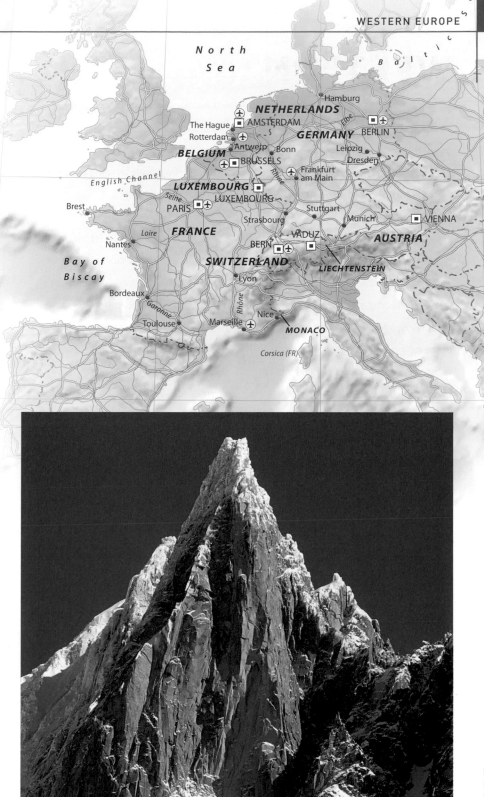

THE ALPS
The pinnacle of Mont Blanc, the highest mountain in Europe.

WESTERN EUROPE

BELGIUM

50° 50' N, 4° 00' E | 30,528 KM² | 11,787 MI² | UTC+1

A small country in northern Europe, Belgium's geographic diversity is matched by the complexity of its political system.

Geography

With coastal plains to the north and forested hills in the south-eastern Ardennes, Belgium is geographically diverse despite its small size. The coastal areas, where the land is lower-lying, are dominated by dunes, and submersion by high seas is prevented by dykes. The centre, richly irrigated by rivers and canals, is given over to agriculture.

History

The country is divided almost equally into two major cultural groups, the French-speaking Walloons to the south and the more prosperous Flemish (Dutch) speakers to the north. Originally part of the Low Countries, Belgium experienced periods of rule by the Holy Roman Empire, Habsburg Spain, revolutionary France and the Netherlands before becoming an independent kingdom in 1831. Often referred to as the 'battlefield of Europe', it has been the scene of fierce fighting over the centuries, including during both the First and Second World Wars. The post-war period was marked by political instability because of tensions between the Walloon and Flemish populations until federalization began in 1980, creating a complex system of self-governing communities and regions.

Economy

Its central position has made Belgium an important trading centre; its prosperity is based on trade, industry and its large service sector, serving the major international organizations, including the European Parliament and NATO, that are located in Brussels. Its main exports are industrial: iron and steel, engineering products, and vehicles. It is a founder member of the European Union and one-third of the Benelux economic union.

BRUSSELS
Brussels' main square with a carpet of flowers.

FACT FILE

LOCAL NAME Kingdom of Belgium

CAPITAL CITY Brussels

CURRENCY Euro (EUR)

MEMBERSHIP Benelux, CE, EAPC, EU, NATO, OAS (observer), OECD, WTO

GOVERNMENT Parliamentary Democracy and Constitutional Monarchy

POPULATION 10,480,390

POP. DENSITY 343/km²; 889/mi²

GDP 376 Billion US$

LANGUAGE(S) Dutch, French, German

ETHNICITY Fleming 58%, Walloon 31%

RELIGION Roman Catholic 75%, Other (includes Protestant) 25%

CLIMATE Temperate Maritime

REGIONAL DIVISIONS 3 Communities (language-based); 3 Regions further divided into 10 Provinces. Capital city Brussels is officially the Brussels Capital Region which is also de facto capital of the European Union

ECONOMIC ACTIVITIES Agriculture, Engineering and Metal Products, Motor Vehicle Assembly, Iron and Steel, Transportation Equipment, Scientific Instruments, Processed Food and Beverages, Chemicals, Basic Metals, Textiles, Refining, Services, Glass

NATURAL RESOURCES Construction Materials, Silica Sand, Carbonates, Coal

NETHERLANDS

52° 30' N, 5° 45' E | 41,526 KM² | 16,033 MI² | UTC+1

This small north European country is one of the most densely populated in the world, with over 15 million people.

Geography

A flat and fertile country, most of the Netherlands lies below sea level on a delta formed by several major rivers, including the Rhine, Maas, Waal and Scheldt, or on reclaimed land. Reclaimed areas include the Zuider Zee, where reclamation began in 1920; its remnant now forms the Ijsselmeer. The rivers are linked by a network of canals over 6,000 kilometres in length, and the major cities and towns are positioned along these trade arteries. The largest city is the capital,

Amsterdam, which is also a world centre for diamond trading.

History

The 'Low Countries', part of the Holy Roman Empire from medieval times, came under Spanish rule in the sixteenth century. Attempts to suppress Protestantism led to rebellion in 1572, and seven northern territories formed the United Provinces of the Netherlands in 1579, creating the modern

KINDERDIJK
Traditional windmills line a canal near Rotterdam.

FACT FILE

LOCAL NAME Kingdom of the Netherlands

CAPITAL CITY Amsterdam

CURRENCY Euro (EUR)

MEMBERSHIP Arctic Council (observer), Benelux, CBSS (observer), CE, EAPC, EU, NATO, OAS (observer), OECD, WTO

GOVERNMENT Constitutional Monarchy and Parliamentary Democracy

POPULATION 16,450,021

POP. DENSITY 396/km²; 1,026/mi²

GDP 639.5 Billion US$

LANGUAGE(S) Dutch, Frisian

ETHNICITY Dutch 80%

RELIGION Roman Catholic 30%, Protestant Church of Netherlands (PKN) 12%, Other Protestant 5%, Muslim 6%

CLIMATE Temperate Maritime

REGIONAL DIVISIONS 12 Provinces further divided into 458 Municipalities; South Holland is the most populous province and Rotterdam (second largest city of the country) is in this province

DEPENDENCIES Aruba, Netherland Antilles (part of Kingdom of Netherlands)

ECONOMIC ACTIVITIES Agriculture, Agro-industries, Electrical Machinery and Equipment, Metal and Engineering Products, Chemicals, Clothing, Diamond Cutting, Petroleum, Construction, Microelectronics, Fishing, Financial and Business Services, Transport Equipment, Flower Import/Export

NATURAL RESOURCES Natural Gas, Petroleum

Dutch state, although their independence was not recognized by Spain until 1648. During the seventeenth century a powerful mercantile navy made possible a boom in commercial activity that led to a 'Golden Age' of colonial expansion and artistic endeavour. Revolutionary France occupied the country from 1795 to 1813. Its neutrality was respected in the First World War, but in 1940 it was invaded and occupied by Germany. The post-war period brought conflicts over independence with its remaining colonies, most of which became independent in the second half of the twentieth century, and the development of a highly liberal society at home.

Economy

Its geographical location and commercial tradition have made the Netherlands a trans-shipment hub for Europe, particularly through Rotterdam and the Europort. Major industries include oil refining and its highly intensive agricultural sector; it is the world's third largest exporter of agricultural produce. A founder member of the European Union and one-third of the Benelux economic union, the Netherlands is also the location of five international courts and the headquarters of Interpol.

ROTTERDAM
Rotterdam is the largest port in Europe.

LUXEMBOURG

49 45' N, 6° 10' E | 2,586 KM² | 998 MI² | UTC+1

Bordering France, Germany and Belgium, the landlocked country of Luxembourg is the world's only Grand Duchy and is also one of the world's richest states.

FACT FILE

LOCAL NAME Grand Duchy of Luxembourg
CAPITAL CITY Luxembourg
CURRENCY Euro (EUR)
MEMBERSHIP Benelux, CE, EAPC, EU, NATO, OAS (observer), OECD, WTO
GOVERNMENT Parliamentary Democracy and Constitutional Grand Duchy
POPULATION 472,066
POP. DENSITY 183/km²; 473/mi²
GDP 38.56 Billion US$
LANGUAGE(S) Luxembourgish, German, French
ETHNICITY Luxembourger 63%, Portuguese 13%, French 5%, Italian 4%, German 2%
RELIGION Roman Catholic 87%, Protestant 3%
CLIMATE Temperate Maritime

Made a Grand Duchy following the Congress of Vienna in 1815, Luxembourg was recognized as a neutral independent state in 1867. The country is broadly divided into two geographical areas: the thickly forested Oesling region in the north and the more fertile and densely populated plateau in the Gutland region in the south. Broad valleys with streams and rivers cross much of the country. Traditional industries such as steel making have diminished in importance in recent decades and Luxembourg's economy has become increasingly dependent on the banking and finance industries. The capital city of Luxembourg is home to more than 150 national banks and nearly 14,000 multinational companies have established holding companies there. It is also the seat of the European Investment Bank and the European Court of Justice.

FRANCE

46° 00' N, 2° 00' E | 643,427 KM² (547,030 KM² IN METROPOLITAN FRANCE) | 248,429 MI² (211,209 MI² IN METROPOLITAN FRANCE) | UTC+1

At the centre of Western Europe, France has been a dominant force in European politics since the sixteenth century.

Geography

Situated on the edge of Western Europe, sharing land borders with seven countries and with a coastline stretching 3,427 kilometres, France is the largest country in the European Union. It has a varied terrain, with rolling coastal plains and hills to the north and west and mountain ranges elsewhere, particularly the Pyrenees in the

FACT FILE

LOCAL NAME French Republic

CAPITAL CITY Paris

CURRENCY Euro (EUR)

MEMBERSHIP AC (observer), BSEC (observer), CBSS (observer), CE, EAPC, EU, G5, G8, G20, NATO, OAS (observer), OECD, WTO

GOVERNMENT Semi-presidential Republic

POPULATION 61,945,598

POP. DENSITY 96/ km²; 249/mi²

GDP 2.047 Trillion US$

LANGUAGE(S) French, Provençal, Breton, Alsatian, Corsican, Catalan, Basque, Flemish

ETHNICITY French 77%, Algerian and Moroccan Berber 2%, Moroccan Arab 2%, Algerian Arab 1%

RELIGION Roman Catholic 88%, Protestant 2%, Muslim 8%

CLIMATE Temperate Maritime, Mediterranean

REGIONAL DIVISIONS 22 Metropolitan Regions and 4 Overseas Regions (Réunion, Martinique, Guadelope and French Guiana) further divided into 100 Departments

DEPENDENCIES Overseas Territories: French Polynesia, French Southern and Antarctic Lands, New Caledonia, Wallis and Futuna; Territorial Collectivity: Mayotte, Saint Pierre and Miquelon; Overseas Collectivity: Saint Barthélemy, Saint Martin

ECONOMIC ACTIVITIES Agriculture, Viticulture, Machinery, Chemicals, Automobiles, Metallurgy, Electronics, Transportation, Aircraft, Textiles, Clothing, Food Processing, Tourism, Iron and Steel, Forestry, Fishing, Oil and Gas Refining, Services, Luxury Goods, Energy

NATURAL RESOURCES Coal, Iron Ore, Bauxite, Zinc, Uranium, Antimony, Arsenic, Potash, Feldspar, Fluorspar, Gypsum, Timber

south-west, the Massif Central plateau in the south, and the Jura and the Alps in the east. France's highest peak is Mont Blanc, which, at 4,807 metres, is also the highest in Western Europe. Major rivers include the Loire, the Seine and the Rhône, and along these lie some of France's largest cities.

PARIS
A night-time view of the River Seine with the Eiffel Tower in the background.

The population of almost 62 million is most densely concentrated in urban areas; elsewhere the land is largely rural, with 33 per cent of the total area given over to arable farming. Its climate is mild and temperate in the north-west, warm continental in the east, and Mediterranean in the south, although higher latitudes experience more extreme temperatures.

History

France was one of the first modern countries to establish a republic, following the bloody French Revolution of 1789. Until then it had been a powerful nation state, ruled by a long succession of monarchs who had made it their duty to uphold Catholic Christianity. The first king to rule all of France was Charlemagne (768–814), whose power had spread to all the way to Rome, but France's power reached its greatest height under Louis XIV, the Sun King (1638–1715), when it became the political and cultural centre of Europe. Following the Revolution, during which many of the aristocracy were guillotined, France was governed by Napoleon Bonaparte, who as Emperor succeeded in conquering much of Europe. France was second only to Britain as a colonial power during the eighteenth and nineteenth centuries, but the devastation of the twentieth century's two world wars greatly weakened France's position as a global power, although it was key to the establishment of the European Union in the 1950s. French culture is world-renowned, from its production of fine wines and high fashion to an artistic legacy that includes the literature of Victor Hugo, Voltaire, Molière and Jules Verne. Despite expressing strong regional differences, the people of France maintain a powerful national identity.

Economy

France was a founder member of the European Union, and is a permanent member of the UN Security Council and a member of NATO. Its highly developed economy has traditionally balanced private and state ownership, although this is now shifting towards privatization, with the government selling off companies such as Air France and France Telecom. Agriculture remains important, although heavy industry and engineering supply a healthy export market. Tourism is also a key industry; France is the most visited country in the world.

CHAMBORD
The Château of Chambord, built in the fifteenth century by King François I, is one of the largest of the many châteaux in the Loire Valley.

MONACO

43° 44' N, 7° 24' E | 1.95 KM² | 0.75 MI² | UTC+1

This tiny, wealthy sovereign state lies on the Mediterranean coast and is completely surrounded on its landward sides by France.

With a population of 32,000 people in an area of 1.95 square kilometres, Monaco is the world's most densely populated sovereign

MONACO
The city of Monaco nestles between the sea and the mountains.

FACT FILE

LOCAL NAME	Principality of Monaco
CAPITAL CITY	Monaco
CURRENCY	Euro (EUR)
MEMBERSHIP	CE, not IMF member
GOVERNMENT	Constitutional Monarchy and Principality
POPULATION	32,796
POP. DENSITY	16,818/km²; 43,728/mi²
GDP	976.3 Million US$
LANGUAGE(S)	French, English, Italian, Monégasque
ETHNICITY	French 47%, Monégasque 16%, Italian 16%
RELIGION	Roman Catholic 90%
CLIMATE	Mediterranean

state. Originally a fortress built by Genoese colonizers in 1215, in 1297 control of the territory was won by Francisco Grimaldi and the Grimaldi family has ruled the state ever since; the current monarch is Prince Albert II. A tax haven and gambling centre, Monaco is popular with businesses, the wealthy and tourists.

LIECHTENSTEIN

47° 16' N, 9° 32' E | 160 KM² | 62 MI² | UTC+1

Established as a principality in 1719, Liechtenstein was a member of a succession of federations of German states, but was the only one to remain independent when the German Empire was formed in 1871.

FACT FILE

LOCAL NAME	Principality of Liechtenstein
CAPITAL CITY	Vaduz
CURRENCY	Swiss Franc (CHF)
MEMBERSHIP	CE, WTO, not WB member, not IMF member
GOVERNMENT	Parliamentary Democracy and Constitutional Monarchy
POPULATION	34,498
POP. DENSITY	216/km²; 556/ mi²
GDP	1.786 Billion US$
LANGUAGE(S)	German, Alemannic
ETHNICITY	Liechtensteiner 66%
RELIGION	Roman Catholic 76%, Protestant 7%
CLIMATE	Continental

Lying landlocked between Switzerland and Austria within the Alps, Liechtenstein, with an area of 160 square kilometres, is the smallest German-speaking country in the world. Its western border is formed by the River Rhine, while in the east it is mountainous. Low business taxes and easy incorporation rules make the state a haven for holding companies and foreign investors, and banking and financial services are the mainstay of the economy.

WESTERN EUROPE

GERMANY

51° 00' N, 9° 00' E | 357,021 KM² | 137,847 MI² | UTC+1

Bordered by nine countries, Germany lies at the very heart of Western Europe and has been a key member of the European Union since its foundation.

Geography

Stretching from the North Sea and the Baltic Sea in the north to Alpine borders with Austria and Switzerland in the south, Germany is a large country with a very varied landscape. The northern region is flat with bogs, marshland and heathland as well as arable land. In the centre the land becomes more hilly and then progressively more mountainous towards the south, rising to the Alps. The hills and mountains are heavily

FACT FILE

LOCAL NAME Federal Republic of Germany

CAPITAL CITY Berlin

CURRENCY Euro (EUR)

MEMBERSHIP AC (observer), BSEC (observer), CBSS, CE, EAPC, EU, G5, G8, G20, NATO, OAS (observer), OECD, WTO

GOVERNMENT Federal Parliamentary Republic

POPULATION 82,534,211

POP. DENSITY 231/km²; 599/mi²

GDP 2.81 Trillion US$

LANGUAGE(S) German, Turkish, Serbo-Croatian, Italian, Kurdish

ETHNICITY German 92%, Turkish 2%

RELIGION Protestant 34%, Roman Catholic 34%, Muslim 4%

CLIMATE Temperate, Maritime

REGIONAL DIVISIONS 16 States further divided into 439 Districts; Bavaria State is the largest in area and has the highest population

ECONOMIC ACTIVITIES Iron and Steel, Coal Mining, Machinery, Vehicle Manufacturing, Engineering, Electronics, Chemicals, Banking, Insurance, Food and Beverages, Textiles, Services, Shipbuilding, Environmental Technology

NATURAL RESOURCES Iron, Hard Coal, Lignite, Potash, Natural Gas, Copper, Nickel, Uranium, Salt, Construction Materials, Timber

MOSELLE
A vineyard in the Moselle Valley in south-western Germany.

BERLIN
Following German reunification parliament returned to Berlin. The historic Reichstag building was renovated by architect Norman Foster.

forested in places, including the Black Forest in the west and the Bavarian Forest to the east. Several major rivers course through Germany, carving deep valleys between the hills and mountains; the Rhine, the Elbe and the Danube are the most significant. Although the capital city is Berlin, Germany's history as a union of independent principalities has resulted in a number of large administrative cities, including Frankfurt, Stuttgart and Munich.

History

From medieval until Napoleonic times, Germanic people populated a number of independent states linked in a loose federation as the Holy Roman Empire (962–1806). At its height, the empire encompassed modern-day Germany and territories to the south and east that included Italy and the Czech Republic. The Holy Roman Empire was dissolved in the face of Napoleon's advance into central Europe, but following his defeat, the German Confederation was founded (1814), bringing together thirty-nine sovereign states. The most powerful was Prussia, which played a key role in European politics in the eighteenth and nineteenth centuries, and whose chancellor, Otto von Bismarck, succeeded in creating a unified German Empire in 1871. The rise in imperialism across Europe led to the outbreak of the First World War, in which Germany suffered defeat and then faced crippling war reparations, creating conditions that contributed to the rise of Adolf Hitler and the outbreak of the Second World War. The post-war division of Germany into a democratic West and a Soviet-controlled East ended in 1990, when the collapse of communism led to Germany's reunification. Notable Germans include scientists such as Albert Einstein, Gabriel Daniel Fahrenheit,

inventors such as Johannes Gutenberg, the founder of the Protestant Reformation Martin Luther, and great composers such as Beethoven, Bach, Brahms and Wagner.

Economy

Germany has Europe's largest economy, although it felt the strain after reunification in bringing the less efficient East up to the standards of the West. Good labour relations and efficiency have transformed the German economy since 1945; it is now a world leader in scientific innovation, technology, engineering and heavy manufacturing. In recent years, an economic downturn has exacerbated the effects of reunification, causing higher unemployment levels that have been a burden on the social security system. Germany also has the third highest immigration levels in the world. Germany was a founder member of the European Union, and is a member of NATO and the United Nations.

SWITZERLAND

47° 00' N, 8° 00' E | 41,290 KM² | 15,942 MI² | UTC+1

Although now famed for its peaceful, orderly society, Switzerland's position at the heart of Western Europe brought it an early history of war and turmoil.

Geography

The northern landscape is generally hilly with rolling pastureland, but it is the central and southern Alpine region and the Jura Mountains dominating the north-western border with France that provide the country's most enduring image. The Swiss Alps cover about two-thirds of the total area; the highest peak is Dufourspitze (4,634 metres). The more densely populated north is the location of several large lakes as well the major cities of Bern, Zurich and Basel.

History

Originally divided into separate sovereign states, or cantons, the Swiss Confederation was formed as a defensive league of cantons in 1291. It expanded in the fourteenth century and became a centre of the Reformation in the sixteenth century. Swiss independence and neutrality were recognized by treaty in 1648. Conquered by Napoleonic France in 1798, in 1815 the country was organized as a confederation of twenty-two cantons. Its centuries of neutrality have led to Switzerland becoming the headquarters of a number of international organizations, including the International Red Cross and the European branches of the United Nations and its agencies.

Economy

One of the world's richest nations, Switzerland has a strong capitalist economy. Banking, insurance, financial services, engineering, chemicals, pharmaceuticals and tourism contribute to its high GDP. Low taxation rates make it attractive to businesses.

FACT FILE

LOCAL NAME Swiss Confederation

CAPITAL CITY Bern

CURRENCY Swiss Franc (CHF)

MEMBERSHIP CE, EAPC, LAIA (observer), OAS (observer), OECD, WTO

GOVERNMENT Direct Democracy Federal Parliamentary Republic

POPULATION 7,512,120

POP. DENSITY 182/km²; 471/mi²

GDP 300.2 Billion US$

LANGUAGE(S) German, French, Italian, Romansch, English

ETHNICITY German 65%, French 18%, Italian 10%, Romansch 1%

RELIGION Roman Catholic 42%, Protestant 35%, Muslim 4%

CLIMATE Temperate and Tundra

REGIONAL DIVISIONS 23 Cantons further divided into 150 districts; 3 Cantons are divided into half-cantons.

ECONOMIC ACTIVITIES Machinery, Chemicals, Pharmaceuticals, Watches, Textiles, Clothing, Transportation Equipment, Precision Instruments, Tourism, Banking and Insurance, Forestry, Pulp and Paper, Agriculture

NATURAL RESOURCES Potential for Hydropower, Timber, Salt

THE ALPS
The Matterhorn straddles the border between Switzerland and Italy.

AUSTRIA

47° 20' N, 13° 20' E | 83,870 KM² | 32,382 MI² | UTC+1

The most mountainous country in Europe, Austria has often been described as the gateway to Central Europe because it shares borders with eight countries.

Geography

The eastern end of the Alpine range covers over 60 per cent of Austria, dominating the west, south and centre. The foothills of the Carpathian Mountains lie in the east. In the north-east the River Danube passes through the capital, Vienna, and its basin is the only lower-lying part of the country.

History

Part of the Roman Empire until the fifth century, from the thirteenth century Austria was the heartland of the Habsburg family's empire, which had become the dominant political power in Europe by the sixteenth century, and Austria still has a slightly faded grandeur. It was the birthplace of some of

VIENNA
The interior of the opera house in Vienna.

the world's finest composers, including Mozart, Strauss and Schubert. Weakened by the Napoleonic Wars and by German expansion in the nineteenth century, the Austro-Hungarian

Empire collapsed in 1918 following defeat in the First World War. Annexed by Nazi Germany in 1933, Austria was under Allied occupation following the Second World War until 1955. Since then Austria has been a neutral republic, enjoying growth and prosperity.

Economy

Tourism and other service industries are the cornerstones of the Austrian economy. In recent years, its location in relation to

Central and Eastern Europe has made Vienna an important business centre. Even with a relatively large immigrant workforce, many from neighbouring Hungary and Slovenia, there is high employment. Austria joined the European Union in 1995 and adopted the euro in 2002.

FACT FILE

LOCAL NAME Republic of Austria

CAPITAL CITY Vienna (Wien)

CURRENCY Euro (EUR)

MEMBERSHIP BSEC (observer), CE, CEI, EU, EAPC, OAS (observer), OECD, WTO

GOVERNMENT Federal Parliamentary Republic

POPULATION 8,391,254

POP. DENSITY 100/km²; 259/mi²

GDP 317.8 Billion US$

LANGUAGE(S) German, Turkish, Serbian, Croatian, Slovene, Hungarian

ETHNICITY Austrians 91%, former Yugoslavs 4%

RELIGION Roman Catholic 74%, Protestant 5%, Muslim 4%

CLIMATE Temperate

REGIONAL DIVISIONS 9 States further divided into 84 Districts and 15 Cities; the state of Vienna is the smallest area yet the most populous

ECONOMIC ACTIVITIES Mechanical Engineering, Metals, Chemicals, Lumber and Wood Processing, Food Products, Communication Equipment, Vehicle Manufacturing, Service Industry, Construction, Paper and Paperboard, Oil and Gas Production, Oil and Gas Refining, Tourism, Wine, Brewing, Agriculture

NATURAL RESOURCES Iron Ore, Lignite, Timber, Oil, Copper, Tungsten, Magnesite, Antimony, Zinc, Hydropower

WESTERN EUROPE

SOUTHERN EUROPE

Sunshine provides its regional character; the Mediterranean, Adriatic and Aegean its flavour. Africa is a breath away; ruins and ancient trade routes testify to the great civilizations of its past.

With Iberia to the west, Italy in the centre and the Balkans to the east, this region is predominantly an area of mountainous peninsulas surrounded by seas scattered with archipelagos. The rocky coasts of Portugal and western and northern Spain are battered by Atlantic breakers, while the shores of southern Spain, Italy, the western Balkans and Greece are lapped by the Mediterranean Sea and its various arms: the Tyrrhenian Sea between western Italy and the islands of Sardinia and Sicily; the Adriatic Sea between eastern Italy and the western Balkan states; the Ionian Sea between

southern Italy and mainland Greece; and the Aegean Sea between eastern Greece and Turkey, studded with the myriad isles of the Sporades, Dodecanese and Cyclades.

The Mediterranean Sea was so named in classical times because it was believed to be the centre of the world. An ancient thoroughfare for trade, migration and conquest, it was the cradle of the civilizations that gave birth to Western culture, which then, through European colonialism, reached the whole world. Ancient Greek civilization, which attained its widest influence in the fourth century BC, developed ideas that are still the bedrock of Western philosophy, political theory, mathematics, architecture,

art, drama and literature. The Romans, the dominant civilization from the second century BC, assimilated much of Greek culture and left their own mark on Western language, law, government, religion and applied sciences such as engineering. Graeco-Roman culture was kept alive after the fall of Rome in the fifth century AD by the eastern part of its empire, the Byzantine Empire, and by the Christian Church.

Both Empire and Church were threatened from the seventh century by the emergence of Islam. Much of Spain fell to the Moors (African Muslims) in the eighth century but they were expelled entirely by 1502. It is in the Balkans that the clash of faiths and cultures has left a bitter legacy. Most of south-eastern Europe was conquered by the Ottoman Empire between 1345 and

Azores (PT)

PORTUGAL
Terraced viticulture near the city of Porto in northern Portugal.

1520 and remained under its rule for several centuries. Independence was wrung from the declining empire by some countries in the nineteenth and early twentieth centuries only after a protracted and bloody struggle. The ancient hatreds of past centuries underlie recent Balkan conflicts and the continuing tensions of the present day.

As the Balkan states recover from past conflict and some start to benefit from membership of the European Union, they increasingly resemble the rest of the region in lifestyle. With proximity to the sea moderating the climate of most of the countries, except at higher altitudes, plentiful sunshine ripens sun-loving fruits and vegetables, and encourages the more relaxed way of life that attracts so many tourists and visitors.

VENICE
The Grand Canal is the main thoroughfare in the historic city of Venice.

SOUTHERN EUROPE

PORTUGAL

39° 30' N, 8° 00' W | 92,391 KM² | 35,672 MI² | UTC+0

This long, narrow country, marked by its north–south divide, is bisected by the River Tagus.

Geography

Located on the Iberian peninsula, to the west and south of Spain, Portugal has a long Atlantic coastline and is the most westerly country in mainland Europe. The mountainous north, with its high plateaux and river valleys, gives way to the lower-lying rolling plains of the south. The weather differs too, being wetter in the north and drier in the south, although the entire country benefits from a warm, Mediterranean climate.

History

Portugal's maritime tradition produced seafaring expertise that put the Portuguese at the forefront of exploration of Africa and the Americas from the late fifteenth century; notable mariners included Bartolomeu Dias, Vasco da Gama, who reached India, and Pedro Álvares Cabral, who sighted Brazil. As a colonial power, Portugal enjoyed considerable prosperity, but the Napoleonic Wars and the independence of Brazil in the nineteenth century brought a gradual decline. After periods of dictatorship and military rule in the twentieth century, Portugal became a democracy with a civilian government in 1976.

Economy

Portugal still relies on its rural economy, with exports of fruit and vegetables, wine and cork being particularly important, but a growing service industry and the production of software have been key areas of growth. Tourism is also a source of considerable revenue. Membership of the European Union since 1986 has lifted the country out of economic decline. It replaced the escudo with the euro in 2002.

THE ALGARVE
A rock formation on the beautiful Algarve coast.

FACT FILE

LOCAL NAME Portuguese Republic

CAPITAL CITY Lisbon

CURRENCY Euro (EUR)

MEMBERSHIP CE, EAPC, EU, LAIA (observer), NATO, OAS (observer), OECD, WTO

GOVERNMENT Parliamentary Republic

POPULATION 10,661,632

POP. DENSITY 115/km²; 299/mi²

GDP 230.5 Billion US$

LANGUAGE(S) Portuguese, Mirandese, Galician, Calo

ETHNICITY Portuguese 92%, mixed-race people from Angola, Mozambique and Cape Verde 2%, Brazilian 1%

RELIGION Roman Catholic 93%, Other Christian 2%

CLIMATE Mediterranean

REGIONAL DIVISIONS 18 Districts and 2 Autonomous Regions (Azores and Madeira), further divided into 308 Municipalities

ECONOMIC ACTIVITIES Agriculture, Textiles, Clothing, Footwear, Wood and Cork, Paper, Chemicals, Auto-parts Manufacturing, Base Metals, Dairy Products, Wine and Foods, Porcelain and Ceramics, Fishing, Glassware, Technology, Telecommunications, Shipbuilding, Tourism

NATURAL RESOURCES Fish, Forests (Cork), Iron Ore, Copper, Zinc, Tin, Tungsten, Silver, Gold, Uranium, Marble, Clay, Gypsum, Salt, Hydropower

SOUTHERN EUROPE

AZORES

38° 50' N, 28° 00' W | 2,322 KM² | 897 MI² | UTC-1

A remote archipelago, the Azores are spread over an area of 600 kilometres in the Atlantic Ocean, 1,400 to 1,800 kilometres west of Portugal. The most westerly of the islands are less than 2,000 kilometres from Canada.

The colonization of the Azores was begun in 1439 by the Portuguese, who claimed to have discovered the islands the previous century, and they are now a self-governing region of Portugal. Of the islands, nine are prominent, including Faial, Terceira and and São Miguel, which is home to over half the population of the Azores. With a subtropical climate, they are all popular tourist destinations, which provides valuable revenue for the territory. Positioned over the junction of three tectonic plates, they are at the heart of the Azores

FACT FILE

LOCAL NAME Autonomous Region of Azores
SOVEREIGN STATE Portugal
CAPITAL/MAIN CITY Ponta Delgada
CURRENCY Euro (EUR)
GOVERNMENT Portuguese Autonomous Region
POPULATION 243,101
POP. DENSITY 105/km²; 271/mi²
GDP 4.121 Billion US$
LANGUAGE(S) Portuguese
ETHNICITY Portuguese
RELIGION Roman Catholic
CLIMATE Temperate Maritime

Hotspot and the volcano Pico, at 2,351 metres, is Portugal's highest mountain.

GIBRALTAR

36° 08' N, 5° 21' W | 6.5 KM² | 2.5 MI² | UTC+1

A rocky promontory at the southernmost tip of the Iberian Peninsula and connected to Spain by a low isthmus, Gibraltar is a UK overseas territory.

Made of limestone, the Rock of Gibraltar is 426 metres high and is one of the most densely populated territories in the world. Sovereignty over this strategically important territory, ceded to Britain in 1713, soured relations between the Spanish and British governments for centuries. After Gibraltarians voted in a 1969 referendum to remain British, Spain closed the border for sixteen years, but it has moderated its claims since residents rejected a proposal for joint sovereignty in 2002. Relations have improved and the territory remains a base for British military and naval forces. Shipping, offshore banking and financial services and tourism account for most

FACT FILE

LOCAL NAME Gibraltar
SOVEREIGN STATE United Kingdom
MAIN CITY Gibraltar
CURRENCY Gibraltar Pound (GIP)
GOVERNMENT Overseas Territory of United Kingdom
POPULATION 28,002
POPULATION DENSITY 4,308/ km²; 11,201/mi²
GDP 1.066 Billion US$
LANGUAGE(S) English, Spanish, Italian, Portuguese
ETHNICITY Gibraltarian 83%, Other British 10%, Moroccan 4%
RELIGION Roman Catholic 78%, Church of England 7%, Other Christian 3%, Muslim 4%, Jewish 2%, Hindu 2%
CLIMATE Mediterranean

of the GDP. The nature reserve at the summit of the rock is home to a colony of macaque monkeys, the famous 'Barbary apes', Europe's only wild monkeys.

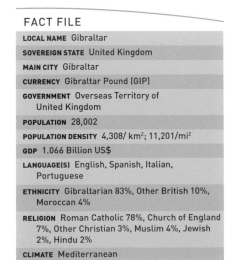

SOUTHERN EUROPE

SPAIN

40° 00' N, 4° 00' W | 504,782 KM² | 194,897 MI² | UTC+1

Having achieved rapid economic growth during the latter decades of the twentieth century, Spain is now recognized as a dynamic member of the European community.

Geography

Spain, the second largest country in Europe, occupies the Iberian peninsula, sharing borders with France, Portugal and the British colony of Gibraltar. It is the closest European country to Africa, separated from Morocco by only 13 kilometres of water. Spain's landscape is varied, from mountainous and verdant in the north to hot desert plains in the south.

FACT FILE

LOCAL NAME Kingdom of Spain

CAPITAL CITY Madrid

CURRENCY Euro (EUR)

MEMBERSHIP CE, EAPC, EU, LAIA (observer), NATO, OAS (observer), OECD, WTO

GOVERNMENT Parliamentary Democracy and Constitutional Monarchy

POPULATION 44,592,770

POP. DENSITY 88/km²; 229/mi²

GDP 1.352 Trillion US$

LANGUAGE(S) Castilian Spanish, Catalan, Galician, Basque

ETHNICITY Spanish 45%, Catalonian 28%, Galician 8%, Basque 6%, Aragonese 5%, Extremaduran 3%, Roma (Gitanos/Gypsy) 2%

RELIGION Roman Catholic 94%

CLIMATE Mediterranean Temperate

REGIONAL DIVISIONS 17 Autonomous Communities and 2 Autonomous Cities, further divided into 50 Provinces

DEPENDENCIES Ceuta and Melilla, on Africa's Mediterranean coast, are Autonomous Cities. Overseas Territories: Canary Islands

ECONOMIC ACTIVITIES Agriculture, Textiles and Apparel (including footwear), Food and Beverages, Metals and Metal Manufacture, Chemicals, Shipbuilding, Automobiles, Machine Tools, Tourism, Clay and Refractory Products, Pharmaceuticals, Medical Equipment, Wine, Forestry and Timber Products, Fishing, Petroleum Refining

NATURAL RESOURCES Coal, Lignite, Iron Ore, Copper, Lead, Zinc, Uranium, Tungsten, Mercury, Pyrites, Magnesite, Fluorspar, Gypsum, Sepiolite, Kaolin, Potash, Hydropower

The north-eastern border with France is dominated by the Pyrenean Mountains, while the lush coastal plains along the Bay of Biscay in the north are commonly known as 'Green Spain'. A high plateau in the centre of the country experiences more extreme temperatures, particularly during the hot

GRANADA
The Alhambra was built as a fortress palace for the medieval Muslim kings of Spain.

summer months, and the capital Madrid sits at the very heart of this region in the Sistema Central mountain range. Further south, beyond the Sierra Morena Mountains, is the Andalusian plain, through which runs the Rio Guadalquivir. Other notable rivers are the Tagus and the Ebro. Spain's territory also includes the Balearic Islands in the Mediterranean Sea, the Canary Islands in the Atlantic Ocean and the towns of Ceuta and Melilla in North Africa, as well as some uninhabited islands in the Strait of Gibraltar.

History

Following the unification of Aragon, Castile, Leon and Navarre in 1469, the Spanish Empire became one of the most influential nations in Europe. Its strategic coastal position provided it with powerful maritime forces which enabled the Spanish monarchy to establish a huge global empire; the Spanish were among the first Europeans to colonize the New World of the Americas and to reach Asia and Africa. The sixteenth and seventeenth centuries were a cultural golden age, with artists such as El Greco and Velázquez and writers like Cervantes flourishing. However, command of the seas was eventually lost to the English and the Dutch. A costly war with France in 1793–5 and a failure to embrace industrialization in the nineteenth century led to economic and political decline, and with colonial insurrection and the Spanish–American War of 1898, Spain lost almost all its empire. Following the disastrous civil war of 1936–9 Spain entered four decades of Fascist dictatorship and largely withdrew from the international stage. Following the death of the dictator Franco in 1975, Spain became a constitutional monarchy under King Juan Carlos and peacefully suppressed attempted military coups in 1978 and 1981. Since then Spain has remained stable and progressive.

BILBAO
The spectacular Guggenheim Museum, covered in 30,000 sheets of titanium, was designed by Frank Gehry and has attracted thousands of visitors to the port city of Bilbao.

It joined the European Union in 1986 and in 2002 adopted the euro as its currency.

Economy

Since an initial boom in the economy in the late 1980s, growth has slowed. Thanks to European Union development funding, the economic infrastructure has improved and unemployment and inflation rates have been brought to acceptable levels. The service industry supplies 66 per cent of the GDP, largely owing to tourism, which provides employment for a large number of Spaniards. Agriculture, textiles and food production also make significant contributions. Increased trade with Latin America and Asia and a highly regulated banking sector have boosted the Spanish economy.

ANDORRA

42° 30' N, 1° 30' E | 468 KM² | 181 MI² | UTC+1

FACT FILE

LOCAL NAME Principality of Andorra

CAPITAL CITY Andorra la Vella

CURRENCY Euro (EUR)

MEMBERSHIP CE, not IMF member, not WB member, WTO (observer)

GOVERNMENT Parliamentary Democracy and Co-principality

POPULATION 82,627

POP. DENSITY 155/km²; 400/mi²

GDP 2.77 Billion US$

LANGUAGE(S) Catalan, French, Castilian, Portuguese

ETHNICITY Spanish 43%, Andorran 33%, Portuguese 11%, French 7%

RELIGION Roman Catholic 89%, Other Christian 4%

CLIMATE Temperate

Lying high in the Pyrenean Mountains, wedged between Spain and France, Andorra has tourism and low taxes to thank for its recent prosperity.

Once shared between Spain and France, Andorra has a population of over 82,000, the majority is a mixture of Spanish, Portuguese and French. Its terrain and relatively isolated location have meant that, historically, Andorra has been cut off from international affairs and economic relations. Popular with visitors both in the summer and the winter, tourism accounts for 80 percent of the GDP.

MALTA

35° 50' N, 14° 35' E | 316 KM² | 122 MI² | UTC+1

The six islands that make up the republic belong to one of the smallest independent countries in Europe.

Lying in the Mediterranean Sea south of the island of Sicily, Malta has been occupied successively by the Phoenicians, Greeks, Carthaginians, Romans, Arabs and Spanish. In 1814 the islands became British and were used as headquarters for their Mediterranean fleet. This strategic role made Malta subject to sustained attack in the Second World War, and the people's resistance won the island a collective George Cross medal from the British monarch. Malta gained its independence in 1964, becoming a republic ten years later. Tourism and income generated from the goods transferred at Maltese ports are two major sources of revenue. Malta joined the European Union in 2004 and adopted the euro in 2008.

VALLETTA
The city of Valletta was founded by the knights of the Order of St John in the sixteenth century.

FACT FILE

LOCAL NAME Republic of Malta

CAPITAL CITY Valletta

CURRENCY Euro (EUR)

MEMBERSHIP C, CE, EU, WTO

GOVERNMENT Parliamentary Republic

POPULATION 408,212

POP. DENSITY 1,292/km²; 3,346/mi²

GDP 9.396 Billion US$

LANGUAGE(S) Maltese, English

ETHNICITY Maltese 94%, British 2%, Arab 2%, Italian 2%

RELIGION Roman Catholic 95%, Other Christian 4%

CLIMATE Mediterranean

SOUTHERN EUROPE

VATICAN CITY
41° 54' N, 12° 27' E | 0.44 KM² | 0.17 MI² | UTC+1

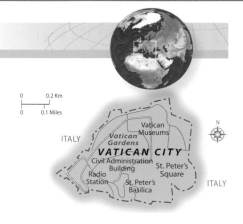

Located in the heart of Rome, the Vatican City State, or Holy See, is the world's smallest independent state.

The Vatican City State is all that remains of the once vast Papal States owned by the Roman Catholic Church and ruled by the Pope. Created as an official seat for the Pope in 1929, it is a series of buildings and gardens that includes the Basilica of St Peter, the Sistine Chapel and the papal apartments. There are around 1,000 inhabitants, and a further 3,400 staff who live outside the City. Its unique non-commercial economy is upheld by contributions from the Roman Catholic Church (Peter's Pence), tourism and investments.

BASILICA OF ST PETER
An aerial view of St Peter's and the Vatican.

FACT FILE

LOCAL NAME The Holy See (State of the Vatican City)
CAPITAL CITY Vatican City
CURRENCY Euro (EUR)
MEMBERSHIP CE (observer), not IMF member, not WB member, OAS (observer), UN (observer), WTO (observer)
GOVERNMENT Theocratic Absolute Elective Monarchy
POPULATION 824
POP. DENSITY 1,873/km²; 4,847/mi²
GDP NA
LANGUAGE(S) Italian, Latin, French, Other
ETHNICITY Italian, Swiss
RELIGION Roman Catholic
CLIMATE Temperate

SAN MARINO
43° 46' N, 12° 25' E | 61.2 KM² | 24 MI² | UTC+1

An enclave in central Italy, San Marino was reputedly founded in the fourth century AD and claims to be the world's oldest surviving republic.

At 61.2 square metres, San Marino is the third smallest independent state in Europe. Situated in the Apennines, its highest peak, Monte Titano, looms over wooded hills and pastures. Although it is socially and politically aligned with Italy, San Marino maintains its own traditions and only reluctantly allows immigration. Visitor numbers are high, however, with tourism providing 50 per cent of GDP. The high standard of living also derives from banking, ceramics, clothing manufacture, and cheese and wine production.

FACT FILE

LOCAL NAME Republic of San Marino
CAPITAL CITY San Marino
CURRENCY Euro (EUR)
MEMBERSHIP CE
GOVERNMENT Parliamentary Republic
POPULATION 29,973
POP. DENSITY 490/km²; 1,249/mi²
GDP 850 Million US$
LANGUAGE(S) Italian
ETHNICITY Sammarinese 86%, Italian 13%
RELIGION Roman Catholic 89%, Other Christian 4%
CLIMATE Mediterranean

SOUTHERN EUROPE

ITALY

42° 50' N, 12° 50' E | 301,230 KM² | 116,306 MI² | UTC+1

As the early centre of Western civilization and then the heart of Christiandom, Italy has an enormous cultural legacy.

Geography

Italy occupies a long peninsula that lies between the Tyrrhenian Sea on the west and the Adriatic Sea on the east. The northern alluvial plains of the River Po valley are encircled by the southernmost reaches of the Alps. There are a number of lakes in this northern region, the largest of which, at 370 square kilometres, is Lake Garda. The Apennine mountain range runs down the centre of the country. Italy is home to several volcanoes, two of which, Etna and Vesuvius, remain active. The Mediterranean islands of Sardinia and Sicily are also part

FACT FILE

LOCAL NAME Italian Republic

CAPITAL CITY Rome

CURRENCY Euro (EUR)

MEMBERSHIP BSEC, CE, EAPC, EU, G8, G20, NATO, OAS (observer), OECD, WTO

GOVERNMENT Parliamentary Republic

POPULATION 58,945,699

POP. DENSITY 196/km²; 507/mi²

GDP 1.786 Trillion US$

LANGUAGE(S) Italian, German, French, Slovene

ETHNICITY Italian 96%

RELIGION Roman Catholic 90%, Other 10% (includes Protestant, Jewish, Muslim)

CLIMATE Mediterranean, Temperate

REGIONAL DIVISIONS 15 Regions and 5 Autonomous Regions, further divided into 107 Provinces

ECONOMIC ACTIVITIES Agriculture, Tourism, Machinery, Iron and Steel, Chemicals, Pharmaceuticals, Food Processing, Textiles, Motor Vehicles, Clothing, Footwear, Ceramics, Electrical Goods, Wine

NATURAL RESOURCES Natural Gas and Crude Oil Reserves, Fish, Coal, Feldspar, Pumice, Marble, Barite, Asbestos, Fluorspar, Pyrite, Zinc, Potash, Mercury

of the republic. Because of the diversity of the landscape, the climate varies between regions, with a humid continental system in the north, a more Mediterranean climate in southern coastal areas, and cooler, wetter and snowy weather at higher altitudes. The country is divided into twenty regions, and the capital, Rome, situated in the centre, is the largest city, with over 4 million residents. Despite this, it is the north of the country that is more densely populated being home to almost half of the total population.

History

Inhabited in pre-Roman times by Etruscans in the north and Greeks in the south, Italy has a long history of civilized culture. It is the legacy of the Roman civilization that is the most enduring; first established in the eighth century BC, at its height the Roman Republic, later the Roman Empire, dominated the known world of its time; remnants of Roman occupation can be found throughout Europe, the Middle East and North Africa. In AD 285 the Empire fractured into western and eastern (Byzantine) empires, each

LIGURIA
Vineyards at Corniglia on the Ligurian coast.

the centre of a Christian church. With the eventual collapse of the western empire in the fifth century, the country divided into a number of independent, frequently warring city states, including Venice, Florence, Naples and the Papal States. Despite the belligerence of the times, the period between the fourteenth and seventeenth centuries saw some of the finest examples of artistic and cultural endeavour in Europe in the Renaissance. With the patronage of powerful popes, rulers and merchants, figures such as Leonardo da Vinci, Michelangelo, Dante and Machiavelli were able to flourish. Such culture was not new: the world's first university had been established at Bologna in 1088. Unification came in 1861–70 under King Victor Emmanuel II, but democracy was temporarily overthrown in the 1920s with the Fascist dictatorship of Benito Mussolini, which lasted until defeat in the Second World War. A democratic republic was installed in 1946, but political instability has dogged the country, producing forty-five governments in forty-seven years until constitutional reform in the 1990s.

Economy

This large capitalist economy is defined by a division between the well-developed, industrial and technologically advanced north and a rural, welfare-dependent south. Attempts to improve competitiveness and reduce the massive public debt have caused some economic difficulty recently. Italy was a founder member of the European Union, adopting the euro as its currency in 1999.

ROME
The Colosseum in Rome, originally called the Flavian Amphitheatre, was completed in AD 80.

SOUTHERN EUROPE

SLOVENIA

46° 07' N, 14° 09' E | 20,273 KM² | 7,828 MI² | UTC+1

Once part of the Austro-Hungarian Empire in Central Europe, Slovenia was a republic of Yugoslavia until independence in 1991.

Slovenia's terrain is mostly mountainous or hilly and thickly forested, especially in the northern Alpine region where it borders Austria, with lower land only in the river valleys and on the narrow stretch of coastline on the Adriatic Sea. For much of its history, Slovenia was under foreign rule, principally that of Austria, until 1918, when it became part of Yugoslavia. It was the most highly westernized of the republics when Yugoslavia disintegrated in 1991. A relatively smooth transition to democracy and free-market economics enabled it to become a member of the European Union and of NATO in 2004.

FACT FILE

LOCAL NAME	Republic of Slovenia
CAPITAL CITY	Ljubljana
CURRENCY	Euro (EUR)
MEMBERSHIP	CE, CEI, EAPC, EU, NATO, OAS (observer), WTO
GOVERNMENT	Parliamentary Republic
POPULATION	2,001,578
POP. DENSITY	99/km²; 256/mi²
GDP	56.19 Billion US$
LANGUAGE(S)	Slovenian (Slovene), Serbo-Croatian
ETHNICITY	Slovene 83%, Serb 2%, Croat 2%, Bosniak 1%
RELIGION	Catholic 58%, Muslim 2%, Orthodox 2%
CLIMATE	Continental, Mediterranean along the coast

CROATIA

45° 10' N, 15° 30' E | 56,542 KM² | 21,831 MI² | UTC+1

In turn part of Hungary, the Habsburg Empire and then Yugoslavia, Croatia has a long history of attempting to assert its independence.

Croatia's long and rocky Adriatic coastline is dotted with islands and is divided from the low plains of the north-east by mountainous highlands. The varied terrain results in a varied climate. Ruled for centuries by Hungary, the area was incorporated into the Austro-Hungarian Empire until 1918, when it became part of Yugoslavia. Croatia's proclamation of independence as Yugoslavia disintegrated in 1991 led to four years of war, internally and in Bosnia-Herzegovina against Serbs opposed to secession. Since 2000, economic growth has been steady and tourism has increased. Croatia has applied to join both the European Union and NATO.

FACT FILE

LOCAL NAME	Republic of Croatia
CAPITAL CITY	Zagreb
CURRENCY	Kuna (HRK)
MEMBERSHIP	BSEC (observer), CE, CEI, EAPC, OAS (observer), WTO
GOVERNMENT	Parliamentary Republic
POPULATION	4,550,273
POP. DENSITY	81/km²; 208/mi²
GDP	68.98 Billion US$
LANGUAGE(S)	Croatian, Serbian, Italian, Hungarian, Czech, Slovak, German
ETHNICITY	Croat 90%, Serb 5%, Other 6% (including Bosniak, Hungarian, Slovene, Czech and Roma)
RELIGION	Roman Catholic 89%, Orthodox 4%, Muslim 1%
CLIMATE	Mediterranean, Temperate

DUBROVNIK
An aerial view of the rooftops and cathedral of the walled city of Dubrovnik.

SOUTHERN EUROPE

BOSNIA AND HERZEGOVINA

44° 00' N, 18° 00' E | 51,209 KM² | 19,772 MI² | UTC+1

The collapse of Yugoslavia was particularly traumatic for Bosnia and Herzegovina with its ethnically mixed population; civil war between Serbs and Bosnians lasted until 1995.

Amost landlocked, Bosnia and Herzegovenia is a predominantly mountainous country with low plains in the north-west and on the 20-kilometre Adriatic coastline. Bosnia, in the north of the country, comprises approximately four fifths of the entire state. Home to three main ethnic groups, the Bosniaks, Serbs and Croats, it has a troubled history. Ruled by the Ottoman Empire from 1463, and by the Austro-Hungarian Empire from 1878, it became part of Yugoslavia

after 1918. Its declaration of independence in 1992 precipitated a civil war that lasted until 1995. The capital city, Sarajevo, endured the longest siege in modern military history

FACT FILE

LOCAL NAME Bosnia and Herzegovina
CAPITAL CITY Sarajevo
CURRENCY Konvertibilna Marka (Convertible Mark) (BAM)
MEMBERSHIP CE, CEI, EAPC, G77, OAS (observer), OIC (observer), WTO (observer)
GOVERNMENT Federal Democratic Republic
POPULATION 3,940,397
POP. DENSITY 77/ km²; 199/mi²
GDP 27.73 Billion US$
LANGUAGE(S) Bosnian, Croatian, Serbian
ETHNICITY Bosniak 48%, Serb 37%, Croat 14%
RELIGION Muslim 40%, Orthodox 31%, Roman Catholic 15%
CLIMATE Temperate, Mediterranean

when Serbian forces surrounded the city for almost four years. A 1995 peace accord introduced a tripartite federal structure, but stability depends on the presence of EU peacekeeping forces.

SERBIA

44° 00' N, 21° 00' E | 77,474 KM² | 29,913 MI² | UTC+1

Serbia resisted the breakup of Yugoslavia, attracting international condemnation for its role in the conflicts of the 1990s, and it has continued to fracture in the twenty-first century.

This large, mountainous but fertile country spent nearly 500 years under Ottoman rule from 1389 to 1878, an experience that fostered the animosity between Serbian Orthodox Christians and Muslims that underlay the Balkan conflicts of the 1990s and Serbia's treatment of its Muslim population in Kosovo. After 1992 Serbia formed a rump Yugoslav state with Montenegro until 2006, when Montenegro seceded. In 2008, Kosovo

also claimed independence, although this has not been recognized by Serbia. Stabilization of Serbia's society continues

FACT FILE

LOCAL NAME Republic of Serbia
CAPITAL CITY Belgrade (Beograd)
CURRENCY Serbian Dinar (RSD)
MEMBERSHIP BSEC, CE, CEI, EAPC, OAS (observer), WTO (observer)
GOVERNMENT Parliamentary Democracy
POPULATION 9,879,595
POP. DENSITY 128/km²; 330/mi²
GDP 77.28 Billion US$
LANGUAGE(S) Serbian, Hungarian, Bosniak, Romani (Gypsy)
ETHNICITY Serb 83%, Hungarian 4%, Romany (Gypsy) 1%, Yugoslavs 1%, Bosniaks 2%
RELIGION Serbian Orthodox 85%, Roman Catholic 6%, Muslim 3%, Protestant 1%,
CLIMATE Mediterranean, Temperate

and it is now a member of the United Nations and is a candidate for membership in the European Union. The economy remains dependent on a mixture of agricultural and industrial production.

SOUTHERN EUROPE

MONTENEGRO

42° 30' N, 19° 18' E | 14,026 KM² | 5,415 MI² | UTC+1

With a history closely tied to its larger neighbour Serbia, in 2006 Montenegro finally asserted its independence.

Bordered by four Balkan states and the Adriatic Sea, Montenegro has a narrow coastal plain and a central mountainous plateau. It was part of the medieval kingdom of Serbia and shared its fortunes until 1878, when it became independent until its incorporation into Yugoslavia after 1918. When Yugoslavia disintegrated, Montenegro formed a federation with Serbia, but declared its independence in 2006 after a referendum.

FACT FILE

LOCAL NAME Montenegro
CAPITAL CITY Podgorica
CURRENCY Euro (EUR)
MEMBERSHIP CE, CEI, EAPC, WTO (observer)
GOVERNMENT Semi-presidential Republic
POPULATION 597,851
POP. DENSITY 43/km²; 110/mi²
GDP 5.918 Billion US$
LANGUAGE(S) Montenegrin, Serbian, Bosnian, Albanian, Croatian
ETHNICITY Montenegrin 43%, Serbian 32%, Bosniak 8%, Albanian 5%, Other (Muslims, Croats, Roma (Gypsy)) 12%
RELIGION Orthodox 74%, Muslim 18%, Roman Catholic 4%
CLIMATE Mediterranean

Already economically separate from Serbia by 2006, Montenegro has since pursued membership of the European Union and other international bodies.

KOSOVO

42° 35' N, 21° 00' E | 10,887 KM² | 4,203 MI² | UTC+1

The new republic of Kosovo was born out of the ethnic tensions that resurfaced during the disintegration of Yugoslavia in the 1990s.

Ottoman control of the Balkans from the fourteenth century resulted in large numbers of Turks and Albanians migrating to this mountainous region, until the Albanian population came to outnumber that of the Serbs. In 1990, the self-governing province was stripped of its autonomy, stimulating

FACT FILE

LOCAL NAME Republic of Kosovo
CAPITAL CITY Pristinë (Pristina)
CURRENCY Euro (EUR); Serbian Dinar (RSD)
MEMBERSHIP Not UN member, not WB member, not IMF member
GOVERNMENT Parliamentary Republic
POPULATION 2,126,708
POP. DENSITY 195/km²; 506/mi²
GDP 4.0 Billion US$
LANGUAGE(S) Albanian, Serbian, Bosnian, Turkish, Romani
ETHNICITY Albanian 88%, Serb 7%, Other 5% (Bosniak, Gorani, Roma, Turk, Ashkali, Egyptian)
RELIGION Muslim, Serbian Orthodox, Roman Catholic
CLIMATE Continental

resistance to Serbia's increasingly harsh repression of the ethnic Albanians in the 1990s. After NATO intervention in 1999, Serbia withdrew and the province was administered by the UN until Kosovo declared its independence in 2008; Serbia still claims sovereignty over Kosovo.

PRISTINA
A man enters a mosque in the capital Pristina.

ALBANIA

41° 00' N, 20° 00' E | 28,748 KM² | 11,100 MI² | UTC+1

Since ending over forty years of communist rule, the southern Balkan state of Albania has espoused democratic capitalism and seeks to join the European Union and NATO.

Apart from a short-lived period of independence under the heroic leader Skanderbeg in the fifth century, Albania was part of the Ottoman Empire until 1912. After Italian occupation from 1914 to 1920, Albania became a republic and then a monarchy under King Zog I. Invaded by Italy in 1939 and then by Germany, from 1946 to 1990 Albania was a communist republic, internationally

isolated under the dictator Enver Hoxha. Democratic reform and westernization were introduced from the late 1980s, but Albania remains one of the poorest countries in Europe.

FACT FILE

LOCAL NAME	Republic of Albania
CAPITAL CITY	Tirana (Tiranë)
CURRENCY	Lek (ALL)
MEMBERSHIP	BSEC, CE, CEI, EAPC, OIC, WTO
GOVERNMENT	Parliamentary Republic
POPULATION	3,207,639
POP. DENSITY	112/km²; 289/mi²
GDP	19.92 Billion US$
LANGUAGE(S)	Albanian, Greek, Vlach, Romani, Macedonian, Macedo Rom
ETHNICITY	Albanian 95%, Greek 3%, Other 2% (Vlach, Roma, Serb, Macedonian, Bulgarian)
RELIGION	Muslim 70%, Albanian Orthodox 20%, Roman Catholic 10%
CLIMATE	Mediterranean

LUSHNJE
Farmers fill baskets and bags with olives to take to the market.

MACEDONIA

41° 50' N, 22° 00' E | 25,333 KM² | 9,781 MI² | UTC+1

The republic asserted its independence from Yugoslavia without opposition, but struggled for recognition because of Greece's opposition to its use of the name Macedonia.

Located in the south of the Balkan peninsula, the republic was originally part of a larger ancient region called Macedonia that was divided between Serbia and Greece in 1913. Part of Yugoslavia after 1918, it achieved independence peacefully in 1991 but experienced intercommunal tension with its ethnic Albanians until 2001. It was the least economically developed republic in Yugoslavia and economic growth was originally hindered by Greece's trade

embargo. The economy remains generally weak, although with a rugged, mountainous landscape and several large lakes, it has potential for tourism.

FACT FILE

LOCAL NAME	Republic of Macedonia
CAPITAL CITY	Skopje
CURRENCY	Macedonian Denar (MKD)
MEMBERSHIP	CE, CEI, EAPC, WTO
GOVERNMENT	Parliamentary Republic
POPULATION	2,039,960
POP. DENSITY	81/km²; 209/mi²
GDP	17.35 Billion US$
LANGUAGE(S)	Macedonian, Albanian, Turkish, Roma, Serbian
ETHNICITY	Macedonian 64%, Albanian 25%, Turkish 4%, Roma 3%, Serb 2%
RELIGION	Macedonian Orthodox 65%, Muslim 33%
CLIMATE	Mediterranean, Temperate

SOUTHERN EUROPE

GREECE

39° 00' N, 22° 00' E | 131,940 KM² | 50,942 MI² | UTC+2

The cradle of Western civilization, Greece is the birthplace of democracy, philosophy, drama and the Olympic Games.

Geography

Situated in the southernmost part of the Balkan peninsula in south-eastern Europe, Greece comprises a mountainous mainland jutting out into the Mediterranean Sea and several island groups totalling around 2,000 islands. Many of the islands are the peaks of submerged mountain ranges that stretch across the Aegean Sea towards Turkey. Only 227 of the islands are inhabited; the largest is Crete, which is over 8,000 kilometres square and marks the southernmost boundary of the Aegean. It has almost 14,000 kilometres of coastline, and a variable but temperate climate, with cool, wet winters and hot, dry summers. Western

Greece is dominated by the Pindus mountain range which threads from the mainland towards Crete via the Peloponnese, a large peninsula separated from the rest of the mainland by the Gulf of Corinth and the Corinthian Canal. The highest mountain in the country is Mount Olympus at 2,918

FACT FILE

LOCAL NAME	Hellenic Republic
CAPITAL CITY	Athens
CURRENCY	Euro (EUR)
MEMBERSHIP	BSEC, CE, EAPC, EU, NATO, OAS (observer), OECD, WTO
GOVERNMENT	Parliamentary Republic
POPULATION	11,171,744
POP. DENSITY	85/km²; 219/mi²
GDP	324.6 Billion US$
LANGUAGE(S)	Greek, English, French
ETHNICITY	Greek 93%
RELIGION	Greek Orthodox 98%, Muslim 1%
CLIMATE	Mediterranean and Temperate
REGIONAL DIVISIONS	13 Peripheries further divided into 51 Prefectures and 1 Autonomous Region; Attica is the most populous Periphery and location of the capital city Athens
ECONOMIC ACTIVITIES	Agriculture, Tourism, Shipping, Textiles, Food and Tobacco Processing, Chemicals, Metal Products, Mining, Petroleum Products, Construction
NATURAL RESOURCES	Lignite, Bauxite, Magnesite, Petroleum, Marble, Lead, Zinc, Nickel, Hydropower Potential

CRETE
The harbour of Rethymno, on Crete, pictured at dusk. Crete is the largest of the Greek islands.

ATHENS
The ruins of the Parthenon, an Ancient Greek temple built in the fifth century BC, is the most famous of the buildings that sit on the Acropolis in the centre of Athens.

metres, while in the central region there are huge canyons such as the Vikos Gorges, which, at a depth of 1,100 metres, is second in size only to the Grand Canyon in the USA.

History

Modern Greece is littered with the remnants of a number of Bronze Age cultures that proved to be highly influential. On Crete, the Minoans were among the first peoples to organize themselves into a complex society based on religion and palace worship, although Crete is perhaps more famous for the legend of the Minotaur; many Ancient Greek societies are remembered principally for the myths spawned by their polytheistic

worship. In Athens, as in the other city states that sprang up around the region, great temples such as the Parthenon were raised to honour gods such as Athena, Apollo and Zeus. After unification by the military king Alexander the Great, Greece became a repository for other influential cultures, falling to the Roman and Byzantine Empires. Under the rule of the Ottoman Empire from the fifth century until 1830, the Greek national identity was suppressed, but following independence the Greeks embarked on a series of territorial wars, including those with Turkey during which thousands of Greeks and Turks were repatriated in 1923. During the Second World War, Greece was occupied first by the Italians and then by the Nazis. A bitter five-year civil war erupted between monarchists and communists after liberation, and the

king was exiled by a military dictatorship from 1967 to 1974, when democracy was restored and the monarchy abolished. Greece has since rebuilt its internal infrastructure and its international relations, joining the European Union in 1981 and adopting the euro as its currency in 2002.

Economy

The service sector is the largest in the Greek economy, based mainly on tourism and shipping. Growth in recent years has been aided partly by EU funding and foreign investment and by the implementation of policies designed to modernize the formerly unstable economy. However, resistance to privatization of the large state-owned sector and the reform of work and pension systems remains.

SOUTHERN EUROPE

EASTERN EUROPE

The demise of communism has not removed the dominance of the Russian Federation over Eastern Europe but political liberalization has brought new prosperity and greater accessibility to and for the world.

As this region continues its emergence from the domination of Communism, replacing its political and economic stranglehold with more liberal regimes, so the individual character of these countries becomes more apparent to the rest of the world. For centuries, the ethnic and cultural diversity of the region was scarcely detectable in these territories, subjugated by the Ottoman, Austrian or Russian empires. For those granted nationhood in the early twentieth century, independence was shortlived, with Soviet-sponsored Communist regimes established after the Second World War holding sway until the sudden collapse of the Iron Curtain in 1989. The areas incorporated into the Soviet Union after the Russian Revolution achieved their independence with the equally unexpected break-up of that federation in 1991.

R U S S I A N   F E D E R A T I O N

Noril'sk

Igarka

Arctic Circle

West Siberian
Plain

Central Siberian
Plateau

Yenisey

Ob

Omsk

Novosibirsk

fertilize these plains, which are the granaries
of the region, and provided the major trade
and transport routes until modern times.
Yet the area's relative backwardness until
recently has been a conservation boon,
preserving large stretches of forest and
wilderness in their ancient state; many of
these are now World Heritage Sites.

The sheer extent of the Russian
Federation encompasses an even greater
geographic diversity. It ranges from the
Caucasus Mountains, which contain Europe's
highest peak, to the areas below sea level
around the northern shores of the Caspian
Sea, and from the temperate climes of the
Black Sea to the Siberian tundra and the
permafrost of its Arctic shores. Having its
political power centred on Moscow keeps
Russia firmly a part of Europe, yet the
enormous expanses east of the Urals are
indisputably Asian in culture and geography.

Since these dramatic events, the pace
of change has been astonishingly fast,
particularly in the Russian Federation
and Ukraine, whose vast resources fired
their newly free-market economies,
rapidly making them bastions of capital
wealth. The economies of the seven most
westerly countries have met the criteria for
membership of the European Union, and
these countries, once part of the defensive
pact of the Soviet bloc, have also become
members of NATO. Such developments in its
former satellites have created tensions with
the Russian Federation, which still dominates

the region politically and economically
through its vast size and resources, and its
control of the supply lines for the petroleum
and natural gas on which much of this newfound prosperity is based.

Geographically the vast North European
Plain is predominant, stretching from the
Carpathian Mountains eastward to the Urals,
which mark the boundary with Asia. Across
these plains swept the fast-moving hordes
from Central Asia that felled the Roman
Empire and made the region such an ethnic
melting-pot. The great river systems of the
Danube, the Dnieper and the Volga drain and

EASTERN EUROPE

POLAND

52° 00' N, 20° 00' E | 312,679 KM² | 120,726 MI² | UTC+1

After centuries of struggle to maintain its identity, Poland became an independent state in the late twentieth century.

Geography

Most of the country lies on the North European Plain. The north-east is home to many large lakes and forests, while the south is dominated by the Carpathian Mountains. Major rivers include the Vistula, on which lies the capital Warsaw, and the Oder, both of which run into the Baltic.

History

An independent kingdom from the ninth century, in 1569 Poland formed a union with Lithuania that heralded a 'Golden Age' until the late eighteenth century, when

Poland was partitioned between Russia (which took the most territory), Prussia and Austria. Independence was restored in 1918, but Poland's occupation by Nazi Germany triggered the Second World War. Although liberated by Soviet forces in 1945, the installation of a communist regime left Poland under Soviet influence until 1989, when Solidarity leader Lech Wałesa was elected president. Significant figures in Polish history include Nicolas Copernicus, Frédéric Chopin and Marie Curie.

Economy

Although Poland has successfully made the transition from a state-owned economy to a free market, unemployment and low standards of living persist. The coal, steel and railway industries have all been privatized and contribute towards the steady increase in growth, alongside a nascent service sector.

Although a member of the European Union, this developing economy currently does not meet the requirements needed to adopt the euro as its currency.

GDANSK
Traditional houses in the port city of Gdansk.

FACT FILE

LOCAL NAME Republic of Poland

CAPITAL CITY Warsaw

CURRENCY Zloty (PLN)

MEMBERSHIP AC (observer), BSEC (observer), CBSS, CE, CEI, EAPC, EU, NATO, OAS (observer), OECD, WTO

GOVERNMENT Parliamentary Republic

POPULATION 38,022,141

POP. DENSITY 122/km²; 315/mi²

GDP 620.9 Billion US$

LANGUAGE(S) Polish, German, Belorussian, Kashubian, Russian

ETHNICITY Polish 97%

RELIGION Roman Catholic 90%, Eastern Orthodox 1%

CLIMATE Temperate

REGIONAL DIVISIONS 16 Provinces further divided into 379 Counties. Masovian is the largest and most populous province

ECONOMIC ACTIVITIES Agriculture, Machine Building, Iron and Steel, Coal Mining, Chemicals, Shipbuilding, Food Processing, Glass, Beverages, Textiles and clothing, Defence industries, Services, Forestry, Wood and Paper products, Tourism

NATURAL RESOURCES Coal, Sulphur, Copper, Gas, Silver, Lead, Salt, Amber

CZECH REPUBLIC
48° 40' N, 19° 30' E | 48,845 KM² | 18,859 MI² | UTC+1

This landlocked country in Central Europe is the most stable and prosperous of the former communist states and joined the European Union in 2004.

The Czech Republic comprises the regions of Bohemia, in the west, and Moravia. The area was under Habsburg rule until 1918 and was part of Czechoslovakia from 1918 to 1992. A communist regime installed in 1948 introduced political and economic reforms (the 'Prague Spring') in 1968 that were suppressed by Soviet troops. Communism fell in 1989 when peaceful student demonstrations led to the 'Velvet Revolution'. A 'Velvet Divorce' from Slovakia occurred in 1993 as a result of growing tensions between the two parts of the federation.

PRAGUE
Bridges over the River Vitava, which flows through the capital city of Prague.

FACT FILE
LOCAL NAME Czech Republic
CAPITAL CITY Prague
CURRENCY Czech Koruna (CZK)
MEMBERSHIP BSEC (observer), CE, CEI, EAPC, EU, NATO, OAS (observer), OECD, WTO
GOVERNMENT Parliamentary Republic
POPULATION 10,183,437
POP. DENSITY 129/km²; 334/mi²
GDP 248.9 Billion US$
LANGUAGE(S) Czech, Slovak, German
ETHNICITY Czech 90%, Moravian 4%, Slovak 2%
RELIGION Roman Catholic 39%, Protestant 2%
CLIMATE Temperate

SLOVAKIA
49° 45' N, 15° 30' E | 78,866 KM² | 30,450 MI² | UTC+1

With the Carpathian Mountains in the north and the fertile Danube plains in the south, Slovakia has a more varied terrain than the Czech Republic, its western neighbour and former federal partner.

Slovakia was settled by Slav tribes in the sixth century, came under Hungarian rule in the tenth century and was part of the Habsburg Empire from the sixteenth century. After 1918 it formed part of Czechoslovakia and experienced communist rule until 1989. Since separation from the Czech Republic in 1993, Slovakia has successfully achieved the difficult transition to a market economy. It joined the European Union in 2004 and aims to adopt the euro in 2009.

FACT FILE
LOCAL NAME Slovak Republic
CAPITAL CITY Bratislava
CURRENCY Slovak Koruna (SKK)
MEMBERSHIP BSEC (observer), CBSS (observer), CE, CEI, EAPC, EU, NATO, OAS (observer), OECD, WTO
GOVERNMENT Parliamentary Democracy
POPULATION 5,392,350
POP. DENSITY 110/km²; 286/mi²
GDP 109.6 Billion US$
LANGUAGE(S) Slovak, Hungarian, Romani, Ukrainian
ETHNICITY Slovak 86%, Hungarian 10%, Roma 2%, Ruthenian/Ukrainian 1%
RELIGION Roman Catholic 69%, Protestant 11%, Greek Catholic 4%
CLIMATE Temperate

EASTERN EUROPE

HUNGARY

47° 00' N, 20° 00' E | 93,030 KM² | 35,919 MI² | UTC+1

A large landlocked country in Central Europe, Hungary has a unique culture and language.

Geography

The country lies mostly on rolling plains, with the Carpathian Mountains along the border with Slovakia and a spur of the Alps in the north-west. The country is bisected by the River Danube, which also separates the towns of Buda and Pest which form the capital Budapest. There are several large lakes, including Lake Balaton, the largest in Central Europe.

History

A kingdom since the eleventh century, Hungary was conquered by the Turks in 1526 and became part of the powerful Habsburg Empire in the seventeenth century. After the collapse of the Austro-Hungarian Empire in 1918, Hungary became independent, and following the Second World War a

Soviet-influenced communist regime took control. The Hungarian Uprising of 1956 was brutally suppressed, but limited liberalization began from the 1960s. In 1989 the opening of Hungary's border with Austria triggered the collapse of communist rule throughout Eastern Europe. Hungarians consider themselves to be distinct from their neighbours, neither Slavic nor northern European. The language, Magyar, shares some features with Finnish, but is otherwise unique.

Economy

The most prosperous and liberal economy in the Soviet Bloc, Hungary made a speedy transition from state control to a free-market economy with strong growth. The mainstays of the economy are agriculture and heavy industry. A member of the European Union since 2004, Hungary has yet to meet the conditions required for adoption of the euro as its currency.

BUDAPEST
The River Danube flows between Buda and Pest.

FACT FILE

LOCAL NAME	Republic of Hungary
CAPITAL CITY	Budapest
CURRENCY	Forint (HUF)
MEMBERSHIP	CE, CEI, EAPC, EU, NATO, OAS (observer), OECD, WTO
GOVERNMENT	Parliamentary Republic
POPULATION	10,000,165
POP. DENSITY	108/km²; 278/mi²
GDP	191.3 Billion US$
LANGUAGE(S)	Magyar (Hungarian), Ukrainian, German, Romani, Romanian
ETHNICITY	Hungarian 92%, Roma 2%
RELIGION	Roman Catholic 52%, Calvinist 16%, Lutheran 3%, Greek Catholic 3%
CLIMATE	Temperate
REGIONAL DIVISIONS	19 Counties, 23 Urban Counties and 1 Capital City further divided into 173 Subregions
ECONOMIC ACTIVITIES	Agriculture, Mining, Metallurgy, Construction Materials, Processed Foods, Textiles, Chemicals, Pharmaceuticals, Automobiles, Forestry, Tourism, Wine
NATURAL RESOURCES	Bauxite, Coal, Natural Gas, Fertile Soils

ROMANIA

46° 00' N, 25° 00' E | 237,500 KM² | 91,699 MI² | UTC+2

Formed from the merger of Moldavia, Wallachia, Transylvania, Bessarabia and Bukovina, modern-day Romania is a melting pot of different peoples.

Geography

The north and centre of Romania are dominated by the Carpathian Mountains, which encircle the Transylvania plateau in the centre of the country. The wide plains of the south are crossed by many rivers, including the River Danube as it flows to the Black Sea in the east. Much of the country remains densely forested, while the temperate climate and swathes of arable land are ideal for agriculture.

History

The original Dacian peoples were Romanized during two centuries as part of the Roman Empire. The fall of Rome was followed by centuries of rule by invading tribes but in the fifteenth century the region came under Ottoman rule. Moldavia and Wallachia merged in the 1860s to create the kingdom of Romania, whose independence was recognized in 1878. Transylvania, Bessarabia and Bukovina were added after the First World War, although parts of Bessarabia and Bukovina were lost to the Soviet Union after 1945. The brutal dictatorship of Ceausescu was overthrown in 1989 in a surge of nationalism, but the struggle for reform has led to ethnic tensions and continued social hardship.

Economy

Progress towards a free-market economy was sluggish, with outdated industries, an unmechanized agricultural sector and low wages all hindering growth. Reform gained impetus as Romania prepared to join the European Union in 2007, but the effects of this and the steady economic growth since 2000 have only recently started to alleviate the country's widespread poverty.

FACT FILE

LOCAL NAME Romania

CAPITAL CITY Bucharest

CURRENCY Leu (RON)

MEMBERSHIP BSEC, CE, CEI, EAPC, EU, LAIA (observer), NATO, OAS (observer), WTO

GOVERNMENT Unitary Semi-presidential Republic

POPULATION 21,344,129

POP. DENSITY 90/km²; 233/mi²

GDP 245.5 Billion US$

LANGUAGE(S) Romanian, Hungarian, Romani

ETHNICITY Romanian 90%, Hungarian 7%, Roma 3%

RELIGION Eastern Orthodox 87%, Protestant 8%, Roman Catholic 5%

CLIMATE Temperate

REGIONAL DIVISIONS 41 Counties and 1 Municipality further divided into 208 Towns, 103 Municipalities, and 2,825 Rural Localities

ECONOMIC ACTIVITIES Agriculture, Electric Machinery and Equipment, Textiles and Footwear, Light Machinery and Auto Assembly, Mining, Timber, Construction Materials, Metallurgy, Chemicals, Food Processing and Beverage Production, Petroleum Refining

NATURAL RESOURCES Petroleum (reserves declining), Timber, Natural Gas, Coal, Iron Ore, Salt, Arable Land, Hydropower

MARAMURES REGION
Haystacks in the fields in the rural Maramures region in the north of Romania.

BULGARIA

43° 00' N, 25° 00' E | 110,910 KM² | 42,823 MI² | UTC+2

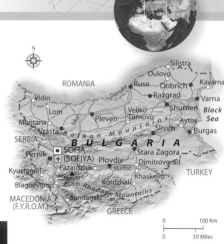

Bulgaria has combated corruption, inflation and unemployment since 1990, to satisfy the requirements for EU membership.

Situated to the north of Greece and Turkey, Bulgaria is a large country with a landscape that varies from mountainous in the south and west to lowland plains on the Black Sea coast and in the valleys of the Danube and Maritsa Rivers. A Bulgarian kingdom established in the seventh century was conquered in 1390 and remained part of the Ottoman Empire for nearly 500 years. Bulgaria was granted independence in 1878,

FACT FILE

LOCAL NAME Republic of Bulgaria
CAPITAL CITY Sofia (Sofiya)
CURRENCY Lev (BGL)
MEMBERSHIP BSEC, CE, CEI, EAPC, EU, NATO, OAS (observer), WTO
GOVERNMENT Parliamentary Republic
POPULATION 7,583,684
POP. DENSITY 68/km²; 177/mi²
GDP 86.32 Billion US$
LANGUAGE(S) Bulgarian, Turkish, Romani
ETHNICITY Bulgarian 84%, Turk 9%, Roma 5%, Other 2% (including Macedonian, Armenian, Tatar, Circassian)
RELIGION Bulgarian Orthodox 83%, Muslim 12%
CLIMATE Temperate

but the monarchy was abolished in 1946 when a communist regime was installed. Multiparty elections were held in 1990, and political and economic reforms were gradually introduced that allowed Bulgaria to join NATO in 2004 and the European Union in 2007.

VARNA
The Cathedral of the Assumption of the Virgin at Varna on the Black Sea coast.

MOLDOVA

47° 00' N, 29° 00' E | 33,843 KM² | 13,067 MI² | UTC+2

Formerly part of the Soviet Union, Moldova has struggled to achieve stability since independence in 1991.

Moldova has historic and cultural links with both Romania, with which it was once merged, and Russia. As part of the Soviet Union from the 1920s, Moldavia's Ukrainian and Russian populations grew, and after 1991 they sought independence for the region east of the River Dniester; Russian peacekeeping troops remain in the region. Despite an effective agricultural sector and wine industry, the economy remains weak because most of the industrialized areas are in the Transdniestria region and relations

FACT FILE

LOCAL NAME Republic of Moldova
CAPITAL CITY Chisinau (Kishinev)
CURRENCY Moldovan Leu (MDL)
MEMBERSHIP BSEC, CE, CEI, EAEC (observer), GUAM, WTO
GOVERNMENT Parliamentary Republic
POPULATION 3,759,599
POP. DENSITY 111/km²; 288/mi²
GDP 9.821 Billion US$
LANGUAGE(S) Moldovan, Russian, Gagauz
ETHNICITY Moldovan/Romanian 79%, Ukrainian 8%, Russian 6%, Gagauz 4%, Bulgarian 2%
RELIGION Eastern Orthodox 98%, Jewish 2%
CLIMATE Temperate

with Moscow are tense because of Moldova's reliance upon Russian energy supplies.

UKRAINE

49° 00' N, 32° 00' E | 603,700 KM² | 233,090 MI² | UTC+2

The second largest country in Europe, Ukraine has struggled to reassert a national identity since independence.

Geography

Ukraine consists mainly of the fertile plains which once made it the 'bread-basket' of the Soviet Union, with the land rising to the Carpathian Mountains in the west. Its southern coastline lies on the Black Sea and the Sea of Azov, which are divided by the Crimean peninsula. The delta of the River Danube forms the border with Romania.

FACT FILE

LOCAL NAME Ukraine

CAPITAL CITY Kiev (Kyiv)

CURRENCY Hryvnia (UAH)

MEMBERSHIP BSEC, CBSS (observer), CE, CEI, CIS, EAEC (observer), EAPC, GUAM, LAIA (observer), OAS (observer), WTO (observer)

GOVERNMENT Semi-presidential Unitary State

POPULATION 45,858,836

POP. DENSITY 76/km²; 197/mi²

GDP 320.1 Billion US$

LANGUAGE(S) Ukrainian, Russian, Romanian, Bulgarian, Hungarian

ETHNICITY Ukrainian 78%, Russian 17%, Belorussian 1%

RELIGION Ukrainian Orthodox – Kyiv Patriarchate 50%, Ukrainian Orthodox – Moscow Patriarchate 26%, Ukrainian Greek Catholic 8%, Ukrainian Autocephalous Orthodox 7%, Roman Catholic 2%, Protestant 2%

CLIMATE Temperate and Mediterranean

REGIONAL DIVISIONS 24 Provinces, 1 Autonomous Republic and 2 Municipalities with Province status, further divided into 490 Districts

ECONOMIC ACTIVITIES Coal, Electric Power and Plant, Ferrous and Non-ferrous Metallurgy, Machinery and Automotive including Tractors and Farming Equipment, Diesel Locomotive Production, Turbines, Aviation Engines, Aircraft and Spacecraft (rocket technology), Food Processing (especially sugar), Oil Refinery, Chemicals and Chemical Plant

NATURAL RESOURCES Iron Ore, Coal, Manganese, Natural Gas, Oil, Salt, Sulphur, Graphite, Titanium, Magnesium, Kaolin, Nickel, Mercury, Timber

History

Once known as the Kyvian Rus, Ukraine was ruled by Lithuania from the fourteenth century and by Poland from the sixteenth century, and was gradually absorbed into the Russian Empire from the seventeenth century. Despite a brief assertion of independence in 1918, it was incorporated into the Soviet Union and suffered severe famines which cost over 8 million lives. Millions more died in the Second World War, when it was a key theatre for battles between German and Soviet forces. The Chernobyl nuclear disaster in 1986 left about 8 per cent of the country contaminated. Independence came in 1991 following the collapse of the Soviet Union, although the new democracy has been destabilized by the marked divide between the Russian-influenced east and the European-influenced west of the country.

Economy

A combination of resistance to reform, corruption and reliance upon trade with Russia, especially for energy supplies, has left the post-Soviet economy stagnant.

Although both industry and agriculture remain outdated, there are some areas of improvement, such as steel exports.

KIEV
The Saint Sophia Cathedral in Kiev.

BELARUS

53° 00' N, 28° 00' E | 207,600 KM² | 80,155 MI² | UTC+2

Reluctantly independent from Russia since 1991, Belarus, formerly 'White Russia', has sought closer political and economic ties with its former 'motherland'.

Geography

The landlocked country is mostly a large plain of marshland, forest and over 11,000 lakes. The three principal rivers are the Neman, the Dnieper and the Prypyats. Most of the country has a continental climate. Winters are generally harsh, with average January temperatures in the capital Minsk ranging from -4°C to -8°C . Summers are warm and damp.

History

The lands that constitute modern Belarus were subject to long periods of foreign rule, especially Polish, allowing the Slavic tribes of the area little opportunity to establish a national identity. From 1795 the area was part of the Russian Empire, but its independence, declared in 1917 during the unrest that followed the Russian Revolution, was short-lived and it was incorporated into the Soviet Union. A key theatre during the Second World War, Belarus suffered massive casualties and infrastructure damage. The country became independent in 1991 with the collapse of the Soviet Union, but post-Soviet governments have pursued closer political, economic and trade relations with Russia, especially since the election of the increasingly authoritarian Alexander Lukashenko in 1994.

Economy

Belarus has experienced a dramatic economic decline since independence, and poverty is widespread. There has been little economic reform since 1994, with much of the economy still under state control, and most sectors have stagnated, although industrial output has grown. The country is dependent on Russia for energy supplies and for industrial raw materials and trade.

ASAREVICHI, EAST OF MAZYR
Belarus farmers use a traditional plough.

FACT FILE

LOCAL NAME Republic of Belarus

CAPITAL CITY Minsk

CURRENCY Belorussian Ruble (BYR)

MEMBERSHIP BSEC (observer), CEI, CIS, EAEC, EAPC, WTO (observer)

GOVERNMENT Presidential Republic

POPULATION 9,635,397

POP. DENSITY 46/km²; 120/mi²

GDP 105.2 Billion US$

LANGUAGE(S) Belorussian, Russian, Polish

ETHNICITY Belorussian 81%, Russian 11%, Polish 4%, Ukrainian 2%

RELIGION Eastern Orthodox 80%, Other (including Roman Catholic, Protestant, Jewish and Muslim) 20%

CLIMATE Temperate

REGIONAL DIVISIONS 6 Provinces, named after their administrative centre cities, and 1 Municipality; these are further divided into 118 Districts

ECONOMIC ACTIVITIES Agriculture, Metal Cutting, Machine Tools, Tractors, Trucks, Earthmovers, Motorcycles, Televisions, Synthetic Fibres, Fertilizer, Textiles, Electrotechnical Products, Agricultural Machinery, Oil Extraction and Processing, Pharmaceutical, Food Industry, Construction Materials

NATURAL RESOURCES Forests, Peat Deposits, Small Quantities of Oil and Natural Gas, Granite, Dolomitic Limestone, Marl, Chalk, Sand, Gravel, Clay

RUSSIAN FEDERATION

60° 00' N, 100° 00' E | 17,075,200 KM² | 6,592,772 MI² | UTC+2 TO +12

Geography

Sharing borders with fourteen other countries, Russia is the largest country in the world; it covers 40 per cent of Europe and all of north Asia and spans eleven time zones.

Geography

The sheer size of Russia's territory results in a range of different landscapes; however the majority of the country is far closer to the North Pole than to the Equator and the terrain, vegetation and climate reflect this. Generally the northern zone is Arctic tundra and moving further south the landscape becomes forested, then grassland or steppe, until it reaches more arid desert in the south. European and Asian Russia are roughly separated by the Ural Mountains which run from the Arctic Circle to the borders of Kazakhstan and cover a distance of 2,100 kilometres. To the west of the Urals is the East European or Russian plain; to their east extends the steppe of the west Siberian plain and the central Siberian plateau, with boreal forests and tundra. Much of the country is inhospitable, and notoriously difficult to farm. Likewise, despite an abundance of natural resources and raw materials, which includes a significant amount of the world's coal and petroleum reserves, the extreme conditions make mining and excavation difficult and expensive.

Further natural boundaries are created by the southern mountain range, the Caucasus, at 5,642 metres the Mount El'brus peak is the highest in Europe. Russia is also home to thousands of rivers and lakes; the freshwater Lake Baikal, which as the world's deepest, is also the largest by volume. Baikal is outsized, however, by the Caspian Sea, which is situated in the south of Russia and extends into northern Iran. The Caspian Sea has a surface area of 371,000 square kilometres and, like Baikal, it is landlocked, although the water is slightly salty. Russia's most famous river is the Volga, situated in the European west and within reach of some of the country's major cities. Its largest city and capital is Moscow and it is from there that this country of over 142 million people is administered.

History

With its origins in the east Slavic state of Kievan Rus, established in the ninth century, Russia has gradually expanded and contracted over the centuries. The disintegration of the Rus during the eleventh and twelfth centuries resulted in the successful invasion of the Mongol Golden Horde. They dominated Russia until the fifteenth century, and with their departure the country was left fragmented into feudal states, the most powerful of which was the Principality of Muscovy. By the seventeenth century the Muscovite Romanov dynasty had established control over an ever increasing territory; under Peter the Great (1682–1725) the country was westernized and modernized, reaching south to the Baltic and east into Siberia. By the nineteenth century the Russian Empire had managed to repel Napoleon and to reach further into Asia and into the Caucasus. However, harsh oppression and defeat in the Russo-Japanese war of 1905 contributed to the first Revolution later that year. Although Tsar Nicholas II managed to maintain control, continued distrust and the economic and human cost of the First World War led to the 1917 Revolution. In the ensuing civil war the royal family were imprisoned, then executed, and Vladimir Lenin rose to become the first ruler of the new communist state. During the premiership of Josef Stalin (1928–53) millions of Russians lost their lives under a brutal communist regime. On Stalin's death, Nikita Krushchev became general secretary, a period marked by Russian explorations into space and the beginning of the arms race and Cold War with the West. During the late 1980s Mikhail Gorbachev's introduction of modernizing reforms led to increased openness, but also precipitated the collapse of the USSR and the assertion of independence of a number of former states such as Lithuania, Latvia and Belarus. With a permanent seat on the Security Council of the United Nations, Russia continues to assert its position on the world stage. It also holds the largest stockpile of weapons of mass destruction in the world.

FACT FILE

LOCAL NAME Russian Federation

CAPITAL CITY Moscow

CURRENCY Russian Ruble (RUB)

MEMBERSHIP APEC, AC, ASEAN (dialogue partner), BSEC, CBSS, CE, CIS, EAEC, EAPC, G8, LAIA (observer), OAS (observer), WTO (observer)

GOVERNMENT Federal Semi-presidential Republic

POPULATION 141,780,031

POP. DENSITY 8/km²; 22/mi²

GDP 2.088 Trillion US$

LANGUAGE(S) Russian, Tatar, Ukrainian, Belorussian, German

ETHNICITY Russian 80%, Tatar 4%, Ukrainian 2%, Bashkir 1%

RELIGION Christian 58% (of which Orthodox 50%, Protestant 6%, Roman Catholic 1%, other Christian 1%), Muslim 8%

CLIMATE Temperate (Humid Continental, Subarctic), Tundra

REGIONAL DIVISIONS 46 Provinces, 21 Republics, 4 Autonomous Districts, 9 Territories (alt. name for province), 2 Federal Cities, and 1 Autonomous Province

ECONOMIC ACTIVITIES Mining and Extractive Industries, Machine Building, Defence Industries, Shipbuilding, Road and Rail Transportation Equipment, Communications Equipment, Agricultural Machinery and Construction Equipment, Electric Power Plant, Medical and Scientific Instruments; Consumer Durables, Textiles, Foodstuffs, Handicrafts

NATURAL RESOURCES Wide natural resource base including major deposits of Oil, Natural Gas, Coal and many Strategic Minerals, Timber

BIRCH FOREST
About 40 per cent of Russia is covered by forest.

ST PETERSBURG
The elegant university buildings and the River Neva in winter. St Petersburg, called Leningrad during the Soviet period, was the capital of Russia for more than 200 years.

Russian contributions to European culture have been particularly strong in the fields of music and literature. Composers such as Tchaikovsky, Rachmaninoff, Stravinsky and Prokofiev are world-renowned. Russian literature includes some of the greatest and most influential writers and poets, from Pushkin and Chekhov to Tolstoy and Dostoyevsky.

Economy

Now a presidential democracy, Russia has undergone a slow transformation from communism to capitalism. Under the presidency of Vladimir Putin, the economy grew steadily; business and investment have increased, consumer confidence has risen and foreign debt has been reduced. Although privatization has increased during the past decade, many key industries remain within state control, inefficient and outdated. Much of the economy relies upon Russia's massive energy reserves; it exports natural gas, oil and coal while remaining fully energy-independent. Minerals, metals and timber also supply

the Russian export market and its outdated heavy manufacturing base supplies a wide range of machinery, from armaments to medical instruments. Despite the reduction of poverty for much of the population, vast inequalities in wealth remain, and corruption and crime are endemic.

MOSCOW
The colourful onion-shaped domes of St Basil's Cathedral in Red Square. The square is also the location of the Kremlin.

ASIA

From Turkey in the west to the Philippines in the east, from Japan in the north to Indonesia in the south, Asia's diverse range of topography and people is immense, yet many people think of Asia and the Orient as a region with common culture and heritage. Just as Asia has the world's highest mountain range in the Himalaya and the world's most fertile river valleys, equally large cultural divides cause the usual human conflict, whether in Afghanistan, Iraq, Myanmar, Sri Lanka or Tibet.

ASIA

ASIA

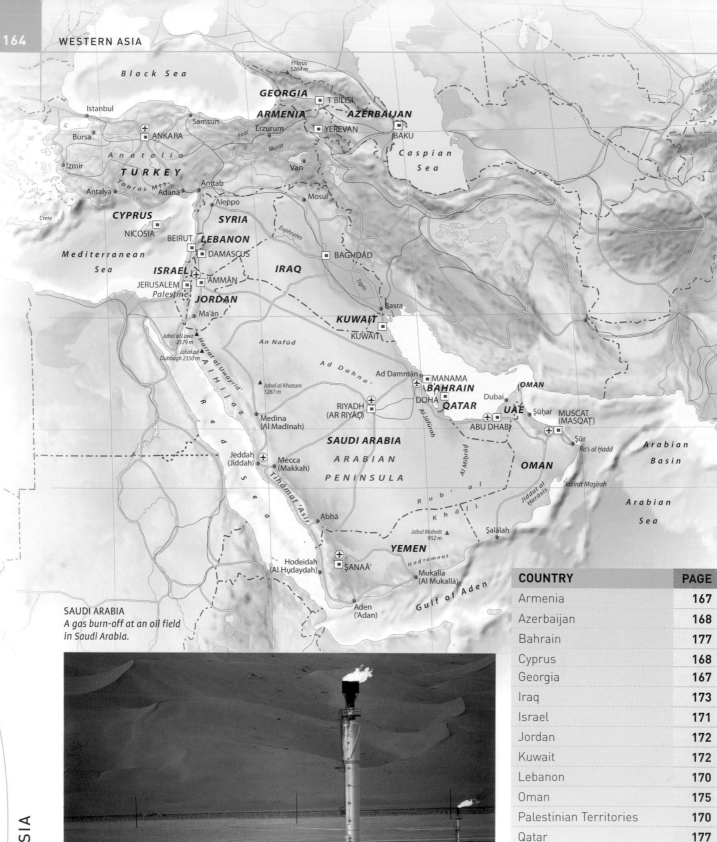

Black Sea

GEORGIA
☐ T'BILISI
ARMENIA   AZERBAIJAN
Istanbul   Samsun   Erzurum   ☐ YEREVAN   ☐ BAKU
Bursa   ☒ ANKARA
İzmir   Anatolia   Murat   Caspian
TURKEY   Van   Sea
Antalya   Tauras Mts   Fırat
Crete   Adana   Amtab
        Aleppo   Mosul
CYPRUS   Euphrates
☐ NICOSIA   SYRIA
BEIRUT ☒ LEBANON   ☐ BAGHDAD
Mediterranean   ☐ DAMASCUS   Tigris
Sea   ISRAEL   IRAQ
JERUSALEM ☒ ☒ 'AMMĀN   Basra
Palestine   JORDAN   KUWAIT
☐ Ma'ān   ☐ KUWAIT
Jabal al Lawz
2579 m   An Nafūd
Jabal ad   Ad Dahna   Ad Dammān   MANAMA
Dubbagh 2350 m   ☒ BAHRAIN   Dubai   OMAN
    ▲ Jabal al Khatam   DOHA   QATAR   ☐ Şūhar   MUSCAT
    1287 m   RIYADH   Abū Dhabi   UAE   (MASQAT)
Medina   (AR RIYĀD)   ☐ ABU DHABI   Şūr
(Al Madīnah)   Al Midwrah   Ra's al Ḥadd
Jeddah   SAUDI ARABIA   Al Mibrāt   Arabian
(Jiddah)   Mecca   ARABIAN   Basin
    (Makkah)   PENINSULA   OMAN   Jazirat Maşirah
            Rub' al   Jiddat al   Arabian
Abhā   Khāli   Harāsis   Sea
            Jabal Mahrāt   Şalālah
            952 m
    Hodeidah   YEMEN   Hadramaut
    (Al Hudaydah)   ☐ ŞANĀ'
            Mukalla
            (Al Mukallā)   Gulf of Aden
    Aden
    ('Adan)

SAUDI ARABIA
A gas burn-off at an oil field in Saudi Arabia.

WESTERN ASIA

WESTERN ASIA

This relatively small region is the cradle of two world religions whose teachings and institutions influence half the world's population. Five of the twelve OPEC countries are here, including the most powerful, Saudi Arabia.

The traditional crossing points between Europe and Asia are the Ural Mountains in the north and Istanbul in the south. Western Asia has always been a conflict zone between east and west and even north and south; Napoleon marched his armies down the coast of the eastern Mediterranean and great battles have been fought there, from the time of the Ancient Greeks to the Crimean War and later the carnage of the Gallipoli landings. A large part of this area comprises the Levant, the Arabian Peninsula and Asia Minor, known in the past as the Near East as opposed to the Far East. In the north of western Asia, countries such as Georgia and

Azerbaijan are sandwiched between two great lakes, the Black Sea and the landlocked Caspian Sea. As in their more southerly neighbours, newfound wealth based on petroleum sits next to relatively poor populations with low standards of living and much subsistence agriculture.

Perhaps the history of conflict in this region has reduced its appeal to tourists, with a few notable exceptions in Turkey, Cyprus and the specific sites of Jordan such as Petra, while the Black Sea and its coast are favoured by Eastern Europeans. The wealthy of the world find great diversion in the Gulf States, particularly the

business hub and playground of Dubai. The terrain and the history of the region are fascinating: from the holy sites of Jerusalem in Israel and Mecca in Saudi Arabia to the monolithic ruins of Baalbec in the Beqaa Valley in Lebanon (part of the same geology that created the Valley of the Dead Sea and even further south, the East African Rift Valley).

BAHRAIN
Skyscrappers around the marina in Bahrain.

TURKEY

39° 00' N, 35° 00' E | 780,580 KM² | 301,384 MI² | UTC+2

Despite undergoing major reforms since Independence, Europe's 'Gateway to Asia' is yet to gain full admittance to the European Union.

Geography

Situated between the Black Sea and the Mediterranean, Turkey straddles both Europe and Asia. Istanbul, the country's largest city, lies in the small European region known as Thrace, which is hilly and fertile with a Mediterranean climate; while the capital, Ankara, is located in the Asian region, or Anatolia, which is largely arid and mountainous.

FACT FILE

LOCAL NAME Republic of Turkey

CAPITAL CITY Ankara

CURRENCY Turkish Lira (TRY)

MEMBERSHIP BSEC, CE, EAPC, ECO, NATO, OAS (observer), OECD, OIC, WTO

GOVERNMENT Parliamentary Republic

POPULATION 75,829,891

POP. DENSITY 97/km²; 252/mi²

GDP 888 Billion US$

LANGUAGE(S) Turkish, Kurdish, Dimli (Zaza), Azeri, Kabardian

ETHNICITY Turkish 80%, Kurdish 20%

RELIGION Muslim 100% (mostly Sunni)

CLIMATE Mediterranean, Continental with hot summer, Semi-arid Steppe

REGIONAL DIVISIONS 7 geographical regions are divided into 81 Provinces, which are further divided into 923 Districts

DEPENDENCIES Controls Turkish Republic of Northern Cyprus, a territory not recognized by any other international body

ECONOMIC ACTIVITIES Agriculture, Textiles, Food Processing, Automotive, Electronics, Mining, Iron and Steel, Petroleum, Construction, Lumber, Paper, Chemicals and Petrochemicals, Beer, Wine, Tourism

NATURAL RESOURCES Coal, Iron Ore, Copper, Chromium, Antimony, Mercury, Gold, Barite, Borate, Celestite (Strontium), Emery, Feldspar, Limestone, Magnesite, Marble, Perlite, Pumice, Pyrites (Sulphur), Clay, Arable Land, Hydropower

History

The first major civilization in Turkey was established by the Hittites around 2000 BC, following which control passed to a succession of empires, including the Greeks, Persians and Romans. Founded in Anatolia in AD 1300, the Ottoman Empire then flourished for over 500 years, but by the nineteenth century, Turkey had become known as 'the Sick Man of Europe'. Independence was gained in 1923, and under the leadership of Mustafa Kemal, or Atatürk, major reforms were instituted in order to strengthen the country and its links with the West. However, the process of democratization has at times led to turmoil, with three military coups occurring between 1960 and 1980, in order to preserve the secular tradition established by Atatürk. Today Turkey's stability is threatened by the prolonged dispute with Greece over Cyprus, and conflict with both Kurdish nationalists and Islamic militants.

Economy

Despite rapid industrialization and the growth of manufacturing and service industries, agriculture remains important to the Turkish economy, employing over 30 per cent of the workforce. The largest industrial sector is textile production; tourism has also grown rapidly in recent years.

ISTANBUL
Hagia Sophia with the Bosporus behind.

GEORGIA

42° 00' N, 43° 30' E | 69,700 KM² | 26,911 MI² | UTC+4

Blighted by civil war and political instability since independence, Georgia's future remains uncertain.

FACT FILE

LOCAL NAME Georgia

CAPITAL CITY T'bilisi

CURRENCY Lari (GEL)

MEMBERSHIP BSEC, CE, CIS, EAPC, OAS (observer), WTO

GOVERNMENT Unitary Semi-Presidential Republic

POPULATION 4,360,801

POP. DENSITY 63/km²; 162/mi²

GDP 20.5 Billion US$

LANGUAGE(S) Georgian, Russian, Armenian, Azeri

ETHNICITY Georgian 84%, Azeri 7%, Armenian 6%, Russian 2%

RELIGION Orthodox Christian 84%, Muslim 10%, Armenian–Gregorian 4%

CLIMATE Humid Subtropical, Continental (hot summer)

Located in the South Caucasus, Georgia is largely mountainous with a continental climate, although the lowlands on the Black Sea are subtropical. Dominated by a succession of conquerors from ancient times until the eighteenth century, Georgia sought Russian protection in 1783, and was later incorporated into the Transcaucasian Republic along with Armenia and Azerbaijan. This was dissolved in 1936, the constituent countries remaining republics within the Soviet Union until its collapse in 1991. Following independence, conflict erupted as the provinces of South Ossetia, Abkhazia and Adzharia attempted to secede from Georgia; sporadic violence continued throughout the 1990s. In the summer of 2008, Georgian troops entered South Ossetia, prompting a violent response by Russia that was condemned by the international community.

ARMENIA

40° 00' N, 45° 00' E | 29,743 KM² | 11,484 MI² | UTC+4

Long subjected to foreign rule, today Armenia is recovering from the conflict and natural disasters it has endured since independence.

Lying in the South Caucasus on a high plateau interlaced with fault lines, Armenia

FACT FILE

LOCAL NAME Republic of Armenia

CAPITAL CITY Yerevan

CURRENCY Dram (AMD)

MEMBERSHIP BSEC, CE, CIS, EAEC (observer), EAPC, OAS (observer), WTO

GOVERNMENT Republic

POPULATION 2,995,890

POP. DENSITY 101/km²; 261/mi²

GDP 17.15 Billion US$

LANGUAGE(S) Armenian, Yezidi, Russian

ETHNICITY Armenian 98%, Yezidi (Kurd) 1%

RELIGION Armenian Apostolic 95%, Other Christian 4%, Yezidi 1%

CLIMATE Continental (warm summer)

is susceptible to frequent earth tremors, and was last devastated by a major earthquake in 1988. The climate is continental, with harsher winters at high altitudes. Historically much larger, Armenia was divided between Russia and the Ottoman Empire by the twentieth century, with the latter implementing a particularly brutal regime. Following a brief period of independence, Armenia was incorporated into the Transcaucasian Republic in 1922 with Georgia and Azerbaijan, before joining the Soviet Union later that year. Independence was gained with the collapse of the USSR in 1991, although a damaging territorial dispute with Azerbaijan over the Nagorno-Karabakh region continues. Like most of the former Soviet states, following independence Armenia had difficulty in adapting its economy from being part of the centrally planned Soviet system. Since 1991 the number of people involved in agriculture has grown rapidly, settling at about 40 per cent of the population. After a period of disruption industry is recovering. Pig iron and copper are Armenia's most valuable exports.

AZERBAIJAN

40° 30' N, 47° 30' E | 86,600 KM² | 33,436 MI² | UTC+4

One of the world's earliest exporters of oil; the industry continues to support Azerbaijan's economy.

Situated in the South Caucasus, Azerbaijan's eastern border is delineated by the Caspian Sea; the rest of the country is enclosed by mountains. Azerbaijan includes the disputed territory of Nagorno-Karabakh, while the autonomous Naxçivan region is cut off by Armenia. Conquered by a succession of empires in ancient times, by the twentieth century Azerbaijan's oil reserves had made it of chief importance to Russia. After the

Russian Revolution, it was incorporated into the Transcaucasian Republic within the

FACT FILE

LOCAL NAME Republic of Azerbaijan

CAPITAL CITY Baku

CURRENCY Azerbaijani Manat (AZN)

MEMBERSHIP BSEC, CE, CIS, EAPC, ECO, GUAM, OAS (observer), OIC, WTO (observer)

GOVERNMENT Presidential Republic

POPULATION 8,533,620

POP. DENSITY 99/km²; 255/mi²

GDP 65.47 Billion US$

LANGUAGE(S) Azerbaijani (Azeri), Lezgi, Russian, Armenian

ETHNICITY Azeri 91%, Dagestani 2%, Russian 2%, Armenian 2%

RELIGION Muslim 93%, Russian Orthodox 3%, Armenian Orthodox 2%

CLIMATE Continental (warm summer)

USSR in 1922. Independence came with the collapse of the Soviet Union in 1991, by which time conflict had erupted with Armenia over Nagorno-Karabakh. An effective ceasefire was implemented in 1994, although the territory remains disputed.

CYPRUS

35° 00' N, 33° 00' E | 9,250 KM² | 3,571 MI² | UTC+2

Although Cyprus has been divided into a Greek republic and a Turkish republic since 1983, only the former is officially recognized by the international community.

The third largest island in the Mediterranean, Cyprus comprises a flat plain bordered by

mountain ranges to the north and south. The climate is Mediterranean, with hot dry summers and mild winters. Inhabited by Greeks since ancient times, by AD 1571 Cyprus had fallen to the Ottoman Empire. In 1925 the island was annexed as a British colony. Greek Cypriots then began a campaign for unification with Greece, sometimes employing guerrilla tactics, and in 1960 Cyprus became independent. Three years later, fighting erupted between Greek and Turkish Cypriots, and in 1974 Turkey sent an occupying army into the north of the country, which it later claimed as an independent republic. Subsequent attempts at reunification have failed, although the south has prospered, largely through tourism.

FACT FILE

LOCAL NAME Republic of Cyprus

CAPITAL CITY Nicosia

CURRENCY Cypriot Pound (CYP); Euro (EUR)

MEMBERSHIP Commonwealth of Nations, CE, EU, OAS (observer), WTO

GOVERNMENT Presidential Republic

POPULATION 863,624

POP. DENSITY 93/km²; 242/mi²

GDP 21.38 Billion US$

LANGUAGE(S) Greek, Turkish, English

ETHNICITY Greek 77%, Turkish 18%

RELIGION Greek Orthodox 78%, Muslim 18%

CLIMATE Mediterranean

KYRENIA
The harbour of Kyrenia with mountains behind.

SYRIA

56° 00' N, 10° 00' E | 185,200 KM² | 71,506 MI² | UTC+2

While Syria's history has been somewhat turbulent, today the country is largely peaceful and looking to strengthen its ties with Europe.

Geography

Syria comprises a fertile Mediterranean coastal plain, divided from the more arid interior by the Jabal an Nusayriyah mountain range. The disputed Golan Heights lie in the south-west beyond the city of Damascus. The River Euphrates flows across the country from Turkey to Iraq.

History

Formerly encompassing the territories of present-day Lebanon, Israel and Jordan, in ancient times Syria played host to a succession of imperial powers, including the Hittites, Assyrians, Persians, Greeks and Romans, before being conquered by Arabs during the seventh century. Control passed from the Ottoman Empire to the French following World War I. Syria became independent in 1946, but the creation of Israel in 1947 sparked a series of Arab–Israeli conflicts, with the Golan Heights being captured by Israel in 1967. A brief period of stability was then undermined by Syria's involvement in the Lebanese civil war in the 1970s and an uprising by the Muslim Brotherhood in 1982. Despite allying itself with coalition forces during the 1991 Persian Gulf War, and condemning terrorist attacks in the US in 2001, prolonged disputes with Israel and Lebanon, and American accusations of links with Iraqi insurgents, continue to threaten Syria's stability.

Economy

Prior to the development of the oil industry during the 1970s, Syria's largest export was cotton, and while agriculture remains a major area of employment, today oil extraction and export is of primary importance.

PALMYRA (TADMUR)
Syria was occupied by many powers. The remains of a Roman temple lie below the castle at Palmyra.

FACT FILE

LOCAL NAME Syrian Arab Republic

CAPITAL CITY Damascus

CURRENCY Syrian Pound (SYP)

MEMBERSHIP G24, G77, LAS, OAPEC, OIC

GOVERNMENT Presidential Republic; Republic under an Authoritarian Military-dominated Regime

POPULATION 20,446,734

POP. DENSITY 110/km²; 286/mi²

GDP 87.09 Billion US$

LANGUAGE(S) Arabic, Kurdish, Armenian, Aramaic, Circassian

ETHNICITY Arab 90%, Kurd, Armenian and other 10%

RELIGION Muslim 86% (Sunni 74%, Alawite 11%) Christian 8%, Druze 3%

CLIMATE Arid, Semi-arid, Mediterranean

REGIONAL DIVISIONS 4 geographical regions are divided into 14 Governorates further divided into 60 Districts

ECONOMIC ACTIVITIES Agriculture, Mining, Petroleum, Textiles, Food Processing, Beverages, Tobacco, Cement, Oil Seeds Crushing, Car Assembly, Construction

NATURAL RESOURCES Petroleum, Phosphates, Chrome and Manganese ores, Asphalt, Iron Ore, Rock Salt, Marble, Gypsum, Hydropower

LEBANON

33° 50' N, 35° 50' E | 10,400 KM² | 4,015 MI² | UTC+2

Once a thriving, cosmopolitan country, today Lebanon is struggling to recover from decades of warfare.

A small country on the eastern Mediterranean, Lebanon consists of a narrow coastal plain divided from the fertile Beqaa Valley by the Lebanon Mountains. The climate varies from subtropical on the coast to alpine at high altitudes. Originally settled by the Phoenicians, Lebanon was part of the Ottoman Empire between 1516 and 1922, following which it prospered under French control. Independence was granted in 1943, but growing tensions between religious groups escalated into civil war in 1975, with neighbouring Israel and Syria being drawn into the conflict. Hostilities persisted until 1990; since then, periodic violence between Hezbollah guerrillas and Israeli forces has

FACT FILE

LOCAL NAME	Lebanese Republic
CAPITAL CITY	Beirut
CURRENCY	Lebanese Pound (LBP)
MEMBERSHIP	G24, G77, LAS, OAS (observer), OIC, WTO (observer)
GOVERNMENT	Parliamentary Democracy with proportional representation
POPULATION	4,142,299
POP. DENSITY	398/km²; 1032/mi²
GDP	42.27 Billion US$
LANGUAGE(S)	Arabic, French, English, Armenian
ETHNICITY	Arab 95%, Armenian 4%
RELIGION	Muslim 60%, Christian 39%
CLIMATE	Mediterranean

hampered reconstruction efforts, as has continued internal conflict between pro- and anti-Syrian factions, leaving Lebanon heavily reliant upon foreign aid.

PALESTINIAN TERRITORIES

GAZA STRIP: 31° 25' N, 34° 20' | WEST BANK: 32° 00' N, 35° 15' E | 6,165 KM² | 2,380 MI² | UTC+2

Disputed by Israel and the Palestinian National Authority, a resolution over the Palestinian Territories may ultimately stimulate wider peace in the Middle East.

Formerly part of a much larger entity, the British Mandate of Palestine, today the Palestinian Territories consist of the Gaza Strip on the Mediterranean, and the West Bank, an area lying west of the River Jordan. The territories have been disputed since the establishment of the Jewish State of Israel in Palestine in 1948, which sparked the Arab–Israeli War of 1948–49, during which the Gaza Strip was seized by Egypt and the West Bank occupied by Jordan. Both were then captured by Israel during the Six Day War in 1967, resulting in the displacement

FACT FILE

LOCAL NAME	Palestine National Authority
CAPITAL CITY	Ramallah (temporary); East Jerusalem (declared)
CURRENCY	New Israeli Shekel (ILS), Jordanian Dinar (JOD)
MEMBERSHIP	G77, not IMF member, not WB member, UN (observer)
GOVERNMENT	Parliamentary Republic
POPULATION	4,146,784
POP. DENSITY	673/km²; 1,742/mi²
GDP	5.32 Billion US$
LANGUAGE(S)	Arabic, English
ETHNICITY	Gaza Strip: Palestinian Arab and others 99%; West Bank: Palestinian Arab and other 83%, Jewish 17%
RELIGION	Gaza Strip: Muslim (predominantly Sunni) 99%, Christian 1%; West Bank: Muslim 75% (predominantly Sunni), Jewish 17%, Christian and other 8%
CLIMATE	Mediterranean, Semi-arid

of millions of Palestinians and growing nationalism and violence within both Israel and the occupied territories. Despite an on-going peace process and recent concessions towards Palestinian self-government, the territories remain in a state of turmoil.

WESTERN ASIA

ISRAEL

31° 30' N, 34° 45' E | 20,770 KM² | 8,019 MI² | UTC+2

Founded as a Jewish state in 1948, the creation of Israel in Palestine has resulted in unrest which remains unresolved to this day.

Geography

Israel's topography ranges from its northern highlands to the large Negev Desert in the south; the west comprises the Mediterranean coastal plain. The eastern border, in part of the Rift Valley, is delineated by the Jordan River and Dead Sea. The climate is generally Mediterranean; parts of the interior may be extremely hot in summer.

History

The region Israel occupies had been held sacred by Jewish people since ancient times, and support for the Zionist ideal of a homeland within Palestine gained momentum during the nineteenth and twentieth centuries, largely because of persecution in Europe. In 1947 Britain withdrew from Palestine; the United Nations partitioned the region into Jewish and Arab states, sparking several Arab–Israeli wars between 1948 and 1973, during which Israel seized further territory, including the Sinai peninsula, West Bank, Gaza Strip and Golan Heights. Israel committed troops to Lebanon in 1982 to combat the Palestinian Liberation Organization, although moves towards peace saw Sinai returned to Egypt and concessions made to Palestinian rule in Gaza and the West Bank. However, the peace process remains threatened by territorial disputes and hostilities between Israel and militant Arab groups.

JERUSALEM
The Western Wall, also known as the Wailing Wall, is Judaism's holiest shrine.

Economy

Israel's highly developed and industrialized economy is largely founded on the production of technological equipment, chemical and metal products, plastics and textiles. Cut diamonds and agricultural produce are exported.

FACT FILE

LOCAL NAME State of Israel

CAPITAL Jerusalem

CURRENCY New Israeli Shekel (ILS)

MEMBERSHIP BSEC (observer), OAS (observer), WTO

GOVERNMENT Parliamentary Democracy

POPULATION 7,044,501

POP. DENSITY 339/km²; 879/mi²

GDP 185.9 Billion US$

LANGUAGE(S) Hebrew, Arabic, English

ETHNICITY Jewish 76% (of which Israel-born 67%, Europe/America-born 23%, Africa-born 6%, Asia-born 4%), Non-Jewish 24%

RELIGION Jewish 76%, Muslim 16%, Arab Christians 2%, Other Christian 0.4%, Druze 2%

CLIMATE Mediterranean, Arid in south

REGIONAL DIVISIONS 6 Districts (of which, Southern is the most populous) are divided into 15 Sub-districts, in turn subdivided into 50 natural regions

ECONOMIC ACTIVITIES Agriculture, Mining, Aviation, Communications, CAD and Manufacture, Medical Electronics, Fibre Optics, Wood and Paper Products, Food, Beverages, Tobacco, Construction, Metal Products, Chemical Products, Plastics, Diamond Cutting, Textiles, Footwear

NATURAL RESOURCES Timber, Potash, Copper Ore, Natural Gas, Phosphate Rock, Magnesium Bromide, Clays, Sand

JORDAN

31° 00' N, 36° 00' E | 92,300 KM² | 35,637 MI² | UTC+2

Since 1948, Jordan has found itself caught up in conflict with both Israel and its militant Arab neighbours.

Containing the Dead Sea, the lowest-lying point on the surface of the Earth, Jordan's western border is formed by the Great Rift Valley, while the Transjordan Plateau in the east is comprised of desert. The territory of Transjordan was established by Britain in 1921, but gained independence as Jordan in 1946. Two years later, the creation of Israel in Palestine would spark a series of Arab–Israeli conflicts. Having accommodated thousands of Palestinian refugees, Jordan found itself

being used as a base by guerrilla fighters and in 1988 it ceded the West Bank to the Palestinian Liberation Organization. Recent years have seen political reform and peace with Israel, but Jordan remains heavily reliant on foreign aid.

FACT FILE

LOCAL NAME	Hashemite Kingdom of Jordan
CAPITAL CITY	'Ammān
CURRENCY	Jordanian Dinar (JOD)
MEMBERSHIP	G77, LAS, OIC, WTO
GOVERNMENT	Constitutional Monarchy
POPULATION	6,118,923
POP. DENSITY	66/km²; 172/mi²
GDP	27.99 Billion US$
LANGUAGE(S)	Arabic, English
ETHNICITY	Arab 98%, Circassian 1%, Armenian 1%
RELIGION	Sunni Muslim 92%, Christian 6% (majority Greek Orthodox)
CLIMATE	Semi-arid, Arid

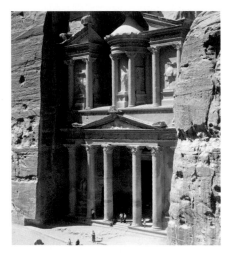

PETRA
The ancient city of Petra, near Ma'ān in southern Jordan, is carved into the red sandstone rock face.

KUWAIT

29° 30' N, 45° 45' E | 17,820 KM² | 6,880 MI² | UTC+3

Claimed by Iraq after independence in 1961, Kuwait has maintained its sovereignty due to its close ties with the West.

One of the smallest countries in the world, Kuwait is largely comprised of desert, with a marshy coastal plain on the Persian Gulf. Kuwait's major development occurred following Arab migration to the region during the eighteenth century and as a British protectorate between 1914 and 1961, during which time oil reserves began to be commercially exploited. In 1990, the country was invaded by Iraq, prompting the 1991 Gulf War, which culminated in Iraqi forces being expelled by a US-led coalition force. Although the country's infrastructure was damaged and several oil fields were set alight by the

retreating Iraqis, Kuwait's vast reserves enabled the country's rapid recovery.

FACT FILE

LOCAL NAME	State of Kuwait
CAPITAL CITY	Kuwait
CURRENCY	Kuwaiti Dinar (KD)
MEMBERSHIP	G77, GCC, LAS, OAPEC, OIC, OPEC, WTO
GOVERNMENT	Constitutional Hereditary Emirate
POPULATION	2,919,143
POP. DENSITY	164/km²; 424/mi²
GDP	130.1 Billion US$
LANGUAGE(S)	Arabic, English
ETHNICITY	Kuwaiti 45%, Other Arab 35%, South Asian 9%, Iranian 4%
RELIGION	Muslim 85% (Sunni 70%, Shi'a 30%), Other (includes Christian, Hindu, Parsi) 15%
CLIMATE	Arid

IRAQ

33° 00' N, 44° 00' E | 437,072 KM² | 168,754 MI² | UTC+3

Located in ancient Mesopotamia, home to some of the world's earliest and greatest civilizations, Iraq today is in turmoil, blighted by three wars in as many decades.

Geography

At the northern end of the Persian Gulf, Iraq has varied topography and climate, from the temperate mountains of the north-east, through the valleys and plains of the Euphrates and Tigris Rivers to the subtropical marshes of the south and east. The west is largely occupied by arid desert.

History

Home to the Babylonian and Assyrian civilizations in ancient times, Mesopotamia became the seat of Islamic power from the eighth century, when Baghdad was founded, to the thirteenth century, when the Mongols invaded. Control later passed to the Ottoman Empire, and after World War I, Iraq was established as a British mandate. Independence came in 1932, and in 1958, following a military coup, Iraq became a republic. Ten years later, the Sunni-dominated Ba'ath Party seized power, and in 1979 Saddam Hussein became president. Since then Iraq has been plunged into three conflicts: the Iran–Iraq War between 1980 and 1988, the 1990–1991 Gulf War following the Iraqi invasion of Kuwait, and the US-led campaign in 2003 which overthrew Hussein's regime and resulted in his trial and execution. Although an interim administration is now in place, Iraq remains highly unstable because of ethnic and religious differences, and continued insurgency against occupying coalition forces.

Economy

Years of conflict and international sanctions have devastated the Iraqi economy, although with vast oil reserves it has the potential to be among Earth's wealthiest nations.

BABYLONIA
A replica of the Ishtar gate, one of the entrances to the ancient city of Babylon, which lay about 55 kilometres south of present-day Baghdad.

FACT FILE

LOCAL NAME Republic of Iraq

CAPITAL Baghdad

CURRENCY New Iraqi Dinar (NID)

MEMBERSHIP G77, LAS, OIC, OPEC, OAPEC, WTO (observer)

GOVERNMENT Parliamentary Democracy

POPULATION 29,492,184

POP. DENSITY 68/km²; 175/mi²

GDP 102.3 Billion US$

LANGUAGE(S) Arabic, Kurdish, Turkoman, Assyrian (Neo-Aramaic), Armenian

ETHNICITY Arab 79%, Kurdish 16%, Turkoman, Assyrian, or other 5%

RELIGION Muslim 97% (Shi'a 60%-65%, Sunni 32%-37%), Christian or other 3%

CLIMATE Arid, Semi-arid, Mediterranean in the north

REGIONAL DIVISIONS 18 Governorates; 1 Region, Kurdistan, with its own local government presiding over 3 of the 18 Governates; Al Anbar is the largest Governorate of Iraq

ECONOMIC ACTIVITIES Agriculture, Mining, Petroleum Production and Export, Chemicals, Textiles, Leather, Construction Materials, Food Processing, Fertilizer, Metal Fabrication/Processing

NATURAL RESOURCES Petroleum, Natural Gas, Phosphates, Sulphur

SAUDI ARABIA

25° 00' N, 45° 00' E | 2,149,690 KM² | 830,000 MI² | UTC+3

The birthplace of Islam during the sixth century, Saudi Arabia is home to the holy cities of Mecca and Medina. However, the country also maintains strong links with the West.

Geography

Occupying around three-quarters of the Arabian Peninsula, Saudi Arabia is a massive country, largely dominated by desert, including the vast Rub'al Khali, or Empty Quarter, although fertile coastal plains are to be found in the east and west. The south-west benefits from monsoon rains, but in general the country is extremely hot and arid.

History

Inhabited by desert nomads and coastal traders in ancient times, by AD 650 the Arabian Peninsula was unified as an Islamic state. However, the Saud dynasty did not come to dominate the region until the eighteenth century, when it was strengthened by an alliance with the religious leader Muhammad ibn Abd al-Wahhab. After struggles with Egypt, the Ottoman Empire and rival Arab dynasties, the Saudis were driven into exile in 1891, but by 1932 the young Abdul Aziz Ibn Saud had reclaimed their lost territory to establish Saudi Arabia. The discovery of oil in 1938 led to rapid economic development, although since the 1960s Saudi Arabia's stability has been threatened by inter-dynastic rivalry, the Arab-Israeli conflicts and disputes with Iran, Iraq and Yemen. Today the greatest threat comes from militant Islamists opposed to the country's cooperation with the West.

Economy

With the largest petroleum reserves on Earth, Saudi Arabia has become the world's leading exporter of oil, which accounts for around 90 per cent of the country's export revenue. However, attempts are being made to diversify the economy.

FACT FILE

LOCAL NAME Kingdom of Saudi Arabia

CAPITAL CITY Riyadh

CURRENCY Saudi Riyal (SAR)

MEMBERSHIP G77, GCC, LAS, OAPEC, OAS (observer), OIC, OPEC, WTO

GOVERNMENT Absolute Monarchy

POPULATION 25,292,816

POP. DENSITY 12/km²; 31/mi²

GDP 564.6 Billion US$

LANGUAGE(S) Arabic

ETHNICITY Arab 90%, Afro-Asian 10%

RELIGION Muslim 100%

CLIMATE Arid

REGIONAL DIVISIONS 13 Provinces/Emirates; Emirate capitals usually share the same name as the Emirate, with Mecca being the most populous

ECONOMIC ACTIVITIES Crude Oil Production and Export, Petroleum Refining, Petrochemicals, Cement, Fertilizer, Plastics, Metals, Commercial Ship Repair, Commercial Aircraft Repair, Construction

NATURAL RESOURCES Petroleum, Natural Gas, Iron Ore, Gold, Copper

MECCA
Thousands of pilgrims circle the Kaaba in the Holy Mosque in Mecca.

YEMEN

15° 00' N, 48° 00' E | 527,970 KM² | 203,850 MI² | UTC+3

Two countries until 1990, Yemen remains a deeply divided nation to this day. It is one of the poorest countries in the Arab world and has one of the highest birthrates in the whole world.

Yemen, in the south-west of the Arabian Peninsula, has narrow coastal plains on the Red Sea and Gulf of Aden; inland are mountains and desert, with the fertile Hadramaut Valley in the southeast. It was once part of the Ottoman Empire, but by the twentieth century, the country was split between Turkish-ruled North Yemen and British-ruled South Yemen. Internal conflicts erupted after the north and south became independent republics in the 1960s, but with peace restored Yemen was reunified in 1990. During the mid-1990s Yemen was plagued by civil war, and conflicts with Saudi Arabia and Eritrea; today stability is threatened by militant insurgents. Oil production has come to dominate the economy but most of the population is involved in agriculture, largely growing subsistence food crops such as grains, pulses and vegetables.

FACT FILE

LOCAL NAME	Republic of Yemen
CAPITAL CITY	San'ā
CURRENCY	Yemeni Rial (YER)
MEMBERSHIP	G77, LAS, OAS (observer), OIC, WTO (observer)
GOVERNMENT	Republic, Parliamentary Democracy
POPULATION	23,066,020
POP. DENSITY	44/km²; 113/mi²
GDP	52.05 Billion US$
LANGUAGE(S)	Arabic
ETHNICITY	Arab 92.8%, Somali 3.7%,
RELIGION	Muslim 99% (of which Shaf'i (Sunni) 60% and Zaydi (Shi'a), 40%
CLIMATE	Arid

OMAN

21° 00' N, 57° 00' E | 212,460 KM² | 82,031 MI² | UTC+4

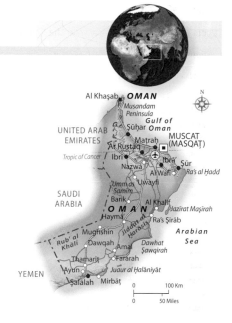

Although Oman has experienced internal disputes and was closed to visitors except those on business until the late 1980s, it is among the most progressive Arab nations.

Situated on the east of the Arabian Peninsula, Oman also includes the territory of Musandam, which is separated by the United Arab Emirates. The country is largely arid desert and rugged mountains, with fertile lands along the Gulf of Oman and in the Dhofar region, which receive monsoon rains between June and September. Summer temperatures can reach 45°C and above. Between the seventeenth and early nineteenth centuries, Oman developed a powerful trading empire, with possessions along the East African coast. Dynastic and tribal struggles threatened its stability, and having developed strong ties with Britain, Oman became a protectorate in 1891. A separatist rebellion flared in Dhofar during the 1960s. Huge oil reserves were then discovered, and since independence in 1971, social and economic reforms have brought lasting peace and prosperity.

FACT FILE

LOCAL NAME	Sultanate of Oman
CAPITAL CITY	Muscat
CURRENCY	Omani Rial (OMR)
MEMBERSHIP	G77, GCC, LAS, OIC, WTO
GOVERNMENT	Monarchy
POPULATION	2,650,820
POP. DENSITY	13/km²; 32/mi²
GDP	61.61 Billion US$
LANGUAGE(S)	Arabic, English, Baluchi, Urdu, Indian
ETHNICITY	Omani Arab 48%, Indo-Pakistani 32%, Other Arab 7%, Persian 3%,
RELIGION	Ibadhi Muslim 75%, Other (includes Sunni Muslim, Shi'a Muslim, Hindu) 25%
CLIMATE	Arid

WESTERN ASIA

UNITED ARAB EMIRATES

24° 00' N, 54° 00' E | 83,600 KM² | 32,278 MI² | UTC+4

A federation of seven principalities or emirates, the United Arab Emirates (UAE) exhibits a degree of unity that has rarely been achieved in the Arab world.

Geography

Located on the Arabian Peninsula with coastlines along the Persian Gulf and the Gulf of Oman, the United Arab Emirates is largely barren desert, with salt flats in coastal areas. The climate is hot and dry, with an average annual rainfall of less than 12 mm, while summer temperatures may exceed 49°C.

History

An important maritime trading site in ancient times, by the early nineteenth century piracy in this region was threatening British shipping interests; in 1820, Britain imposed the first of several truces on the Arab states. Thus they became known as the Trucial States, and by 1892 the region had become a British protectorate. Britain withdrew in 1981, following which the emirates of Abu Dhabi, Dubai, Ajmān, Al Fujayrah, Ash Shāriqah and Umm al Qaiwain joined to form the United Arab Emirates, with Ras al Khaimah, being incorporated the following year. Bahrain and Qatar opted to become independent countries. Despite occasional problems with Saudi Arabia, Oman, and Iran, the United Arab Emirates has remained politically stable for many years.

Economy

Although some agriculture takes place at scattered oases, the economy of the United Arab Emirates is primarily founded upon the oil industry, which accounts for around 90 per cent of export earnings, while the port of Dubai has become a major financial centre and tourist destination, where Western visitors are permitted a less restricted lifestyle than in many Islamic countries. Interestingly, over 90 per cent of the United Arab Emirates' labour force are foreign workers.

FACT FILE

LOCAL NAME United Arab Emirates

CAPITAL CITY Abu Dhabi

CURRENCY Emirati Dirham (AED)

MEMBERSHIP G77, GCC, LAS, OAPEC, OIC, OPEC, WTO

GOVERNMENT Federal Constitutional Monarchy

POPULATION 4,502,582

POP. DENSITY 54/km²; 140/mi²

GDP 167.3 Billion US$

LANGUAGE(S) Arabic, Persian, English, Hindi, Urdu

ETHNICITY Emirati 19%, Other Arab and Iranian 23%, South Asian 50%, Other expatriates (includes Westerners and East Asians) 8%

RELIGION Muslim 96% (84% Sunni, 16% Shi'a), Other (includes Christian, Hindu) 4%

CLIMATE Arid

REGIONAL DIVISIONS 7 Emirates; Abu Dhabi is the largest and most populous emirate but Dubai has the strongest commercial reputation.

ECONOMIC ACTIVITIES Petroleum and Petrochemicals, Fishing, Aluminium, Cement, Fertilizers, Commercial Ship Repair, Construction Materials, Boat Building, Handicrafts, Textiles

NATURAL RESOURCES Petroleum, Natural Gas

DUBAI
The luxury Burj Al Arab Hotel, built to resemble a traditional Arab dhow boat, was constructed on an artificial island almost 300 metres off the coast of Dubai.

BAHRAIN

26° 00' N, 50° 33' E | 665 KM² | 257 MI² | UTC+3

Bahrain was the first Gulf State to export oil after its discovery in 1932, and today is the financial hub of the Arab world.

Bahrain is a group of islands in the Persian Gulf; the largest, Bahrain Island, is linked to Saudi Arabia by a causeway. The terrain is mainly arid, low-lying desert, having very

hot summers and milder winters. Bahrain became an important trading centre over 4,000 years ago, and following Persian domination has been ruled by the al-Khalifa dynasty since the late 1700s. It was a British protectorate from 1861 until 1971. Sporadic

FACT FILE

LOCAL NAME	Kingdom of Bahrain
CAPITAL CITY	Manama
CURRENCY	Bahraini Dinar (BHD)
MEMBERSHIP	G77, GCC, LAS, OAPEC, OIC, WTO
GOVERNMENT	Constitutional Monarchy
POPULATION	766,071
POP. DENSITY	1152/km²; 2,981/mi²
GDP	24.5 Billion US$
LANGUAGE(S)	Arabic, English, Farsi, Urdu
ETHNICITY	Bahraini 62%
RELIGION	Muslim 81%, Christian 9%
CLIMATE	Arid

unrest occurs between the majority Sunni population and the minority Shi'as; recent reforms have eased tensions. Bahrain still relies heavily upon oil exports, but the economy has diversified, and now includes a major banking sector.

MANAMA
The Al Fateh Mosque at night.

QATAR

25° 30' N, 51° 15' E | 11,437 KM² | 4,416 MI² | UTC+3

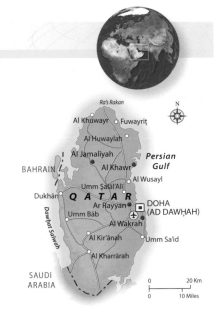

Since the 1990s, Qatar, one of the founder members of OPEC, has become one of the most prosperous and liberal of the Gulf States.

The Qatar Peninsula in the Persian Gulf is mainly dry, barren and low-lying, with extremely hot summers and warm winters. Formerly inhabited by Bedouin nomads, today around 90 per cent of the population live in the capital, Doha. During the late eighteenth century, the country was settled by the Kuwaiti al-Khalifa clan, who went on to conquer Bahrain. Later, Qatar came

to be dominated by the al-Thanis. In 1916 it became a British protectorate. Following independence in 1971, Qatar chose not to join

FACT FILE

LOCAL NAME	State of Qatar
CAPITAL CITY	Doha
CURRENCY	Qatari Rial (QAR)
MEMBERSHIP	G77, GCC, LAS, OAS (observer), OIC, OPEC, WTO
GOVERNMENT	Constitutional Monarchy
POPULATION	855,896
POP. DENSITY	75/km²; 194/mi²
GDP	57.69 Billion US$
LANGUAGE(S)	Arabic, English
ETHNICITY	Arab 40%, Indian 18%, Pakistani 18%, Iranian 10%
RELIGION	Muslim 78%, Christian 9%
CLIMATE	Arid

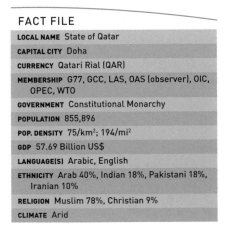

the United Arab Emirates, and it has since prospered as a result of economic and social reforms, with oil as its chief export.

WESTERN ASIA

CENTRAL AND EASTERN ASIA

Over the last hundred years the majority of these two regions has been hidden under the cloak of a communist regime. Today the countries in these regions are increasingly playing an important role in the world economy and politics.

These two regions combined occupy a large portion of the Earth's land surface and are geographically varied, from high mountains and passes in Tian Shan, to vast grassland steppes and great deserts in the hinterland and extensive coastlines. Nomadic peoples continue to live in the steppes but large towns and cities attract great numbers from the traditional way of life.

Central Asia comprises five former republics of the Soviet Union: Kazakhstan, Kyrgyzstan, Tajikistan, Turkmenistan and Uzbekistan. Eastern Asia's eight countries are more diverse, ranging from enormous China and Mongolia to more compact Japan and North and South Korea. The countries bordering the Pacific are now best known for their intensive industrialization, especially electronic consumer goods. At one time Hong Kong was the focus of western interest in Eastern Asia but now it is spread more widely. However, liberalized trading, probably

helped by recent sovereignty over Hong Kong, has transformed China from a regional giant to a world giant economy.

While central and eastern Asia do not draw the same level of tourism as south-east Asia, there is increasing traffic in and out of these countries, especially business-related in eastern Asia.

MONGOLIA

Selenge Mörön

Erdenet

Darhan

ÚLAN BATOR

Gobi Altayn Nuruu

Gobi Desert

Hohhot

Jining

Baotou

BEIJING

Tangshan

Huang He

Shijiazhuang

Tianjin

Bo Hai

Dalian

Taiyuan

Qinghai Hu

Lanzhou

Jinan

Zibo

Qingdao

Xining

Xi'an

Luoyang

C H I N A

Yangtze

Chengdu

Chongqing

Yangtze

Wuhan

Nanjing

Hangzhou

Shanghai

Nanchang

Changsha

Guiyang

Fuzhou

Xun Jiang

Kunming

Mekong

Guangzhou

Hong Kong

Shantou

Kaohsiung

Zhanjiang

Haikou

Hainan

Amur

Qiqihar

Harbin

Jilin

Vladivostok

Shenyang

Ch'ŏngjin

Anshan

NORTH KOREA

Sea of Japan (East Sea)

Korea Bay

P'YŎNGYANG

Inch'ŏn

SEOUL

SOUTH KOREA

Taejŏn

Taegu

Kwangju

Pusan

Korea Strait

Yellow Sea

Kita Kyūshū

Fukuoka

Nagasaki

Kagoshima

Kyūshū

Hokkaidō

Sapporo

Aomori

Honshū

J A P A N

TOKYO

Kawasaki

Kyōto

Yokohama

Osaka

Hiroshima

Shikoku

T'AIPEI

TAIWAN

COUNTRY	PAGE
China	184
Hong Kong (CN)	187
Japan	190
Kazakhstan	180
Kyrgyzstan	182
Mongolia	183
North Korea	188
Republic of China (Taiwan)	187
South Korea	189
Tajikistan	182
Turkmenistan	181
Uzbekistan	181

JIAYUGUAN, CHINA
The city of Jiayuguan at the western end of the Great Wall.

CENTRAL AND EASTERN ASIA

KAZAKHSTAN

48° 00' N, 68° 00' E | 2,717,300 KM² | 1,049,155 MI² | UTC+6

Under Russian control during the twentieth century, large areas of Kazakhstan were allocated to arable farming. Today the country is more reliant upon its large mineral reserves.

Geography

The largest country in Central Asia, Kazakhstan's topography varies from the eastern and south-eastern highlands to the western lowlands around the Caspian Sea. Part of the Aral Sea also lies in Kazakhstan, although two-thirds of the landscape is dominated by arid steppe. The climate is continental, although conditions vary with altitude.

FACT FILE

LOCAL NAME Republic of Kazakhstan

CAPITAL CITY Astana

CURRENCY Tenge (KZT)

MEMBERSHIP CIS, EAEC, EAPC, ECO, OAS (observer), OIC, WTO (observer)

GOVERNMENT Presidential Republic; Authoritarian presidential rule, with little power outside the executive branch

POPULATION 15,531,645

POP. DENSITY 6/km²; 15/mi²

GDP 167.6 Billion US$

LANGUAGE(S) Kazakh, Russian

ETHNICITY Kazakh (Qazaq) 53%, Russian 30%, Ukrainian 4%, Uzbek 3%, German 2%, Tatar 2%, Uygur 1%

RELIGION Muslim 47%, Russian Orthodox 44%, Protestant and other 9%,

CLIMATE Continental, Arid, Semi-arid

REGIONAL DIVISIONS 5 Economic Regions include 14 Provinces and 3 Cities; Provinces have the same name as their administrative centres (with few exceptions)

ECONOMIC ACTIVITIES Agriculture, Oil, Petrochemical and other Chemical, Mining, Iron and Steel, Tractors and Other Agricultural Machinery, Electric Motors, Construction Materials, Textiles, Sugar Refining

NATURAL RESOURCES Petroleum, Natural Gas, Coal, Iron Ore, Manganese, Chrome Ore, Nickel, Cobalt, Copper, Molybdenum, Lead, Zinc, Bauxite, Gold, Uranium

History

Originally settled by Turkic peoples, but conquered by Mongols during the thirteenth century, by the sixteenth century the region was home to the Kazakhs, whose various tribes had emerged to form a powerful nomadic kingdom. This fragmented into three major hordes, with power being further eroded by Mongol attacks during the late seventeenth and early eighteenth centuries. Because of these incursions, the Kazakhs looked to Russia for protection, and by the nineteenth century the region had been absorbed into the Russian Empire, becoming the Kazak Soviet Socialist Republic in 1936. During the twentieth century, forced resettlement, collective farming and nuclear testing caused resentment amongst the Kazakhs, who welcomed independence in 1991. Despite political reforms, the government has been criticized.

Economy

Formerly based on nomadic farming, Kazakhstan's economy was transformed by state farms and industry during the Soviet era, but suffered badly after the break-up of the Soviet Union in 1991. The economy has begun to recover recently, largely because of natural resources, including oil, gas, coal and metals.

TIAN SHAN MOUNTAINS
The Tian Shan mountains lie in the border region of Kazakhstan, Kyrgyzstan and the autonomous region of western China.

UZBEKISTAN

41° 00' N, 64° 00' E | 447,400 KM² | 172,742 MI² | UTC+5

Natural resources may help to transform the economy of this former Soviet republic.

FACT FILE

LOCAL NAME Republic of Uzbekistan

CAPITAL CITY Tashkent

CURRENCY Soum (UZS)

MEMBERSHIP CIS, EAEC, EAPC, ECO, OIC, WTO (observer)

GOVERNMENT Republic; Authoritarian presidential rule, with little power outside the executive branch

POPULATION 27,768,982

POP. DENSITY 62/km²; 161/mi²

GDP 64.15 Billion US$

LANGUAGE(S) Uzbek, Russian, Tajik

ETHNICITY Uzbek 8%, Russian 6%, Tajik 5%, Kazakh 3%, Karakalpak 3%, Tatar 2%

RELIGION Muslim 88% (mostly Sunnis), Eastern Orthodox 9%

CLIMATE Arid, Semi-arid Steppe in east

Although mountainous in the east, where the fertile Fergana Valley lies, much of Uzbekistan is covered by desert plains and steppe grassland; the shrinking Aral Sea lies in the autonomous Qoraqalpogh region in the north-west. The climate is continental, with cold winters and hot, dry summers. Originally part of the Persian Empire, Uzbekistan was settled by Turkic peoples during the fifteenth century AD, who founded three distinct states within the region. During the late nineteenth century, the area succumbed to Russian control, becoming the Uzbek Soviet Socialist Republic from 1924 until independence in 1991. Political reforms have been slow, although the country has allied with the West against Islamic militancy. Uzbekistan is among the world's largest cotton producers; natural gas and mineral reserves also contribute to the economy.

TURKMENISTAN

40° 00' N, 60° 00' E | 488,100 KM² | 188,456 MI² | UTC+5

A former Soviet republic, Turkmenistan is looking to Arab nations for assistance in developing its oil and gas industries.

Central Asia's second largest country and one of the least densely populated, Turkmenistan is mainly desert, including one of the world's largest deserts, the Karakum, meaning Black Sands. The Caspian Sea forms the country's western border; the southern border regions are mountainous. The climate is continental, with hot summers and cold winters. Following Persian, Macedonian and Arab conquest, Turkmenistan was settled by Turkic tribes during the fifteenth century AD. By 1884, Russia had effectively conquered the whole of Central Asia. Despite local resistance, the area became the Turkmen Soviet Socialist Republic in 1924. Independence came with the collapse of the Soviet Union in 1991; since then Turkmenistan has been under dictatorial rule, and despite exporting oil, gas and cotton, has struggled to make economic reforms.

FACT FILE

LOCAL NAME Turkmenistan

CAPITAL CITY Asgabat

CURRENCY Turkmen Manat (TMM)

MEMBERSHIP CIS, EAPC, ECO, G77, OIC

GOVERNMENT Single-party State Republic; Authoritarian presidential rule, with little power outside the executive branch

POPULATION 5,030,972

POP. DENSITY 10/km²; 27/mi²

GDP 26.73 Billion US$

LANGUAGE(S) Turkmen, Russian, Uzbek

ETHNICITY Turkmen 85%, Uzbek 5%, Russian 4%

RELIGION Muslim 89%, Eastern Orthodox 9%

CLIMATE Arid, Semi-arid Steppe

KARAKUM
The Karakum, or Gara Gum, Desert occupies some 70 per cent of Turkmenistan's territory.

CENTRAL AND EASTERN ASIA

KYRGYZSTAN

41° 00′ N, 75° 00′ E | 198,500 KM² | 76,641 MI² | UTC+6

Of the former Soviet republics, Kyrgyzstan is widely considered to be leading the way in political and economic reform.

FACT FILE

LOCAL NAME	Kyrgyz Republic
CAPITAL CITY	Bishkek
CURRENCY	Som (KGS)
MEMBERSHIP	CIS, EAEC, EAPC, OIC, ECO, WTO
GOVERNMENT	Unicameral Democratic Republic
POPULATION	5,376,432
POP. DENSITY	27/km²; 70/mi²
GDP	10.5 Billion US$
LANGUAGE(S)	Kyrgyz, Uzbek, Russian, Dungun
ETHNICITY	Kyrgyz 65%, Uzbek 14%, Russian 13%
RELIGION	Muslim 75%, Russian Orthodox 20%
CLIMATE	Continental to Polar in high Tien Shan, Subtropical in south-west, Temperate in northern foothill zone

Landlocked in Central Asia, Kyrgyzstan is an almost entirely mountainous country, although part of the low-lying Fergana Valley is within its borders. The climate is continental, with cold winters and hot summers, but around 3 per cent of the terrain is permanently covered by snow and ice. Home to nomadic herders in ancient times, Kyrgyzstan was conquered by the Mongols and Chinese, before becoming a Russian province in 1876. By 1936, the region had become the Kirgiz Soviet Socialist Republic. Independence as Kyrgyzstan came in 1991, although the decade was marred by ethnic violence between Kyrgyz and Uzbeks and armed incursions by Islamic militants. Despite attempts at reform, political unrest remains a problem, although the country's economy is improving. Exports include cotton and wool.

TAJIKISTAN

39° 00′ N, 71° 00′ E | 143,100 KM² | 55,251 MI² | UTC+5

Blighted by war after independence in 1991, Tajikistan remains the poorest of the former Soviet republics.

The smallest of the Central Asian republics, Tajikistan is highly mountainous, although steppe grassland occupies much of the west, and the country extends into the Fergana Valley in the north-east. The autonomous region of Gorno-Badakhshan lies in the east. The climate is continental, with extreme winters in the highlands. Originally settled by Persians, Tajikistan was later conquered by Arabs, Turks and Mongols; between the sixteenth and nineteenth centuries, Uzbeks dominated, although the majority of the population are from the Tajik ethnic group, whose language and cultural traditions are similar to those of the Iranian people. By the early twentieth century, Russia had control over the area, and in 1929 it became the Tajik Soviet Socialist Republic. Following moves

FACT FILE

LOCAL NAME	Republic of Tajikistan
CAPITAL CITY	Dushanbe
CURRENCY	Somoni (TJS)
MEMBERSHIP	CIS, EAEC, EAPC, ECO, OIC, WTO (observer)
GOVERNMENT	Unitary Presidential Republic
POPULATION	6,838,716
POP. DENSITY	48/km²; 124/mi²
GDP	11.82 Billion US$
LANGUAGE(S)	Tajik, Russian
ETHNICITY	Tajik 80%, Uzbek 15%, Russian 1%, Kyrgyz 1%
RELIGION	Sunni Muslim 85%, Shi'a Muslim 5%
CLIMATE	Continental, Semi-arid to Polar in Pamir Mountains

towards independence during the 1980s, Tajikistan became an independent republic in 1991; from 1992 to 1997 the country was plagued by civil war arising from ethnic and political disputes, leaving its economy severely damaged. Aluminium and cotton, the main cash crop during the Soviet era, are the principal sources of income.

CENTRAL AND EASTERN ASIA

MONGOLIA

46° 00' N, 105° 00' E | 1,564,116 KM² | 603,909 MI² | UTC+8

Famed as the seat of Genghis Khan's vast Mongol Empire in the thirteenth century, Mongolia remains steeped in its nomadic traditions.

Geography

The largest landlocked country in the world, Mongolia can be divided into three principal geographic regions: the mountainous, forested north, the central steppe grasslands, and the arid south, which includes part of the Gobi Desert. The climate is continental with warm summers and long, cold winters.

History

Long inhabited by various nomadic Mongol tribes, Mongolia was united during the thirteenth century AD under Genghis Khan, whose armies would conquer territory stretching from the Caspian Sea, through Central Asia, into northern India and east into China; the largest continuous terrestrial empire ever known. However, by the time the empire reached its greatest extent, it consisted of separate khanates, and by the seventeenth century, present-day Mongolia was under Chinese control as Outer Mongolia. Following the collapse of the Chinese Qing dynasty in 1911, China and Russia vied for control over Outer Mongolia, and in 1924 the Mongolian People's Republic was founded along Soviet lines. Full independence arrived in 1946, although Mongolia maintained strong ties with Russia. Recently, major reforms have introduced multi-party democracy and a free-market economy.

Economy

Despite the introduction of collectivized farming and industry during the twentieth century, Mongolia's principal economic activity remains herding, and the country boasts the world's highest ratio of livestock to people. However, it is also rich in natural resources, including oil and gas, and several precious minerals.

FACT FILE

LOCAL NAME Mongolia

CAPITAL CITY Ulan Bator

CURRENCY Togrog/Tugrik (MNT)

MEMBERSHIP CP, G77, WTO

GOVERNMENT Mixed Parliamentary/Presidential Republic

POPULATION 2,653,679

POP. DENSITY 2/km²; 4/mi²

GDP 8.42 Billion US$

LANGUAGE(S) Khalkha Mongol, Turkic, Russian

ETHNICITY Mongol (mostly Khalkha) 95%, Turkic (mostly Kazakh) 5%

RELIGION Tibetan Buddhist 50%, Shamanist and Christian 6%, Muslim 4%

CLIMATE Arid (cool), Semi-arid (cool), Subarctic

REGIONAL DIVISIONS 4 Economic Regions (Western, Khangain, Central and Eastern) are divided into 21 Provinces and 1 Municipality, Ulan Bator, which has province status

ECONOMIC ACTIVITIES Construction and Construction Materials, Mining (Coal, Copper, Molybdenum, Fluorspar, Tin, Tungsten, Gold), Oil, Agriculture, Food and Beverages, Processing of Animal Products, Cashmere and Natural Fibre Manufacturing

NATURAL RESOURCES Oil, Coal, Copper, Molybdenum, Tungsten, Phosphates, Tin, Nickel, Zinc, Fluorspar, Gold, Silver, Iron

TSAGAANNUUR
Traditional Mongolian tents or yurts in the snow.

CHINA

35° 00' N, 105° 00' E | 9,596,960 KM² | 3,705,407 MI² | UTC+8

The third largest country in the world, China is not only home to over one billion people, or around 20 per cent of the world's population, making it the most populous country on Earth, but it also contains the world's highest peak and third longest river. Having embraced international trade, China also has one of the world's fastest growing economies, but this modernization has failed to extend into the political arena.

Geography

Although China encompasses a huge variety of geographic regions, it may be broadly divided into three principal areas: the mountains and high plateaux of the west, which extend from Central Asia in the north to the Tibetan plateau, Himalayas and Mount Everest in the south; the deserts and basins of the north, which stretch across the country above the Great Wall to the plains and mountains of the north-east; and the densely populated, alluvial plains of the east, which range from the edge of the Inner Mongolian grasslands, south through the deltas of the Yellow (Huang He) and Yangtze Rivers, to the rolling southern hills. The Yangtze is one of many major rivers to rise in the Tibetan plateau, but at 6,300 kilometres it is Asia's longest, flowing east to enter the East China Sea near the huge industrial port of Shanghai, the country's most populous city. Formerly known as Peking, China's capital, Beijing, is somewhat smaller, but it is the nation's political and cultural hub.

Like its landscape, China's climate is highly varied, with conditions in the east of the country ranging from continental in the north, through temperate and subtropical to tropical in the far south, with coastal areas experiencing high rainfall and typhoons during the summer months. The interior is much drier, with a desert climate prevailing in much of the north-west, and while the Tibetan plateau is also arid, it is subject to near Arctic conditions at higher elevations.

History

Inhabited for many thousands of years, China is thought to have given rise to one of the earliest human civilizations with the foundation of the Bronze Age Xia dynasty;

FACT FILE

LOCAL NAME People's Republic of China (PRC)

CAPITAL CITY Beijing

CURRENCY Renminbi (RMB) counted in units of Yuan (CNY)

MEMBERSHIP AC, APEC, ASEAN (dialogue partner), G20, G24 (observer), G77, LAIA (observer), OAS (observer), SAARC (observer), WTO

GOVERNMENT Single Party State; Socialist Republic

POPULATION 1,336,310,750

POP. DENSITY 139/km²; 361/mi²

GDP 6.99 Trillion US$

LANGUAGE(S) Mandarin, Yue (Cantonese), Wu (Shanghainese), Minbei (Fuzhou), Minnan (Hokkien-Taiwanese), Xiang, Gan, Hakka

ETHNICITY Han (Chinese) 92%, Chuang (Zhuang) 1%, Manchu 1%, Hui 1%, Miao (Hmong) 1%, Uygur 1%, Tuchia 1%, Yi 1%, Mongol 0.47%, Tibetan 0.44%

RELIGION Non-religious 42%, Daoist (Taoist) and Chinese folk religions 29%, Buddhist 8%, Atheist 8%, Christian 7%, Indigenous beliefs 4%

CLIMATE Extremely diverse: Subtropical, Humid, Continental, Subarctic, Tundra, Arid (cool), Semi-arid (cool)

REGIONAL DIVISIONS 8 Economic Regions are divided into 22 Provinces, 5 Autonomous Regions and 4 Municipalities; PRC claims Taiwan as its 23rd province

DEPENDENCIES Hong Kong, Macau (special administrative regions) Paracel Islands (occupied) Spratly Islands (claimed)

ECONOMIC ACTIVITIES Agriculture, Mining and Ore Processing, Iron, Steel and Other Metals, Machine Building, Armaments, Textiles and Apparel, Petroleum, Cement, Chemicals, Consumer Products (including Footwear, Toys, and Electronics), Food Processing, Transportation Equipment (including Automobiles, Rail Cars and Locomotives, Ships, Aircraft), Telecommunications Equipment, Commercial Space Launch Vehicles, Satellites

NATURAL RESOURCES Coal, Iron Ore, Petroleum, Natural Gas, Mercury, Tin, Tungsten, Antimony, Manganese, Molybdenum, Vanadium, Magnetite, Aluminium, Lead, Zinc, Uranium, Hydropower (world's largest producer)

establishing a dynastic tradition that would endure from around 2000 BC until the twentieth century. The country was first unified under the Qin dynasty in the third century BC, although its territory was significantly expanded during the Han dynasty (206 BC–AD 220), when trading routes were also established to the Middle East. Periods of internecine warfare followed, although China witnessed a flourishing in art and science from the seventh to the thirteenth centuries under the Tang and Song dynasties, which coincided with increased migration to the south of the country. However, power returned to the north with the Mongol invaders who founded the Yuan dynasty during the thirteenth century, and again with the Manchus, who established the Qing dynasty in the seventeenth. After

this time, China began to experience a falling living standard, precipitated by its massive population growth, and by the nineteenth century imperial power had become increasingly fragmented, with social unrest, political corruption and Western intervention leading to a series of conflicts and rebellions, including the Opium Wars, the Sino-Japanese War and the Taiping and Boxer Rebellions. Hong Kong and other major ports were ceded to Britain after 1842, while Japan took control of Taiwan in 1895; in 1912, at the abdication of the last emperor, China was declared a republic.

GUILIN HILLS
The spectacular Guilin Hills in southern China are made from limestone.

As rival warlords then fought for power, two opposing movements emerged to fill the political vacuum: the nationalist Kuomintang, and the Chinese Communist Party. From 1937 until the end of World War II both were engaged in resisting the Japanese invasion of China, but from 1945 to 1949, China was plunged into civil war. Hostilities ended with the retreat of the Kuomintang to Taiwan, leaving Communist Party chairman Mao Zedong to proclaim the People's Republic of China on the mainland. The following year Tibet, which had been independent since 1911, was reabsorbed. Initially communism brought much-needed stability to China, but the rapid industrialization of Mao's 'Great Leap Forward' and the violent purges sparked by the Cultural Revolution were to prove disastrous, resulting in the deaths of up to 20 million people. Since Mao's death in 1976, major economic reforms have taken place, including the establishment of 'special economic zones' to encourage foreign trade and investment, but political freedoms have remained suppressed, and calls for democracy brutally crushed, as in the massacre of hundreds of demonstrators in Beijing's Tiananmen Square in 1989. More recently, Hong Kong and Macau have been returned to China by Britain and Portugal respectively, the country has been admitted to the World Trade Organization, and Beijing has played host to the Olympic Games. However, international relations have remained strained by disputes over the sovereignty of Taiwan and Tibet, and China's strict control of political expression.

Economy

Having developed an economy based on agriculture and trade since ancient times, China was transformed under communism, with economic activity being brought almost entirely under state control. However, rapid industrial expansion and the collectivization of farming were to prove ultimately ineffective, and a new programme of reforms was begun in the late 1970s. This move away from the Soviet model of central control has allowed for an increase in private enterprise, ownership, foreign investment, trade and tourism, particularly in special administrative regions such as Hong Kong and Shanghai. Today China has one of the world's fastest growing economies, and is a world-leading producer of several crops, metals, coal and consumer goods, although there remains an ideological conflict between state control and the desire for a free-market economy.

BEIJING
The National Stadium, a symbol of modernity, was built for the 2008 summer Olympics.

Hong Kong

One of two special administrative regions in China, the other being Macau, Hong Kong has fully embraced capitalism under the 'one country, two systems' policy.

Comprised of the Kowloon peninsula and New Territories on mainland China, as well as Hong Kong Island, Lantau Island and numerous smaller islands, Hong Kong's terrain is largely rugged and mountainous. The climate is tropical, with monsoon rains and typhoons in summer. Long established as a trading centre, Hong Kong Island was ceded to Britain in 1842 after the First Opium War, followed by Kowloon in 1860 and the New Territories in 1898. Trade continued to

HONG KONG
Skyscapers line the coast of Hong Kong.

flourish and Hong Kong became one of the largest container ports in the world. In 1997 it was returned to China, becoming a special administrative region with a high degree of autonomy over its economic affairs. Hong Kong remains one of the world's major commercial, banking and industrial centres, and also attracts millions of tourists each year.

REPUBLIC OF CHINA (TAIWAN)

23° 30' N, 121° 00' E | 35,980 KM² | 13,892 MI² | UTC+8

Regarded as a rebel province by the Chinese government, the Republic of China, comprising Taiwan and the smaller P'enghu, Chinmen and Matsu Islands, has effectively operated as an independent nation since 1949.

FACT FILE

LOCAL NAME Republic of China

CAPITAL CITY T'aipei

CURRENCY New Taiwan Dollar (TWD)

MEMBERSHIP APEC, not IMF member, not UN member, not WB member, WTO

GOVERNMENT Multi-party Democracy

POPULATION 22,920,946

POP. DENSITY 637/km²; 1,650/mi²

GDP 695.4 Billion US$

LANGUAGE(S) Mandarin Chinese, Taiwanese (Min), Hakka

ETHNICITY Taiwanese (including Hakka) 84%, Mainland Chinese 14%, Indigenous 2%

RELIGION Mixture of Buddhist and Taoist 93%, Christian 5%

CLIMATE Humid Subtropical

Taiwan is a large island around 160 kilometres from the coast of mainland China, dominated by a central mountain range running from north to south, with fertile coastal plains in the west. The climate is subtropical, with monsoons in both summer and winter. Claimed by China during the late seventeenth century, in 1895 Taiwan was ceded to the Japanese, who controlled the island until the end of World War II. It was then seized by Chinese nationalists fleeing from the communist regime on the mainland, and proclaimed the Republic of China. Despite the imposition of martial law, with US aid and protection Taiwan prospered, undergoing massive economic growth and industrialization. However, during the 1970s, as global relations with mainland China

mellowed, Taiwan found itself marginalized. Political reforms and continued economic growth since the 1980s have seen the domestic situation improve, although tensions persist with China, which has threatened to invade should independence be officially declared.

NORTH KOREA

40° 00' N, 127° 00' E | 120,540 KM² | 46,541 MI² | UTC+9

A communist dictatorship since 1948, North Korea has recently begun accepting foreign investment. However, the regime still attracts harsh criticism from Western governments.

Geography

Occupying the northern part of the Korean Peninsula, North Korea is dominated by rugged mountains, with lowland areas largely confined to the west coast along the Yellow Sea. The climate is continental: cold winters and hot summers. Rainfall averages 1,000 mm, mostly falling in summer.

History

Formerly divided into three principal kingdoms linked to Japan and China, Korea was unified between the tenth and nineteenth centuries AD, although by the late 1800s both Japan and Western nations were seeking greater regional influence. Japan seized power in 1910, but the country was liberated by Allied forces in 1945, the USSR overseeing the Japanese surrender north of the thirty-eighth parallel, the US controlling the south. By 1948, both nations had installed separate governments, and in 1950 the Korean War began with a Northern invasion of the South. The conflict, in which the USSR and China supported the North and US troops backed the South, was concluded in 1953, after which North Korea developed an increasingly isolated and totalitarian regime under Kim Il Sung, and later his son, Kim Jong Il. Recent years have seen major steps towards reconciliation between North and South Korea, but serious international concerns remain over North Korea's regime and its development of nuclear weapons.

Economy

Modelled on Soviet lines since 1948, the economy is almost entirely state-controlled, with nationalized industries and collectivized farming. Following widespread famine during the 1990s, economic reforms have begun.

FACT FILE

LOCAL NAME Democratic People's Republic of Korea

CAPITAL CITY Pyongyang

CURRENCY North Korean Won (KPW)

MEMBERSHIP G77, not IMF member, not WB member

GOVERNMENT Juche Socialist Republic: Communist State, One-Man Dictatorship

POPULATION 23,866,883

POP. DENSITY 198/km²; 513/mi²

GDP 40 Billion US$

LANGUAGE(S) Korean

ETHNICITY Korean 99%, Chinese 0.2%

RELIGION Indigenous beliefs 12%, Ch'ondogyo (Religion of the Heavenly Way) 13%, Christian 2%, Buddhist 2%

CLIMATE Temperate

REGIONAL DIVISIONS 14 divisions comprising 9 Provinces; 3 Special Administrative Regions; 2 directly governed Cities, of which Pyongyang is the largest city of North Korea

ECONOMIC ACTIVITIES Military Products, Machine Building, Electric Power, Chemicals, Mining (Coal, Iron Ore, Limestone, Magnesite, Graphite, Copper, Zinc, Lead, Precious Metals), Metallurgy, Textiles, Food Processing, Tourism

NATURAL RESOURCES Coal, Lead, Tungsten, Zinc, Graphite, Magnesite, Iron Ore, Copper, Gold, Pyrites, Salt, Fluorspar, Hydropower

DEMILITARIZED ZONE
The border between North and South Korea.

SOUTH KOREA

37° 00' N, 127° 30' E | 98,480 KM² | 38,023 MI² | UTC+9

Once an impoverished agricultural country, in little more than a generation South Korea has transformed itself into one of the world's fastest-growing industrial powers.

Geography

Comprising the southern half of the Korean Peninsula, South Korea is largely mountainous, although broad coastal plains occupy parts of the south and west. The climate is generally temperate, with cold winters and hot summers. Heavy rains and typhoons often affect the south in summer.

History

Despite long periods of independence, Korea was dominated by Chinese and Japanese influences for hundreds of years, and was annexed by Japan in 1910, before being divided by the US and USSR for administrative purposes after World War II. Attempts at reunification stalled in 1947, and in 1948 two separate republics were created, prompting a civil war between 1950 and 1953, which also involved Chinese and American forces. Following a brief period of authoritarian rule, major economic reforms were introduced during the 1960s, enabling the rapid industrialization of the country. However, government corruption and the suppression of human rights remained major concerns until the introduction of democratic reforms in the 1980s and 1990s. Since the late 1990s, South Korea has also paved the way for reconciliation with North Korea, although the North's nuclear programme has at times threatened this process.

Economy

Traditionally agricultural, South Korea's economy has been radically transformed since the 1960s, with US financial aid and Japanese war reparations enabling the country to develop into an important industrial power.

SEOUL
Nearly half of the population of South Korea live in the Seoul metropolitan area.

FACT FILE

LOCAL NAME Republic of Korea

CAPITAL CITY Seoul

CURRENCY South Korean Won (KRW)

MEMBERSHIP APEC, ASEAN (dialogue partner), CP, G20, LAIA, OAS (observer), OECD, SAARC (observer), WTO

GOVERNMENT Presidential Republic

POPULATION 48,387,832

POP. DENSITY 491/km²; 1,273/mi²

GDP 1.201 Trillion US$

LANGUAGE(S) Korean

ETHNICITY Korean 98%, Japanese 2%

RELIGION Buddhist 23%, Protestant 20%, Roman Catholic 7%

CLIMATE Temperate, Continental, Subtropical

REGIONAL DIVISIONS 16 Divisions comprising 8 Provinces, 1 Special Self-governing Province, 6 Metropolitan Cities and 1 Special City, the capital, Seoul

ECONOMIC ACTIVITIES Electronics, Telecommunications, Automobile Production, Chemicals, Shipbuilding, Steel

NATURAL RESOURCES Coal, Tungsten, Graphite, Molybdenum, Lead, Hydropower potential

CENTRAL AND EASTERN ASIA

JAPAN

36° 00' N, 138° 00' E | 377,835 KM² | 145,883 MI² | UTC+9

Known as 'the land of the rising sun', Japan is a country of ancient traditions and modern technology, which has risen from the ashes of World War II to become one of the world's leading economic powers.

Geography

An island nation in the North Pacific comprised of the exposed peaks of submerged mountains and volcanoes, Japan is made up of the main islands of Honshu, Hokkaido, Kyushu, and Shikoku, as well as thousands of smaller islands. About 80 per cent of the terrain is mountainous, much of which is heavily forested. The largest area of flat land is the Kanto plain in east central Honshu, which is dominated by the Tokyo metropolitan area: a conurbation consisting of Japan's capital Tokyo as well as many other smaller towns and cities. Mount Fuji, the country's highest peak, lies south-west of the capital.

Spanning some 1,600 kilometres from north to south, Japan has a climate that varies considerably, with Hokkaido subject to cold winters and fairly cool summers, while Tokyo experiences short winters, and summers that are hot and humid. Further south conditions are subtropical, with monsoon rains and typhoons affecting the Pacific coast in summer. The climate also varies from east to west on account of Japan's central mountains, with eastern parts receiving greater snowfall in winter.

History

It is thought that Ainu people, possibly of Polynesian origin, first settled Japan well over

10,000 years ago, with successive waves of migrants arriving from the Korean peninsula during the Yayoi period, between 300 BC and AD 300. By the fifth century, the nation was divided between various clans, the most powerful of which was the Yamato, who were the first to adopt the title of *tenno*, or emperor. Chinese influence increased under the Yamato emperors, including the introduction of Buddhism and Chinese administrative systems, although by the ninth century the Fujiwara family had eclipsed the Yamato. The Fujiwara or Heian period lasted until the late twelfth century, when the Minamoto warrior clan rose to power to establish the Kamakura shogunate, heralding the introduction of a feudal system overseen by military rule. It was also during the Kamakura Period that two Mongol invasions were repulsed by typhoons, since referred to as the kamikaze, or divine wind. Briefly unified, Japan then descended into years of civil war as rival warlords vied for power, but despite this, the country enjoyed a major flourishing in Zen-inspired arts,

FACT FILE

LOCAL NAME Japan

CAPITAL CITY Tokyo

CURRENCY Yen (JPY)

MEMBERSHIP APEC, ASEAN (dialogue partner), CE (observer), CP, G8, G10, G20, LAIA, OAS (observer), OECD, SAARC (observer), WTO

GOVERNMENT Constitutional Monarchy with a parliamentary government

POPULATION 127,938,000

POP. DENSITY 339/km²; 877/mi²

GDP 4.29 Trillion US$

LANGUAGE(S) Japanese

ETHNICITY Japanese 99%

RELIGION Observing both Shinto and Buddhist 84%

CLIMATE Humid Subtropical, Temperate, Subarctic

REGIONAL DIVISIONS 8 traditional regions are divided into 47 Prefectures; Tokyo is the most populous prefecture of Japan

ECONOMIC ACTIVITIES Motor Vehicle Manufacturing, Electronic Equipment, Machine Tools, Steel and Nonferrous Metals, Shipbuilding, Chemicals, Textiles, Processed Foods

NATURAL RESOURCES Negligible Mineral Resources, Fish

and by the sixteenth century the nation had been reunified. By this time the Portuguese had also reached Japan's shores, bringing with them guns and Christianity, and they were followed by Dutch and English traders. However, during the Edo period, as the samurai code of Bushido, 'the way of the warrior', became deeply entrenched, Christianity and foreign trade were rejected, and in 1639 the country closed its borders. They were reopened in 1854, following which the shogunate, which had capitulated to Western pressure, was overthrown, and in 1868 the emperor was restored at Edo, which was renamed Tokyo. Ironically, Japan then began to look increasingly to the West for inspiration; the feudal system was dissolved and samurai stripped of status, and the country was politically, industrially and militarily modernized. Its new military might was first revealed in the Sino-Japanese and Russo-Japanese conflicts in the late nineteenth and early twentieth centuries, following which Japanese expansionism saw its invasion of China in 1937 and involvement in World War II, which was brought to an end in August 1945 by the use of atomic bombs against the cities of Hiroshima and Nagasaki. The US then imposed a new constitution,

TOKYO
Tokyo reflects the mixture of modernity and tradition in Japanese society.

which introduced numerous political, social and economic reforms, and by the 1970s Japan had emerged as one of the world's leading industrial nations. Political and economic turmoil returned during the 1980s and 1990s, as Japan's economic bubble finally burst, but the country remains an important major global power to this day. Having renounced warfare after World War II, its defence forces have recently begun to be employed in international support and peacekeeping operations.

Economy

Having undergone two major periods of economic restructuring in modern times, today Japan is one of the world's leading economic powers, with the second highest gross domestic product, and one of the highest average living standards of any nation. During the Meiji Restoration in the mid-nineteenth century, Japan emerged from decades of isolation to enjoy rapid growth and industrialization, while the country's post-World War II recovery was regarded as an 'economic miracle', with the country enjoying an unprecedented rate of growth. Despite a lack of natural resources, Japan has been able to develop a highly advanced manufacturing industry, becoming a world leader in the production of steel, ships, automobiles and high-tech consumer goods.

MOUNT FUJI
Mount Fuji last erupted in 1707–08.

CENTRAL AND EASTERN ASIA

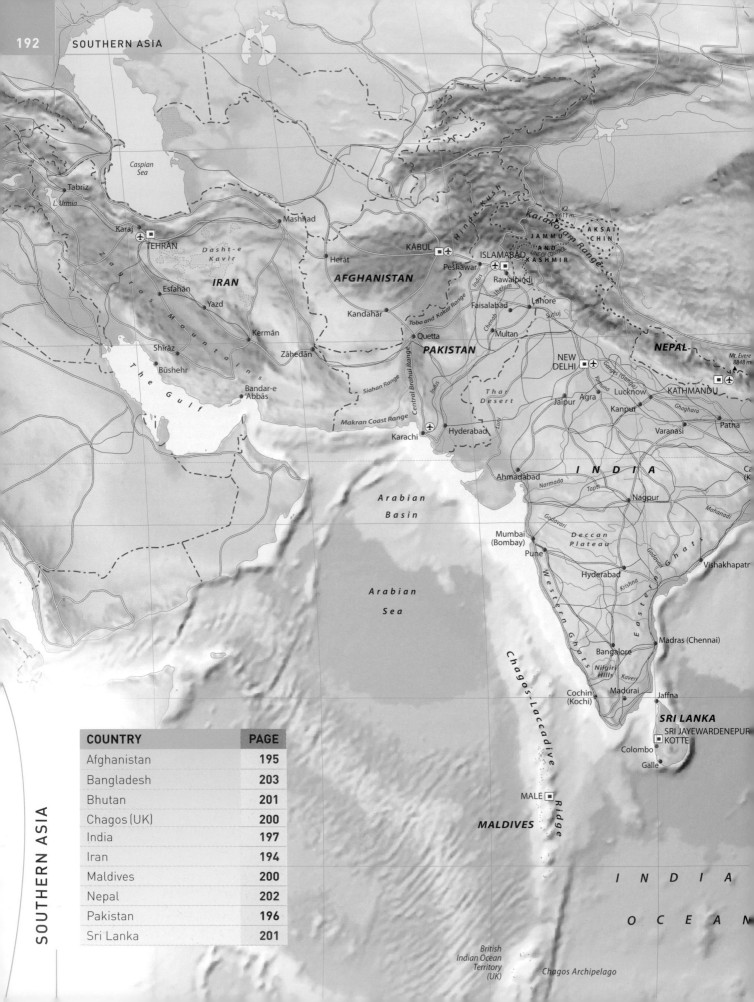

SOUTHERN ASIA

Caspian
Sea

Tabriz

L. Urmia

Karaj
TEHRĀN

Mashhad

Dasht-e
Kavīr

IRAN

Esfahan

Yazd

Herāt

KĀBUL
AFGHANISTAN
Peshawar

ISLAMABAD
Rawalpindi

JAMMU
AND
KASHMIR

Hindu Kush

Karakoram Range

AKSAI
CHIN

82
2611 m

LINE OF CONTROL

Kandahār

Faisalabad
Lahore

Chenab

Jhelum

Indus

Sutluj

Kermān

Shīrāz

Zāhedān

Quetta
PAKISTAN

Multan

NEPAL

Mt. Evere
8848 m

KATHMANDU

Bandar-e
Abbās

Būshehr

Zagros
Mountains

The
Gulf

Siahan Range

Central Brahui Range

Makran Coast Range

Indus

Thar
Desert

NEW
DELHI

Ganges (Ganga)

Yamuna

Lucknow

Jaipur
Āgra

Kanpur

Ghaghara

Varanasi

Patha

Karachi

Hyderabad

INDIA

Ca
(K

Ahmadābad

Narmada

Tapti

Nagpur

Mahanadi

Arabian
Basin

Godavari

Deccan
Plateau

Mumbai
(Bombay)
Pune

Hyderabad

Krishna

Godavari

Eastern Ghats

Vishakhapatr

Arabian
Sea

Western Ghats

Bangalore

Nilgiri
Hills

Kaveri

Madras (Chennai)

Chagos-Laccadive

Cochin
(Kochi)

Madurai

Jaffna

SRI LANKA

SRI JAYEWARDENEPUR
KOTTE

Colombo

Galle

MALE

MALDIVES

Ridge

INDIA

British
Indian Ocean
Territory
(UK)

Chagos Archipelago

OCEAN

SOUTHERN ASIA

This complex region bridges many cultures and is increasingly at the heart of political turmoil and conflict that affects the whole world. The history of the East and West also converges here, from military engagement in Afghanistan to colonial rule in India.

Southern Asia is geographically diverse: from the mountainous ranges of the Hindu Kush to the legendary beaches of Goa and the jewelled isles of the Maldives. As a region it has a wonderful cultural heritage entangled in a legacy of struggle and conflict. The dominance of western culture in the world has sidelined the sophistication and beauty of the art, poetry and music of Iran and India and the fascinating history of the region is largely unknown outside its boundaries.

India is the dominant country of the region with its large population and rapidly growing world-class economy, yet it doesn't have the political leverage to guarantee peace in the region, especially with the complex politics of Afghanistan and Pakistan and, closer to home, Kashmir, making active conflict zones a continuing threat to lasting peace.

No region on earth gives more reason for hope or cause for despair – where aspiring individuals and businesses prosper and enjoy the luxuries of modern civilization while poor neighbours or lower castes live in deep poverty. For large numbers the solution has been emigration, either permanently or as migrant workers, to richer countries in Western Asia or further afield, especially the UK where Indian, Pakistani and Bangladeshi migrants flocked in the last century.

AMRITSAR
The Golden Temple at Amritsar in northern India is the holiest shrine of the Sikh religion. Called Harmandir Sahib (House of God) by the Sikhs, the first temple on the site was built in 1601.

IRAN

32° 00' N, 53° 00' E | 1,648,000 KM² | 636,296 MI² | UTC+3:30

An Islamic republic since a fundamentalist revolution of 1979, today Iran remains isolated and is viewed with suspicion by Western governments; attempts at reform have been opposed by the nation's religious leaders.

Geography

Mainly mountainous, with a large barren plateau in the east, and narrow plains along the Caspian Sea and the Persian Gulf, much of Iran is arid; precipitation is greatest in the north. Average annual temperatures are lowest in the western mountains and increase towards the south.

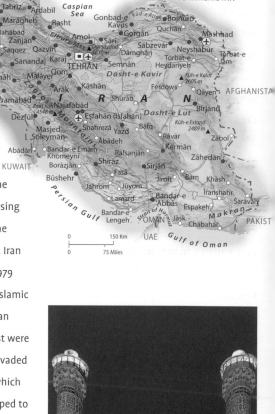

History

Known as Persia until 1935, Iran was once home to the Persian Empire. By the seventh century AD, the region had been invaded by Arabs, who introduced Islam. A succession of dynasties followed; Shi'a Islam became dominant under the Safavid dynasty, who ruled until the eighteenth century. Despite the increasing influence of Britain and Russia from the nineteenth to the twentieth centuries, Iran maintained its independence, but in 1979 the monarchy was overthrown in the Islamic Revolution. The country was declared an Islamic republic, and ties with the West were severed. The following year Iran was invaded by Iraq, beginning the Iran–Iraq War, which continued until 1988, when the UN helped to negotiate a ceasefire. Since then attempts have been made to introduce political reform and improve international relations, but concerns remain over the country's nuclear programme and possible sponsorship of Islamic terrorism.

Economy

Traditionally agricultural, Iran was transformed following the discovery of oil in 1908. Petroleum soon became a major export, and by the 1970s the country had been massively industrialized. Oil remains of primary importance; natural gas, metals and textiles are also exported.

FACT FILE

LOCAL NAME Islamic Republic of Iran

CAPITAL CITY Tehran

CURRENCY Iranian Rial (IRR)

MEMBERSHIP CP, ECO, G24, G77, OIC, OPEC, SAARC (observer), WTO (observer)

GOVERNMENT Theocratic Republic, governed by the Supreme Ruler of Iran via an elected President and a unicameral parliament

POPULATION 72,211,695

POP. DENSITY 44/km²; 114/mi²

GDP 753 Billion US$

LANGUAGE(S) Persian (Farsi), Kurdish, Arabic, Turkish

ETHNICITY Persian 51%, Azeri 24%, Gilaki and Mazandarani 8%, Kurd 7%, Arab 3%

RELIGION Muslim 98% (Shi'a 89%, Sunni 9%), Other (includes Zoroastrian, Jewish, Christian, and Baha'i) 2%

CLIMATE Arid; Semi-arid; Subtropical (along Caspian coast)

REGIONAL DIVISIONS 30 Provinces are divided into 324 Sub-provinces which are further divided into 865 Counties

ECONOMIC ACTIVITIES Petroleum, Petrochemicals, Mining, Fertilizers, Caustic Soda, Textiles, Cement and Other Construction Materials, Agriculture, Food Processing (particularly Sugar Refining and Vegetable Oil Production), Ferrous and Non-ferrous Metal Fabrication, Armaments

NATURAL RESOURCES Petroleum, Natural Gas, Coal, Chromium, Copper, Iron Ore, Lead, Manganese, Zinc, Sulphur

ESFAHAN
The entrance to the Imam (Shah) Mosque in Esfahan.

AFGHANISTAN

33° 00' N, 65° 00' E | 647,500 KM² | 250,001 MI² | UTC+4:30

Ravaged by decades of war, Afghanistan remains the scene of conflict, despite the appointment of the country's first democratically elected government in 2004.

Geography

Landlocked in the centre of southern Asia, Afghanistan is dominated by the mountains of the Hindu Kush, extending across the country from the east. The south and west are occupied by desert and semi-desert regions. The climate is extreme, with very cold winters and hot, dry summers.

History

Once part of the Persian Empire, Afghanistan was conquered by a succession of rulers. Islam was introduced by Arab invaders in the seventh century. The country was subsequently controlled by the Mongols and Mughals, and briefly unified during the eighteenth century. British fears over Russian expansion sparked three Anglo-Afghan wars during the nineteenth and early twentieth centuries. Independence came in 1921, but conflict between Islamic traditionalists and left-wing reformers followed. In 1979 Soviet forces invaded the country, supporting a leftist regime. Troops were withdrawn in 1989, but civil war persisted as US-backed Mujaheddin guerrillas challenged the government; by the late 1990s the Taliban faction had seized power. Following terrorist attacks in the US in 2001, a US–British coalition ousted the Taliban, who had links to the al-Qaeda organization. Since then Taliban fighters have contended with coalition forces.

Economy

Devastated by years of conflict, and with little arable land, Afghanistan is an extremely poor country. Agriculture is of primary importance; sheep and goats are raised, and wheat grows in scattered fertile valleys. Afghanistan is also thought to be the world's largest producer of opium.

BAMIYAN PROVINCE
An irrigation system in fields in Bamiyan Province, in the centre of Afghanistan.

FACT FILE

LOCAL NAME Islamic Republic of Afghanistan

CAPITAL CITY Kabul

CURRENCY Afghani (AFA)

MEMBERSHIP CP, ECO, G77, OIC, SAARC, WTO (observer)

GOVERNMENT Islamic Republic

POPULATION 28,225,646

POP. DENSITY 44/km²; 113/mi²

GDP 35 Billion US$

LANGUAGE(S) Afghan Persian (Dari), Pashto, Uzbek, Turkmen, Balochi, Pashai

ETHNICITY Pashtun 42%, Tajik 27%, Hazara 9%, Uzbek 9%, Aimak 4%, Turkmen 3%

RELIGION Sunni Muslim 80%, Shi'a Muslim 19%

CLIMATE Arid; Semi-arid

REGIONAL DIVISIONS 34 Provinces are divided into 398 Districts; Kabul is the most populated province and its capital Kabul is also the national capital

ECONOMIC ACTIVITIES Agriculture, Mining and Extraction of Minerals and Gemstones, Small-Scale Production of Textiles, Food Processing and Beverages, Telecommunication, Soap, Furniture, Shoes, Fertilizer, Cement, Construction, Handwoven Carpets, Natural Gas

NATURAL RESOURCES Natural Gas, Petroleum, Coal, Copper, Chromite, Talc, Barites, Sulphur, Lead, Zinc, Iron Ore, Salt, Precious and Semi-precious Stones

SOUTHERN ASIA

PAKISTAN

30° 00' N, 70° 00' E | 803,940 KM² | 310,403 MI² | UTC+5

Pakistan was founded as an autonomous Muslim state in 1947, but political stability remains elusive.

Geography

Pakistan may be divided into three main geographic regions: the northern highlands, the western Baluchistan plateau and the eastern Indus plain, dominated by the Indus River. Climate varies considerably according to altitude, with mountainous areas colder than the Indus plain, which is mild in winter and hot in summer.

History

Home to the Indus Valley Civilization 4,500 years ago, the region now occupied by Pakistan was conquered by the Persians, Greeks and Arabs, and later the Mughals, who went on to rule most of the Indian subcontinent. The British East India Company exerted increasing control throughout the eighteenth century; in 1858, following the Sepoy Mutiny, direct imperial rule was established. This lasted until 1947, when calls for an independent Muslim state were answered with the creation of Pakistan, consisting of West Pakistan and East Bengal. However, conflict flared with India over the Kashmir region, which remains disputed, and East Bengal (East Pakistan) gained independence as Bangladesh in 1971. Since then Pakistan has endured considerable political strife and extensive periods of martial law, and tensions with India have persisted. Recently Pakistan has joined the US in a commitment to combating Islamic terrorism, although condemning US incursions into its territory.

Economy

At its creation Pakistan was a poor agricultural nation, and despite major economic growth and industrialization, agriculture remains important, along with textiles and chemical products. The economy has suffered from mismanagement, foreign debt and massive defence spending.

FACT FILE

LOCAL NAME Islamic Republic of Pakistan

CAPITAL CITY Islamabad

CURRENCY Pakistani Rupee (PKR)

MEMBERSHIP C, CP, ECO, G24, G77, SAARC, OAS (observer), OIC, WTO

GOVERNMENT Semi-presidential Federal Islamic Republic; Bicameral Legislature

POPULATION 166,961,297

POP. DENSITY 208/km²; 538/mi²

GDP 410 Billion US$

LANGUAGE(S) Punjabi, Sindhi, Siraiki, Pashtu, Urdu, Balochi, Hindko, Brahui, English (lingua franca – elite and most government ministries), Burushaski

ETHNICITY Punjabi 44%, Pashtun (Pathan) 15%, Sindhi 14%, Sariaki 11%, Urdu 8%, Balochi 4%

RELIGION 95% Muslim

CLIMATE Arid, Semi-arid, Temperate in north-west, Arctic in mountainous north

REGIONAL DIVISIONS 4 Provinces, 1 Territory and 1 Capital Territory (Azad Kashmir and northern areas have their own respective political and administrative structure) with further sub-division into 124 Districts and 7 Tribal Agencies

DEPENDENCIES None, but claims India-occupied Jammu and Kashmir

ECONOMIC ACTIVITIES Agriculture, Textiles and Apparel, Food Processing, Pharmaceuticals, Cement and Other Construction Materials, Sugar, Paper Products, Fertilizer, Shrimp

NATURAL RESOURCES Extensive Natural Gas Reserves, Petroleum, Coal (poor quality), Iron Ore, Copper, Salt, Limestone

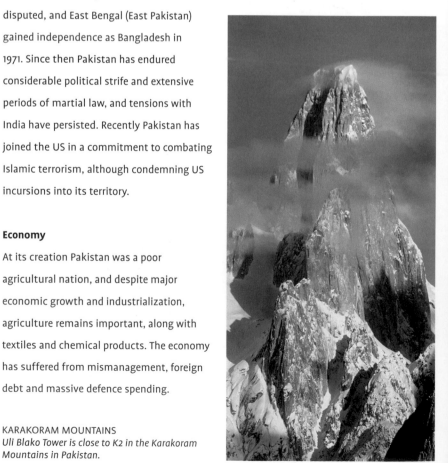

KARAKORAM MOUNTAINS
Uli Blako Tower is close to K2 in the Karakoram Mountains in Pakistan.

INDIA

20° 00' N, 77° 00' E | 3,287,590 KM² | 1,269,346 MI² | UTC+5:30

With a population of over one billion, India is the world's second most populous country after China and possesses one of the world's fastest-growing economies. It is also incredibly diverse, with almost twenty major languages in use and thousands of ethnic groups represented.

Geography

One of the world's largest countries, India is roughly triangular in shape, and may be broadly divided into three principal geographic regions: the Himalayan Mountains, which extend 2,500 kilometres across the north of the country from the disputed Kashmir region in the west to Arunachal Pradesh in the east; the Gangetic or Northern Plains, which stretch from the Thar Desert on the border with Pakistan, east to Bangladesh; and the Indian Peninsula, which is largely occupied by the Deccan

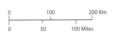

AGRA
The Taj Mahal was built by the Mughal emperor Shah Jahan in memory of his favourite wife Mumtaz Mahal.

Plateau, and bounded by the Arabian Sea in the west and the Bay of Bengal in the east, extending to the Indian Ocean in the south. The country's capital, New Delhi, is in the north on the Yamuna River, the main tributary of the Ganges, India's most important and sacred river, which enters from the Himalayas north-east of Delhi before flowing south-east to Bangladesh and the Bay of Bengal.

The climate is mainly tropical or subtropical, with considerable variation across the country and according to the time of year. The northern plains experience the greatest range of temperatures, with cool winters and hot summers, while mountainous areas are subject to cold winters and cool summers, and the south remains fairly hot throughout the year. Generally, India experiences three seasons; a cool winter from October to March, a hot, dry season, which persists until June, and the monsoon season, which brings heavy rains from mid-June to September.

History

India's earliest known society, the Indus Valley Civilization, emerged in what is now Pakistan around 4,500 years ago, although by 1,700 BC, northern India was controlled by the Aryan founders of the Vedic civilization, out of which Hinduism was to emerge. Following incursions into the Indus Valley by Alexander the Great in 326 BC, unification was achieved by the Mauryan Empire, which saw the rise of Buddhism under Emperor Asoka, but after his death in 232 BC the empire dissolved. The Guptan Empire brought another period of unity during the third century AD, but from about 450 AD, the north was conquered by successive waves of invaders, including Arabs and Turks who began to introduce Islam to India. A Muslim sultanate was established at Delhi in 1206, with Islamic rule being consolidated in the sixteenth century under the Mongol descendants who founded the Mughal Empire.

Art and architecture flourished under the Mughal emperors, with the Taj Mahal being completed in 1648. However, Emperor Aurangzeb's policy of enforced Islamization provoked perpetual conflict that led to the disintegration of the empire from around the early 1700s. The British East India Company began to extend its authority over the country, and following the Rebellion of 1857, control passed to the British Crown. The British instigated a process of industrialization and development of infrastructure, but a lack of participation in Indian affairs fostered resentment, and led to the formation of the Indian National Congress in 1885 and the Muslim League in 1906. Despite some concessions by the British towards political reform, Congress soon began to call for Indian self-governance, and from 1920 opposition to British rule was united under the leadership of Mohandas Gandhi, who advocated peaceful civil disobedience as a means to effect political change. From about 1930, the Muslim League began to demand independence from both Britain and the Hindu majority in India; by the end of World War II, during which Indian troops had been mobilized in support of British forces, differences between the Muslim League, led by Muhammad Ali Jinnah, and Congress, under Jawaharlal Nehru, were clearly irreconcilable, with the result that Britain decided to partition the country in 1947, creating the Muslim nation of Pakistan, whilst giving India its independence. However, terrible violence flared in the wake of this decision, particularly in the Punjab, which had large Sikh, Muslim and Hindu populations, while conflict between India and Pakistan over Kashmir still persists. Distrust was also heightened during the 1990s as both countries began nuclear testing. Since independence, India has enjoyed long periods of peace and prosperity, and its economy has been transformed, but underlying tensions between ethnic and religious groups have frequently led to sporadic violence.

Economy

Since the early 1990s major reforms, including relaxation of government controls on foreign trade and investment, have enabled the economy, formerly dependent on agriculture, to become one of the world's fastest-growing. High-tech activities such as IT, software and consumer electronics now have increased significance. However, agriculture remains important to the Indian economy, employing 65 per cent of a workforce of around 438 million people; tea, cotton, wheat, rice, sugarcane, bananas and spices are major crops. India is also a world-leading producer of coal, iron ore and bauxite. Yet despite recent advances, economic development across India has been uneven, with many people existing in abject poverty, and although illegal, child labour also remains a major problem.

FACT FILE

NATIONAL NAME Republic of India

CAPITAL New Delhi

CURRENCY Indian Rupee (INR)

MEMBERSHIP ASEAN (dialogue partner), C, CP, G15, G20, G24, G77, LAS (observer), OAS (observer), SAARC, WTO

GOVERNMENT Federal Republic Parliamentary Democracy

POPULATION 1,186,185,625

POP. DENSITY 361/km²; 935/mi²

GDP 2.989 Trillion US$

LANGUAGE(S) Assamese, Bengali, Bodo, Dogri, Gujarati, Hindi, Kannada, Kashmiri, Konkani, Maithili, Malayalam, Manipuri, Marathi, Nepali, Oriya, Punjabi, Sanskrit, Santhali, Sindhi, Tamil, Telugu, Urdu

ETHNICITY Indo-Aryan 72%, Dravidian 25%, Mongoloid and other 3%

RELIGION Hindu 81%, Muslim 13%, Christian 2%, Sikh 2%

CLIMATE Tropical in south, Temperate and Continental in north, Arid and Semi-arid in north-west

REGIONAL DIVISIONS 4 major physiographic Divisions are divided into 28 States and 7 Union Territories

ECONOMIC ACTIVITIES Agriculture, Textiles, Chemicals, Food Processing, Sugar, Iron and Steel, Transportation Equipment, Pulp and Paper, Cement, Mining, Petroleum, Machinery, Software

NATURAL RESOURCES Coal, Iron Ore, Manganese, Mica, Bauxite, Titanium Ore, Chromite, Natural Gas, Diamonds, Petroleum, Limestone, Arable Land

TIGERS
The Bengal tiger is one of the world's most endangered species.

SOUTHERN ASIA

MALDIVES

3° 15' N, 73° 00' E | 300 KM² | 116 MI² | UTC+5

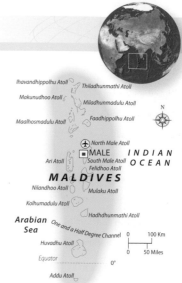

While thousands of tourists experience the Maldives as a tropical paradise, the indigenous population live under a somewhat repressive regime.

The Maldives' 1,000 coral islands form less than 1 per cent of its territory, the rest being maritime, and are incredibly low-lying, no higher than 3 metres above sea level. The climate is humid and tropical, temperatures averaging around 25°C. The Maldives were first settled from southern India and Sri Lanka, and after conversion from Buddhism to Islam during the twelfth century, were ruled by a succession of sultans. The Portuguese held control briefly during the sixteenth century; from 1887 to 1965 the islands were a British protectorate. Tourism has supported the economy since independence. Political reforms have been slow, sparking social unrest that has sometimes been brutally suppressed.

FACT FILE

LOCAL NAME Republic of Maldives
CAPITAL CITY Male
CURRENCY Rufiyaa (MVR)
MEMBERSHIP C, CP, G77, OIC, SAARC, WTO
GOVERNMENT Presidential Republic
POPULATION 311,056
POP. DENSITY 1,037/km²; 2,682/mi²
GDP 1.588 Billion US$
LANGUAGE(S) Maldivian Dhivehi, English (government officials)
ETHNICITY Maldivians 99%, Sinhalese 1%
RELIGION Sunni Muslim
CLIMATE Humid Tropical

NORTH MALE
North Male Atoll attracts divers from all over the world.

CHAGOS

6° 00' S, 71° 30' E | 54,400 KM² | 21,004 MI² | UTC+5

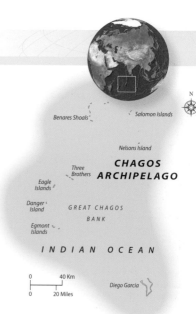

The Chagos Islands have been in legal dispute since controversial resettlement in the 1970s.

Part of the British Indian Ocean Territory, which comprises over 2,000 tropical islets in the Indian Ocean, the Islands were discovered by the Portuguese in the sixteenth century AD, but became a French possession during the eighteenth century. Control passed to Britain around 1810, the islands being governed from Mauritius and retained when Mauritius gained independence in 1968. Soon afterwards, the native Chagossians were forcibly removed to facilitate construction of a joint British and US military facility on the island of Diego Garcia, where copra plantations were previously established. Today economic activity centres on the military base and commercial fishing. It is hoped that the Chagossians may soon be allowed to return.

FACT FILE

LOCAL NAME British Indian Ocean Territory
SOVEREIGN STATE United Kingdom
MAIN CITY Diego Garcia
CURRENCY British Pound (GBP); US Dollar (USD)
MEMBERSHIP None
GOVERNMENT British Overseas Territory
CLIMATE Tropical Marine

SOUTHERN ASIA

BHUTAN

27° 30' N, 90° 30' E | 47,000 KM² | 18,147 MI² | UTC+6

Bhutan is the only country to measure Gross National Happiness, in line with its Buddhist principles.

Situated between India and Tibet in the Himalayas, Bhutan is mountainous in the north, with an alpine climate; parts of the south are occupied by subtropical plains and forests. By the seventeenth century Bhutan was united under Ngawang Namgyal. His death in 1651 was followed by civil war; power struggles persisted until the twentieth century, when a hereditary monarchy was installed with British support. Recent decades have brought modernization and political reform, although discrimination

FACT FILE

LOCAL NAME	Kingdom of Bhutan
CAPITAL CITY	Thimphu
CURRENCY	Ngultrum (BTN); Indian Rupee (INR)
MEMBERSHIP	CP, G77, SAARC, WTO (observer)
GOVERNMENT	In Transition to Constitutional Monarchy; Special Treaty Relationship with India
POPULATION	666,918
POP. DENSITY	14/km²; 37/mi²
GDP	3.36 Billion US$
LANGUAGE(S)	Dzongkha, Tibetan, Nepalese
ETHNICITY	Bhote 50%, Ethnic Nepalese 35% (includes Lhotsampas), Indigenous or migrant tribes 15%
RELIGION	Tibetan Buddhist 75%, Hindu 25%
CLIMATE	Tropical in south, Temperate in central area, Subarctic in north

against the Nepalese minority sparked violence during the 1990s. Bhutan has recently embraced democracy; parliamentary elections were held in 2007 and 2008. Agriculture occupies over 90 per cent of the workforce, although cement is exported to India.

SRI LANKA

7° 00' N, 81° 00' E | 65,610 KM² | 25,332 MI² | UTC+5:30

This large island, the 'Pearl of the Indian Ocean', has recently suffered disasters, both natural and manmade.

Sri Lanka may be divided into two climatic regions: a wet zone in the south and west, and a dry zone in the north and east. After Sinhalese and Tamil rule, from the sixteenth century European colonies were established. Independence was granted by Britain in 1948. Known as Ceylon under British rule, the country became Sri Lanka in 1972. Although democratic since independence, ethnic

FACT FILE

LOCAL NAME	Democratic Socialist Republic of Sri Lanka
CAPITAL CITY	Colombo (commercial), Sri Jayewardenepura Kotte (administrative)
CURRENCY	Sri Lankan Rupee (LKR)
MEMBERSHIP	C, CP, G15, G24, G77, OAS (observer), SAARC, WTO
GOVERNMENT	Democratic Socialist Republic
POPULATION	21,128,773
POP. DENSITY	322/km²; 834/mi²
GDP	81.29 Billion US$
LANGUAGE(S)	Sinhala, Tamil
ETHNICITY	Sinhalese 74%, Sri Lankan Moors 7%, Indian Tamil 5%, Sri Lankan Tamil 4%
RELIGION	Buddhist 69%, Muslim 8%, Hindu 7%, Christian 6%
CLIMATE	Tropical

NUWARA ELIYA
Tea pickers at Nuwara Eliya in the central highlands of Sri Lanka, where some of the world's finest orange pekoe tea is grown.

tensions between the Sinhalese majority and Tamil separatists sparked a civil war in 1983, which remains unresolved. The economy is largely agricultural, with tea, coconuts and rubber as major crops; clothing and gemstones are also exported. The country is gradually recovering from a devastating tsunami in 2004.

SOUTHERN ASIA

NEPAL

28° 00' N, 84° 00' E | 147,181 KM² | 56,827 MI² | UTC+5:45

Nepal, the birthplace of Buddha, has Buddhist and Hindu traditions dating back thousands of years, but today it is a secular state, led by a democratically elected communist party.

Geography

Situated in the Himalayas between India and Tibet, with which it shares the world's highest peak, Mount Everest, Nepal is a largely mountainous country, with a lowland region in the south. The climate is alpine, extremely cold at high altitudes, becoming tropical in the far south.

History

Parts of Nepal have been inhabited for many thousands of years, but it was first unified under the eighteenth-century Shah dynasty, after which territorial disputes with the British East India Company led to the Anglo-Nepalese War of 1814–16. Instability followed, although relations with Britain improved; Nepal offered assistance during the Sepoy rebellion in India and in both world wars. The autocratic rule of the Rana dynasty was ended during the 1950s by King Mahendra, who installed himself as absolute monarch. By 1990, calls for democratic reform brought about a multi-party system. Soon afterwards the Communist (Maoist) Party of Nepal rebelled, and in 2001 several members of the royal family were murdered. Insurrection persisted until 2006; in 2008 the monarchy was abolished, and a republic was declared, with the chairman of the Communist Party as prime minister.

Economy

One of the world's poorest countries, Nepal's economy is primarily agricultural, with sugarcane, jute and tobacco. Textiles and tourism are growing sectors, and there are plans to export hydroelectric power to India, although the country remains highly dependent upon foreign aid. Gurkha soldiers, who have supported British forces since the 1800s, contribute significantly to the economy from their salaries.

THE HIMALAYAS
At 8,848 metres, Everest is the world's highest mountain.

FACT FILE

LOCAL NAME Federal Democratic Republic of Nepal

CAPITAL CITY Kathmandu

CURRENCY Nepalese Rupee (NPR)

MEMBERSHIP CP, G77, SAARC, WTO

GOVERNMENT Democratic Republic

POPULATION 28,757,414

POP. DENSITY 195/km²; 506/mi²

GDP 29.04 Billion US$

LANGUAGE(S) Nepali, Maithali, Bhojpuri, Tharu (Dagaura/Rana), Tamang, Newar, Magar, Awadhi

ETHNICITY Ettri 16%, Brahman-Hill 13%, Magar 7%, Tharu 7%, Tamang 6%, Newar 5%, Muslim 4%, Kami 4%, Yadav 4%

RELIGION Hindu 81%, Buddhist 11%, Muslim 4%, Kirant 4%

CLIMATE Tropical, Temperate,Tundra

REGIONAL DIVISIONS 5 Developmental Regions are divided into 14 Zones and further into 75 Districts

ECONOMIC ACTIVITIES Agriculture, Tourism, Carpets, Textiles, Paper, Rice, Jute, Sugar and Oilseed Mills, Cigarettes, Cement and Brick Production, Tourism

NATURAL RESOURCES Quartz, Water, Timber, Hydropower, Small Deposits of Lignite, Copper, Cobalt, Iron Ore

BANGLADESH

24° 00′ N, 90° 00′ E | 144,000 KM² | 55,599 MI² | UTC+6

Formerly East Pakistan, Bangladesh became independent in 1971. However, it has remained politically unstable, and its problems are compounded by frequent natural disasters.

Geography

Bangladesh, on the Bay of Bengal, is largely surrounded by India, although it shares a border with Myanmar in the south-west. Most of the country comprises the flat and low-lying alluvial plains of the Ganges, Jamuna (Brahmaputra) and Meghna Rivers, and with a tropical, monsoonal climate, is frequently devastated by flooding and cyclones.

History

Historically, Bangladesh formed part of the Bengal region, which was first united by the Buddhist Pala dynasty in the eighth century AD, and later became part of the Mughal Empire, following the introduction of Islam during the twelfth century. By the nineteenth century the region was under British control, and at the partitioning of India in 1947 the area became known as East Bengal, renamed East Pakistan in 1955. In 1971 civil war erupted, but by the end of the year Indian intervention had ended the conflict, and Bangladesh gained its independence. Since then the country has endured terrible famines and floods, political instability, social unrest and years of military rule. Although democracy was restored in 1991, the political scene still evinces violence and corruption.

Economy

Despite being among the world's largest producers of rice, Bangladesh is one of the poorest countries, with most people engaged in subsistence farming. However, jute and tea are grown as cash crops, and in recent years large reserves of natural gas have been discovered both on- and offshore.

THE GANGES
Fishermen working the Ganges Delta.

FACT FILE

LOCAL NAME People's Republic of Bangladesh
CAPITAL CITY Dhaka
CURRENCY Taka (BDT)
MEMBERSHIP C, CP, G77, SAARC, WTO (observer)
GOVERNMENT Parliamentary Republic
POPULATION 161,317,625
POP. DENSITY 1,120/km²; 2,901/mi²
GDP 206.7 Billion US$
LANGUAGE(S) Bangla, English
ETHNICITY Bengali 98%, other 2% (includes tribal groups, non-Bengali Muslims)
RELIGION Muslim 83%, Hindu 16%
CLIMATE Tropical
REGIONAL DIVISIONS 6 Divisions are divided into 64 Districts; Divisions are named after their divisional administrative centres
ECONOMIC ACTIVITIES Agriculture, Cotton Textiles, Jute, Garments, Tea Processing, Paper Newsprint, Cement, Chemical Fertilizer, Pharmaceuticals, Light Engineering, Sugar
NATURAL RESOURCES Natural Gas, Timber, Coal

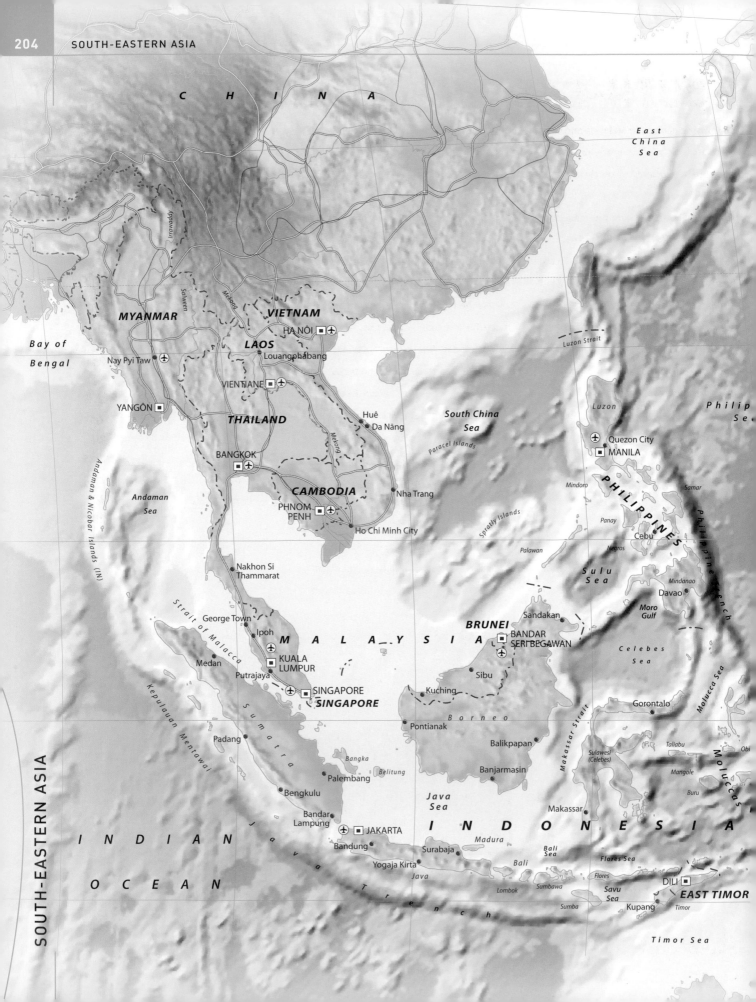

C H I N A

East China Sea

MYANMAR

Irrawaddy

Salween

Mekong

VIETNAM

HA NÔI

LAOS

Louangphabang

Luzon Strait

Bay of Bengal

Nay Pyi Taw

VIENTIANE

THAILAND

Huê
Da Nång

Luzon

Philippi ne Se

YANGÔN

BANGKOK

CAMBODIA

South China Sea

Paracel Islands

Quezon City
MANILA

Mindoro

PHILIPPINES

Andaman & Nicobar Islands (IN)

Andaman Sea

PHNOM PENH

Nha Trang

Ho Chi Minh City

Spratly Islands

Panay

Samar

Cebu

Negros

Mindanao

Nakhon Si Thammarat

Palawan

Sulu Sea

Davao

Philippine Trench

Moro Gulf

Sandakan

George Town

Ipoh

M A L A Y S I A

BRUNEI
BANDAR SERI BEGAWAN

Celebes Sea

Strait of Malacca

Medan

KUALA LUMPUR

Putrajaya

Sibu

Kuching

Molucca Sea

Kepulauan Mentawai

SINGAPORE
SINGAPORE

B o r n e o

Gorontalo

Taliabu

Obi

Sumatra

Pontianak

Sulawesi (Celebes)

Moluccas

Padang

Balikpapan

Mangole

Bangka

Belitung

Banjarmasin

Buru

Palembang

Makassar Strait

Bengkulu

Java Sea

Makassar

I N D O N E S I A

I N D I A N

Bandar Lampung

JAKARTA

Madura

Bandung

Surabaja

Bali Sea

Flores Sea

DILI

O C E A N

Yogaja Kirta

Java

Bali

EAST TIMOR

Lombok

Sumbawa

Savu Sea

Flores

Sumba

Timor

Kupang

Timor Sea

SOUTH-EASTERN ASIA

Comprising peninsular Malaysia and the maritime area of islands and archipelagos, South-eastern Asia is home to nearly 10 per cent of the world's population. For the last 500 years this region has played a key role in East-West trade.

For some a haven of travel and exploration, for others the location of the darkest chapter of modern history, this region has been a focus of world attention in the last 50 years with international involvement in two bloody conflicts since World War Two, which had its own terrible stories under Japanese invasion. The Korean War could be viewed as a traditional conflict but the extraordinary tactics used by both sides in the Vietnam War have left scars on succeeding generations. Oppressive regimes in Cambodia and Laos are part of a fabric of terror that is slowly receding and the natural beauty of the area and its wonderful cultural heritage guarantee a more secure future for peaceable economies.

South-east Asia arguably provided the first step in the global economy; as the East Indies, from the sixteenth century it attracted colonial exploitation and settlement by Portugal, Spain, Britain and France, who set about liberating the local riches from timber and spices to rubber. The region's role in the global economy remains important, from the factories of the Philippines to the commercial hub of Singapore. The less lucrative but significant backpacker culture gives travellers a taste of the world's exotic treats.

SINGAPORE
The famous Raffles Hotel in Singapore.

SOUTH-EASTERN ASIA

MYANMAR

22° 00' N, 98° 00' E | 678,500 KM² | 261,970 MI² | GMT +/- | UTC+6:30

The Union of Myanmar, formerly known as Burma, is the largest country in mainland south-east Asia.

Geography

The country lies in the tropical monsoon region of Asia, with its coastal regions receiving over 5,000 mm of rain annually. The terrain consists of central lowlands ringed by steep, rugged highlands. Much of the country is covered by tropical rain forest. The fertile plain surrounding Irrawaddy River is the most densely populated area of the country.

History

The country's earliest groups were the Mon, who arrived in the south from c. 950 BC, and the Pyu, who arrived c. 100 BC. The area was

an independent Buddhist kingdom from the eleventh to thirteenth centuries, when it fell to Mongol invaders, before becoming a satellite of China. In the nineteenth century Britain controlled the region and incorporated it into its Indian Empire in 1885. The thirty years after independence, which came in 1948, saw economic stagnation and isolation from the international community. In the 1990 elections the main opposition party won a landslide victory but the ruling junta refused to hand over power. The military regime declared a 'roadmap to democracy' in 2002, which resulted in a constitution being drafted in 2008.

Economy

Despite substantial natural resources, years of mismanagement and isolation have made Myanmar one of the poorest countries in Asia. Infrastructure remains undeveloped and levels of education are low, affecting its ability to produce a skilled workforce. Its major agricultural product is rice which covers about 60 per cent of the country's total cultivated land area. Other industries include wood products and gems such as rubies.

FACT FILE

LOCAL NAME	Union of Myanmar
CAPITAL CITY	Rangoon
CURRENCY	Kyat (MMK)
MEMBERSHIP	ASEAN, CP, G77, WTO
GOVERNMENT	Military Dictatorship
POPULATION	49,220,559
POP. DENSITY	73/km²; 188/mi²
GDP	91.13 Billion US$
LANGUAGE(S)	Burmese (Myanmar)
ETHNICITY	Burman 68%, Shan 9%, Karen 7%, Rakhine 4%, Chinese 3%, Indian 2%, Mon 2%
RELIGION	Buddhist 89%, Muslim 4%, Baptist 3%, Roman Catholic 1%, Animist 1%
CLIMATE	Tropical Monsoon
REGIONAL DIVISIONS	7 Divisions and 7 States are divided into 64 Districts
ECONOMIC ACTIVITIES	Agriculture, Agricultural Processing, Petroleum Refining, Natural Gas, Wood and Wood Products, Mining, Cement and Other Construction Materials, Pharmaceuticals, Fertilizer, Garments, Jade and Gems, Telecommunication, Insurance, Banking
NATURAL RESOURCES	Petroleum, Timber, Tin, Antimony, Zinc, Copper, Tungsten, Lead, Coal, Marble, Limestone, Precious Stones, Natural Gas, Hydropower

BAGAN
There are over 2,000 ancient pagodas, stupas and shrines at Bagan.

ANDAMAN AND NICOBAR ISLANDS
11° 41' N, 92° 46' E | 8,249 KM² | 3,185 MI² | UTC +5.30

These islands, the peaks of a submerged mountain chain, lie in the Indian Ocean between the Andaman Sea and the Bay of Bengal.

The Andaman and Nicobar Islands are sparsely populated and largely unspoiled, although they were badly affected by a tsunami in 2004. Many are hilly and swathed in tropical woodland. The climate is hot and humid with high annual rainfall. Although inhabited for thousands of years, Western settlement began during the eighteenth century, when Danes, Austrians and British arrived. In 1869 the islands were annexed by Britain and combined under a single administration in 1872. They fell to the Japanese during World War II, but in 1947, when India gained independence from Britain, they became Indian territories. Principal economic activities include woodworking, fishing, agriculture, and some tourism.

ANDAMAN ISLANDS
The Andaman and Nicobar territories comprise more than 550 islands of which fewer than forty are inhabited.

FACT FILE

LOCAL NAME	Union Territory of Andaman and Nicobar Islands
SOVEREIGN STATE	India
MAIN CITY	Port Blair
CURRENCY	Indian Rupee (INR)
MEMBERSHIP	None
GOVERNMENT	Union Territory of India
POPULATION	3,56,152
POP. DENSITY	43/km²; 112/mi²
GDP	320.7 Million US$
LANGUAGE(S)	English, Hindi, Tamil, Bengali
ETHNICITY	Negrito tribes (the Great Andamanese, Onge, Jarawa and Sentinalese), Two Mongoloid tribes (Nicobarese and Shompens) and others (Immigrants or Settlers)
RELIGION	Hindu 68%, Christian 24%, Muslim 8%
CLIMATE	Tropical

SPRATLY AND PARACEL ISLANDS
8° 38' N, 111° 55' E 16° 30' N, 112° 00' E | 5 KM² 10 KM² | 2 MI² 4 MI² | GMT +/- | UTC+8 UTC+8

The uninhabited Paracel and Spratly Islands are subject to territorial disputes because of vast offshore oil and gas reserves.

FACT FILE

LOCAL NAME	Spratly Islands, Paracel Islands
SOVEREIGN STATE	Spratly Islands are claimed by China, Taiwan and Vietnam; parts of them are claimed by Malaysia and the Philippines; occupied by China, also claimed by Taiwan and Vietnam
POPULATION	No indigenous population
CLIMATE	Tropical

These islands, between Vietnam and the Philippines, comprise a number of coral atolls in the South China Sea. The climate is tropical, and typhoons frequently occur. The Paracel Islands are disputed by China, Taiwan and Vietnam; the Spratly Islands are additionally claimed by Malaysia, the Philippines and Brunei. There are no permanent inhabitants, although the Chinese have a garrison in the Paracel Islands, and military installations are maintained throughout the Spratly Islands by all of the contesting nations except Brunei, which has however claimed exclusive fishing rights around Louisa Reef in the south. Conflict last flared in the Spratly Islands in 1988, but both groups are potential flashpoints.

SOUTH-EASTERN ASIA

VIETNAM

16° 00' N, 106° 00' E | 329,560 KM² | 127,244 MI² | UTC+7

The Socialist Republic of Vietnam, the easternmost country on the Indochina Peninsula, measures only 50 kilometres across at its narrowest point.

Geography

About 80 per cent of the country's terrain is mountainous, with densely populated fertile plains in the north and south around the Red River and Mekong Delta respectively. The climate is tropical in the south and monsoonal in the north with a hot, rainy season (May to September) and a warm, dry season (October to March).

History

Successive Chinese dynasties ruled Vietnam from 111 BC until AD 938, when it regained its independence until becoming part of French Indochina in 1887. In 1954 Vietnam was divided into two states: the North, ruled by the communist leader Ho Chi Minh, and the South, led by Dien Bien. As communist insurgent activity increased in South Vietnam, Dien's government became increasingly dependent on American support. Conflict escalated and America entered the war in 1963, finally withdrawing all troops in 1973. Following this, North Vietnam invaded the South and the country was reunified as the Socialist Republic of Vietnam in 1976, which is still governed by the Communist Party.

Economy

Although Vietnam's economy was shattered by the war, the enactment of Vietnam's 'renovation' policy in 1986 has led to the country being among the fastest-growing economies in Asia. Manufacturing, information technology and high-tech industries form a large and fast-growing part of the national economy. However, more than half the population is still involved in agriculture and there is a marked divide between the relatively affluent urban areas and the poorer rural regions.

FACT FILE

LOCAL NAME Socialist Republic of Vietnam

CAPITAL CITY Ha nôi

CURRENCY Dong (VND)

MEMBERSHIP APEC, ASEAN, CP, G77, WTO

GOVERNMENT Socialist Republic

POPULATION 88,537,273

POP. DENSITY 269/km²; 696/mi²

GDP 221.4 Billion US$

LANGUAGE(S) Vietnamese, English, French, Tai, Muong, Nung, Chinese

ETHNICITY Kinh (Viet) 86%, Tay 2%, Thai 2%, Muong 2%, Khome 1%, Hoa 1%, Nun 1%, Hmong 1%

RELIGION Buddhist 9%, Catholic 7%, Hoa Hao 2%, Cao Dai 1%

CLIMATE Tropical in south, Humid Subtropical in north

REGIONAL DIVISIONS 59 Provinces and 5 Municipalities which are grouped into 8 Regions for administrative convenience

DEPENDENCIES Claims Spratly and Paracel Islands (occupied by China)

ECONOMIC ACTIVITIES Agriculture, Fisheries, Food Processing, Garments, Shoes, Machine Building, Mining, Coal, Steel, Cement, Chemical Fertilizer, Glass, Tyres, Oil, Paper

NATURAL RESOURCES Phosphates, Coal, Manganese, Bauxite, Chromate, Offshore Oil and Gas Deposits, Forests, Hydropower

THE MEKONG
The Mekong Delta occupies approximately 40,000 square metres of land.

THAILAND

15° 00' N, 100° 00' E | 514,000 KM² | 198,457 MI² | UTC+7

The Kingdom of Thailand, the only South-east Asian country to have avoided colonization, has one of the largest Buddhist populations in the world.

Geography

Thailand is composed of plains in the centre, plateaux in the north-east, mountain ranges in the north and west, and the Gulf of Thailand with islands and an isthmus eventually joining Malaysia in the south. The climate is tropical and monsoonal.

History

National identity first emerged under the Sukothai Kingdom (1238–1376) through the introduction of Thai writing and codification of Theravada Buddhism. In 1782 the first Chakri monarch ascended the throne, consolidated the area, formerly known as Siam, and introduced a wide range of reforms. In 1932 a bloodless coup stripped the king of his absolute powers, transforming the country into a constitutional monarchy and handing power to a mixed military-civilian government. Since this time periods of civilian rule have been interrupted by years of military rule and Thailand has failed to establish a stable system of government. Elections in 2007 were designed to bring in democracy but so far attemps to bring political stability have failed.

Economy

Over recent years Thailand's economy has experienced rapid growth, with much of the economic activity centred around Bangkok. However, agriculture is still a major employer and Thailand is the world's largest exporter of rice, exporting more than 6.5 million tonnes annually. More than half of the available land area is used for rice production. Tourism is an increasingly important source of revue.

FACT FILE

LOCAL NAME Kingdom of Thailand

CAPITAL CITY Bangkok

CURRENCY Baht (THB)

MEMBERSHIP APEC, ASEAN, CP, G77, OAS (observer), OIC (observer), WTO

GOVERNMENT Parliamentary Democracy and Constitutional Monarchy

POPULATION 64,316,133

POP. DENSITY 125/km²; 324/mi²

GDP 519.4 Billion US$

LANGUAGE(S) Thai, English (secondary language of the élite)

ETHNICITY Thai 75%, Chinese 14%

RELIGION Buddhist 95%, Muslim 5%

CLIMATE Tropical

REGIONAL DIVISIONS 76 Provinces are grouped into 4 Regions; Bangkok is the most populous province

ECONOMIC ACTIVITIES Agriculture (Sugar, Rice, Rubber), Mining, Tourism, Textiles and Garments, Agricultural Processing, Beverages, Tobacco, Cement, Light Manufacturing (e.g.Jewellery and Electric Appliances), Computers and Components, Integrated Circuits, Furniture, Plastics, Automobiles and Automotive Parts

NATURAL RESOURCES Tin, Rubber, Natural Gas, Tungsten, Tantalum, Timber, Lead, Fish, Gypsum, Lignite, Fluorite

PHI PHI LEE ISLAND, NEAR PHUKET
Tourists flock to Thailand's beautiful coastline, and the bustling city of Bangkok.

CAMBODIA

13° 00' N, 105° 00' E | 181,040 KM² | 69,900 MI² | UTC+7

Devastated by war, Cambodia remains one of the world's poorest nations.

Although bordered by highlands, Cambodia largely comprises low-lying plains around the Mekong River and Tonlé Sap, a large freshwater lake. Once the seat of the Khmer empire and the Angkor kingdom, Cambodia was a protectorate within French Indochina from 1863 to 1954, following which the country briefly prospered, before being drawn into the Vietnam War around 1969. The country fell to the communist Khmer Rouge group in 1975; up to a quarter of the population perished under Pol Pot's brutal regime. Vietnamese forces overthrew the Khmer Rouge in 1979, sparking conflict and instability that continued until political reforms in the 1990s. Official corruption remains a major concern, and economic recovery has been slow.

FACT FILE

LOCAL NAME	Kingdom of Cambodia
CAPITAL CITY	Phnom Penh
CURRENCY	Riel (KHR)
MEMBERSHIP	ASEAN, G77, WTO
GOVERNMENT	Parliamentary Democracy under a Constitutional Monarchy
POPULATION	14,697,217
POP. DENSITY	81/km²; 210/mi²
GDP	25.9 Billion US$
LANGUAGE(S)	Khmer, French, English
ETHNICITY	Khmer 90%, Vietnamese 5%
RELIGION	Theravada Buddhist 95%
CLIMATE	Tropical

ANGKOR WAT
Built by the Khmer kings in the twelfth century, the vast temple complex fell into disuse and was lost in the dense jungle until 1861, when it was rediscovered by Henri Mahout, a French explorer.

LAOS

18° 00' N, 105° 00' E | 236,800 KM² | 91,429 MI² | UTC+7

Laos remains a one-party communist state, although it has opened its borders to trade and tourism in recent years.

Laos is dominated by mountains and high plateaux, with low-lying plains along the Mekong River and a tropical climate. First united under the Lan Xang kingdom in 1353, Laos suffered repeated incursions from Burma, Siam (Thailand) and Vietnam, until being incorporated into French Indochina during the nineteenth century. Independence came in 1954; civil war then erupted between royalist forces with clandestine US backing and the communist Pathet Lao group, supported by North Vietnam. The Pathet Lao seized power in 1975, leaving the country marginalized until the economic reforms of the 1980s and 1990s, although Laos remains one of poorest nations in south-east Asia, with much subsistence farming.

FACT FILE

LOCAL NAME	Lao People's Democratic Republic
CAPITAL CITY	Vientiane
CURRENCY	Kip (LAK)
MEMBERSHIP	ASEAN, CP, OIC, G77, WTO (observer)
GOVERNMENT	Single-Party Socialist Republic
POPULATION	5,962,765
POP. DENSITY	25/km²; 65/mi²
GDP	12.65 Billion US$
LANGUAGE(S)	Lao, French, English
ETHNICITY	Lao 55%, Khmou 11%, Hmong 8%
RELIGION	Buddhist 65%, Animist 33%, Christian 1%
CLIMATE	Tropical Monsoon

MALAYSIA

2° 30' N, 112° 30' E | 329,750 KM² | 127,317 MI² | UTC+8

Malaysia is separated into two regions by the South China Sea: Peninsular Malaysia and Malaysian Borneo.

Geography

The two separate areas of Malaysia share a similar terrain: both are comprised of coastal plains rising to densely forested hills and mountains. The climate is equatorial with annual monsoons.

History

In ancient times the Malay Peninsula was settled by waves of immigrants from the north and was later subject to Indian and Islamic influences. A series of indigenous trading empires culminated in that of Malacca, which fell first to the Portuguese in the sixteenth century, then to the Dutch, and then finally to the British in the late eighteenth century. In 1948, the British-ruled territories on the Malay Peninsula formed the Federation of Malaya, which became independent in 1957. Malaysia was formed in 1963 when the former British colonies of Singapore and the east Malaysian states of Sabah and Sarawak on the northern coast of Borneo joined the federation. The post-independence period was marred by conflict with Indonesia, Singapore's exit from the federation in 1965 and race riots in 1969 – Malaysia has since maintained a delicate ethno-political balance.

Economy

Since the 1970s the economy has been transformed from a producer of raw materials to an emerging multi-sector economy. It is mainly driven by the services sector, which contributed about half of GDP in 2007. Exports of electronic goods, palm oil and rubber are significant, as are oil and gas.

FACT FILE

LOCAL NAME Malaysia

CAPITAL CITY Kuala Lumpur

CURRENCY Ringgit (MYR)

MEMBERSHIP APEC, ASEAN, C, CP, G15, G77, OIC, WTO

GOVERNMENT Constitutional Monarchy and Parliamentary Democracy

POPULATION 27,026,582

POP. DENSITY 82/km²; 212/mi²

GDP 357.4 Billion US$

LANGUAGE(S) Bahasa Malaysia, English, Chinese (Cantonese, Mandarin, Hokkien, Hakka, Hainan, Foochow), Tamil, Telugu, Malayalam, Panjabi, Thai

ETHNICITY Malay 50%, Chinese 24%, Indigenous 11%, Indian 7%

RELIGION Muslim 60%, Buddhist 19%, Christian 9%, Hindu 6%, Confucianism, Taoism, Other Chinese religions 3%

CLIMATE Tropical

REGIONAL DIVISIONS 2 geographical regions, West and East, are divided into 13 States and 3 Federal Territories

DEPENDENCIES Claims parts of Spratly Islands

ECONOMIC ACTIVITIES Rubber and Oil Palm Processing and Manufacturing, Light Manufacturing, Electronics, Tin Mining and Smelting, Logging, Timber Processing, Tourism, Petroleum Production and Refining, Agriculture Processing

NATURAL RESOURCES Tin, Petroleum, Timber, Copper, Iron Ore, Natural Gas, Bauxite

KUALA LUMPUR
At 452 metres high, Petronas Towers are a symbol Malaysia's level of economic development.

SOUTH-EASTERN ASIA

INDONESIA

5° 00' S, 120° 00' E | 1,919,440 KM² | 741,100 MI² | UTC+7

Indonesia, home to the world's largest Muslim population, is an archipelagic country of 17,508 islands, of which 6,000 are inhabited. It is the fourth most populated country in the world.

FACT FILE

LOCAL NAME Republic of Indonesia

CAPITAL CITY Jakarta

CURRENCY Indonesian Rupiah (IDR)

MEMBERSHIP APEC, ASEAN, CP, G15, G20, G77, OIC, OPEC, WTO

GOVERNMENT Presidential Republic

POPULATION 234,342,422

POP. DENSITY 122/km²; 316/mi²

GDP 837.8 Billion US$

LANGUAGE(S) Bahasa Indonesia, English, Dutch, Javanese

ETHNICITY Javanese 41%, Sundanese 15%, Madurese 3%, Minangkabau 3%, Betawi 2%, Bugis 2%, Banten 2%, Banjar 2%

RELIGION Muslim 86%, Protestant 6%, Roman Catholic 3%, Hindu 2%

CLIMATE Tropical

REGIONAL DIVISIONS Indonesia consists of 5 major islands, 2 major archipelagos and other smaller islands, together divided into 30 Provinces, 2 Special Regions and 1 Special Capital City district

ECONOMIC ACTIVITIES Agriculture, Petroleum and Natural Gas, Textiles, Apparel, Footwear, Mining, Mineral Production and Processing, Cement, Chemical Fertilizers, Wood processing, Rubber, Food and Beverages, Tourism, Aircraft Manufacturing

NATURAL RESOURCES Petroleum, Tin, Natural Gas, Nickel, Timber, Bauxite, Copper, Fertile Soils, Coal, Gold, Silver

Geography

Stretching along the equator in South-east Asia, the five largest islands of Indonesia are Java, Sumatra, Kalimantan (the Indonesian part of Borneo), New Guinea (shared with Papua New Guinea) and Sulawesi. The terrain of the islands is predominantly coastal lowlands, with the larger islands having mountainous interiors which are covered in dense tropical rain forest. The climate is tropical, with more moderate temperatures in the highlands.

History

From AD 600 the powerful Srivijaya naval kingdom flourished, bringing Hindu and Buddhist influences, followed by the Majapahit kingdom, which influenced much of Indonesia. The introduction of Islam dates from the thirteenth century and was propagated by Muslim traders reaching

SUMATRA
Orang utans, found in the rain forests of Sumatra, are one of the world's most endangered species.

northern Sumatra. The Dutch controlled Indonesia from the early seventeenth century until 1949, when independence was formally recognized. The leader of the independence movement, Sukarno, became the region's first president until he was outmanoeuvred by the head of the military, General Suharto, in 1968. Since the resignation of Suharto in 1998 Indonesia has seen four different presidencies.

Economy

Indonesia's economy has stabilized in recent years, having suffered badly during the Asian financial crisis of the late 1980s. Reforms have brought some progress but poor infrastructure and corruption impede investment and growth. Some 25 per cent of GDP is derived from trade, with exports mainly in the hydrocarbon, mining and agricultural sectors, and imports in manufactured goods; but agriculture employs almost half of the country's 95 million workers.

SINGAPORE

1° 22' N, 103° 48' E | 693 KM² | 268 MI² | UTC+8

The Republic of Singapore is an island which lies to the south of the Malay Peninsula, to which it is joined by a 1.2-kilometre-long causeway, carrying a road, railway and water pipeline across the Straits of Johor.

The island's terrain is mainly lowland, with gently undulating central plateaux. The climate is hot and humid, with no clearly defined seasons, although December and January are the wettest months. From AD 200 the island was an outpost for the Sumatran Srivijaya empire and became a significant trading settlement, but declined from the late 1300s. In 1819 the British East India Company established a trading post on the island, which later became a prominent commercial centre as a port of call along the spice route. In 1963, having achieved independence from Britain, Singapore merged with Malaya, Sabah and Sarawak to form Malaysia. Two years later, however, it seceded from the federation and became an independent republic. Since then the country has seen three presidents, the most recent being Lee Hsien Loong, who took office in 2004. Since independence it has achieved almost uninterrupted economic growth for over three decades. It has strong international trading links and a per capita GDP equal to that of the leading nations of Western Europe. Foreign direct investment and a state-led drive to industrialization have created a modern economy focused on electronics manufacturing, petrochemicals, tourism and financial services alongside traditional entrepôt trade.

SINGAPORE SKYLINE
Almost 75 per cent of Singapore is urban. It is one of the world's most densely populated countries.

FACT FILE

LOCAL NAME	Republic of Singapore
CAPITAL CITY	Singapore
CURRENCY	Singapore Dollar (SGD)
MEMBERSHIP	APEC, ASEAN, C, CP, G77, WTO
GOVERNMENT	Parliamentary Republic
POPULATION	4,490,117
POP. DENSITY	6,479/km²; 16,754/mi²
GDP	228.1 Billion US$
LANGUAGE(S)	Mandarin, English, Malay, Tamil, Hokkien, Cantonese, Teochew
ETHNICITY	Chinese 77%, Malay 14%, Indian 8%
RELIGION	Buddhist 43%, Muslim 15%, Taoist 8%, Hindu 4%, Catholic 5%, Other Christian 10%
CLIMATE	Tropical

BRUNEI

4° 30' N, 114° 40' E | 5,770 KM² | 2,228 MI² | UTC+8

Brunei has a high standard of living, although political freedoms are severely limited.

Brunei, on Borneo's northern coast, is mainly hilly and densely forested, with large swamps along the coastal plain. The climate is hot and humid, with frequent rain. Thought to have been settled during the eighth century AD, Brunei later became a Javanese dependency; by the fifteenth century it had become an independent Islamic sultanate. British influence then increased, and from 1888 until 1984 Brunei was a British protectorate. Since the discovery of oil in 1929, Brunei has become one of the

FACT FILE

LOCAL NAME	State of Brunei, Abode of Peace
CAPITAL CITY	Bandar Seri Begawan
CURRENCY	Bruneian Dollar (BND)
MEMBERSHIP	APEC, ASEAN, C, G77, OIC, WTO
GOVERNMENT	Absolute Islamic Sultanate
POPULATION	398,142
POP. DENSITY	69/km²; 179/mi²
GDP	19.64 Billion US$
LANGUAGE(S)	Malay, English, Chinese
ETHNICITY	Malay 66%, Chinese 11%, Indigenous 3%
RELIGION	Muslim 67%, Buddhist 13%, Christian 10%, Other (includes Indigenous Beliefs) 10%
CLIMATE	Tropical

wealthiest Asian nations, and the sultan is among the world's richest men. Oil, natural gas and related products form 90 per cent of Brunei's exports; much of the nation's food must be imported.

EAST TIMOR

8° 50' S, 125° 55' E | 15,007 KM² | 5,794 MI² | UTC+9

Blighted by decades of war, East Timor is one of the world's least developed countries.

Comprising the eastern part of the island of Timor, the enclave of Oecussi-Ambeno and the islands of Atauro and Jaco, East Timor is largely mountainous, with narrow coastal plains. The climate is hot and humid, with monsoon rains between December and March. It was a Portuguese possession from the sixteenth century until 1975, when civil war erupted between rival independence movements. Indonesia then seized control; Timorese guerrillas resisted robustly until 1999, when East Timor voted for independence. Violence then escalated, and has surfaced sporadically since independence was granted in 2002. The economy is largely agricultural; a deal with Australia to exploit offshore gas and oil reserves may prove profitable.

COASTAL VILLAGE
Traditional houses made from bamboo.

FACT FILE

LOCAL NAME	Democratic Republic of Timor-Leste
CAPITAL CITY	Dili
CURRENCY	US Dollar (USD)
MEMBERSHIP	G77, PIF (observer)
GOVERNMENT	Presidential Parliamentary Republic
POPULATION	1,192,515
POP. DENSITY	80/km²; 206/mi²
GDP	2.61 Billion US$
LANGUAGE(S)	Tetum, Portuguese, Indonesian, English
ETHNICITY	East Timorese 80%, Other (nearly all Indonesian and particularly West Timorese) 20%
RELIGION	Roman Catholic 98%, Muslim 1%, Protestant 1%
CLIMATE	Tropical

PHILIPPINES

13° 00' N, 122° 00' E | 300,000 KM² | 115,831 MI² | UTC+8

The Philippine archipelago is made up of 7,107 islands divided into three main areas: Luzon in the north, the Visayas in the central area, and Mindanao and the Sulu Archipelago to the south.

Geography

Much of the island terrain is mountainous and is prone to earthquakes and volcanic eruptions, although about one-third of territory is coastal lowlands. The climate is tropical with seasonal monsoons and the islands are frequently hit by typhoons.

History

Around 6,000 years ago the first settlers, Malays, reached the region. From around the eleventh century onwards Chinese, Indonesian and Arab traders arrived, with Islam reaching the islands in the fourteenth century. The Spanish established a settlement in the sixteenth century, introducing Catholicism and naming the region Las Islas Filipinas, after their monarch Phillip II. The country remains largely Christian; the Philippines and East Timor are the only Christian countries in Asia. Spain was forced to cede the Philippines to the USA 1898. Independence was finally granted in 1946, with Ferdinand Marcos, the country's first president, retaining power for twenty years – his resignation in 1986 was eventually forced by a 'people power' movement in the captial Manila.

Economy

Despite having a growing economy, the combination of the Philippines' extremely rapid population growth, the fastest in Asia, and a large national debt means that many people still live in poverty. Much of the country's income is derived from money sent home by the enormous number of Filipinos working abroad. The workforce is still primarily engaged in agriculture, with most manufacturing based around Manila and the island of Luzon.

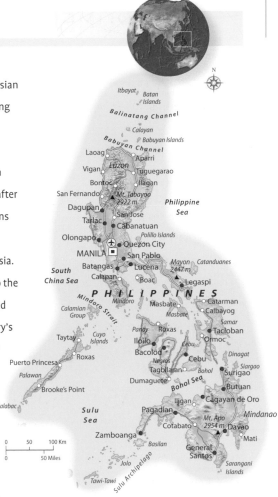

FACT FILE

LOCAL NAME Republic of the Philippines

CAPITAL CITY Manila

CURRENCY Philippine Peso (PHP)

MEMBERSHIP APEC, ASEAN, CP, G24, G77, OAS (observer), WTO

GOVERNMENT Unitary Presidential Constitutional Republic

POPULATION 89,651,078

POP. DENSITY 299/km²; 774/mi²

GDP 299.6 Billion US$

LANGUAGE(S) Filipino, English, Tagalog, Cebuano, Ilocano, Hiligaynon/Ilonggo, Bicol, Waray, Pampango, and Pangasinan

ETHNICITY Tagalog 28%, Cebuano 13%, Ilocano 9%, Bisaya/Binisaya 8%, Hiligaynon Ilonggo 8%, Bikol 6%, Waray 3%

RELIGION Roman Catholic 81%, Muslim 5%, Evangelical 3%, Iglesia ni Kristo 2%, Aglipayan 2%, Other Christian 5%

CLIMATE Tropical Maritime

REGIONAL DIVISIONS 3 Island Groups are divided into 17 Regions further subdivided into 81 Provinces and 136 Cities.

DEPENDENCIES Claims parts of Spratly Islands

ECONOMIC ACTIVITIES Agriculture, Electronics Assembly, Textiles and Garments, Footwear, Pharmaceuticals, Chemicals, Wood Products, Food Processing and Beverages, Petroleum Refining, Fishing

NATURAL RESOURCES Timber, Petroleum, Nickel, Cobalt, Silver, Gold, Salt, Copper

LUZON ISLAND
Terraces are cut into the hillside to increase the amount of land available to grow rice.

SOUTH-EASTERN ASIA

AFRICA

A continent of extremes, Africa has rich agriculture yet expanding desert. Home of some of the world's poorest countries its mines yield rich mineral deposits and tourists spend millions visiting its stunning attractions from wildlife parks to rivers, waterfalls and mountains. Africa is believed to be the cradle of mankind with rich prehistoric sites and its future holds much mystery as it struggles to find a sustainable place in the modern world.

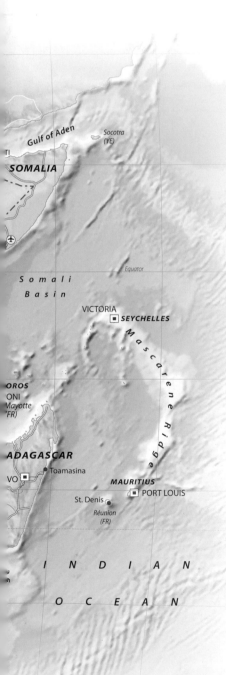

NORTHERN AFRICA

Sharing much of its history with Europe yet combining African and Arabian culture, this unique region is a critical area for Africa's economic and environmental future.

With the Atlantic Ocean to the west, the Mediterranean Sea to the north and the Red Sea to the east, Northern Africa has been susceptible to seaborne invasion and influence – from the Phoenician founders of Carthage in ancient times through Ottoman rule and European occupations of last century. The region has its own ancient native populations, historically divided into Berber people in the northwest and Egyptians in the east but from a modern perspective the region is both Arabized and Islamic.

This region, excluding Egypt and Sudan, is generally called the Maghreb by Arab speakers, meaning place of sunset or west. The language of the native population, however, is Berber, part of the same language family as Arabic. The word 'Berber' or 'Barber' links to the name Barbary Coast, first given by Europeans. Berber gives a local dialect to Arabic, which is the main language of the region. Generally the Arabization of the Maghreb has been a natural outcome of independence from France, the main colonial power in

Madeira (PT)

Canary Is. (ES)

LAÂ

WE

Nouâdhibo

LUXOR, EGYPT
The Ancient Egyptian temple complex at Karnak is situated on the east bank of the River Nile, close to the modern town of Luxor.

the area, although French remains the bureaucratic and commercial language in former colonies.

Separating Northern Africa from the rest of the continent is the vast Sahara Desert. Climate change over millennia has turned the Sahara from a fertile populated region into barren wilderness. However, with new technology, the natural reserves of the Sahara, which include oil and solar energy, may bring new importance to this wasteland.

The greatest natural feature affecting the people and culture of this region is the Nile Valley. Its pharaonic civilization shows agrarian and technological advances that are hard to comprehend. Later Egyptian civilization created centres of learning such as Alexandria that illuminated and informed the Greek and Roman worlds. Even today the Nile is at the heart of Egypt's economy with tourism and agriculture highly dependent on the second-longest river in the world, linking Egypt and its close and troubled neighbour, Sudan.

LIBYA
An oasis with date palms in the Sahara Desert.

NORTHERN AFRICA

MOROCCO

32° 00' N, 5° 00' W | 446,550 KM² | 172,414 MI² | UTC+0

Lying just fourteen kilometres from continental Europe, Morocco is often referred to as 'the gateway to Africa'.

Geography

Morocco is the only African country with an Atlantic and a Mediterranean coastline, tempering the climate of the fertile coastal plains. These plains are separated from the arid Sahara Desert by the Atlas Mountains, which are divided by the Moulouya River valley.

History

Originally inhabited by the Berbers, the area was later occupied by the Phoenicians, Carthaginians, Romans and Vandals. A series of Arab incursions in the early seventh century introduced Islam. European interest during the nineteenth century led to France and Spain establishing protectorates of parts of Morocco in the early twentieth century. Independence was gained in 1956 as a monarchy, although Ceuta and Melilla remain Spanish and a cause of tension with Spain. Between 1975 and 1979, Morocco annexed the Western Sahara, and despite a ceasefire in 1989, the territory remains disputed. Morocco's exotic blend of European, Arabic and African influences and relative political stability have made towns such as Marrakech and Fès popular tourist destinations.

Economy

The mainstay of the economy is the export of agricultural produce such as grain, fruit and vegetables. Fishing, phosphate mining and fertilizer production provide other sources of revenue, and tourism and manufacturing are growing.

FACT FILE

LOCAL NAME Kingdom of Morocco

CAPITAL CITY Rabat

CURRENCY Moroccan Dirham (MAD)

MEMBERSHIP WTO, OIC, LAS, AFDB

GOVERNMENT Constitutional Monarchy

POPULATION 34,343,219

POP. DENSITY 77/km²; /199/mi²

GDP 467.1 Billion US$

LANGUAGE(S) Arabic, Berber dialects, French (for business, government and diplomacy)

ETHNICITY Arab-Berber 99%

RELIGION Muslim 99%, Christian 1%

CLIMATE Mediterranean, becoming more extreme in the interior

REGIONAL DIVISIONS 16 Regions, the most densely populated being Greater Casablanca; 62 Prefectures and Provinces

DEPENDENCIES Claims Western Sahara

ECONOMIC ACTIVITIES Agriculture Phosphate Rock Mining and Processing, Food Processing, Leather Goods, Textiles, Construction, Tourism

NATURAL RESOURCES Phosphates, Iron Ore, Manganese, Lead, Zinc, Fish, Salt

ANTI-ATLAS MOUNTAINS
The village of Adal sits against the sandstone rockface in the Anti-Atlas Mountains.

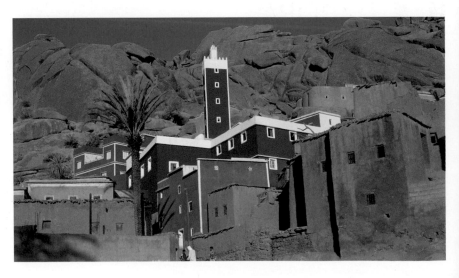

CEUTA
35°53' N, 5°18' W | 28 KM² | 11 MI² | UTC+1

MELILLA
35°18' N, 2°56' W | 20 KM² | 8 MI² | UTC+1

Ceuta and Melilla are two Spanish enclaves on the Moroccan coast, and are the only territories of the European Union located on the African continent. Both were former Carthaginian and Roman settlements, before being ruled by Berber dynasties.

During the fifteenth century Ceuta was conquered by the Portuguese and Melilla fell to Spain. The Spanish would then take Ceuta in 1580. Today, both are ports involved in trade, fishing and boat-building. Both enclaves are surrounded by fences which are intended to prevent illegal immigration into the European Community. However, these are only partially successful.

FACT FILE
LOCAL NAME	Ceuta
SOVEREIGN STATE	Spain
POPULATION	78,320
POP DENSITY	2,709/km²; 7,120/mi²
CURRENCY	Euro (EUR)
LANGUAGE(S)	Spanish, Arabic

FACT FILE
LOCAL NAME	Melilla
SOVEREIGN STATE	Spain
POPULATION	69,440
POP DENSITY	3,472/km²; 8,680/mi²
CURRENCY	Euro (EUR)
LANGUAGE(S)	Spanish, Tarifit-Berber

CANARY ISLANDS
28°06' N, 15°24' W | 7,447 KM² | 2,878 MI² | UTC

FACT FILE
LOCAL NAME	Autonomous Community of the Canary Islands
SOVEREIGN STATE	Spain
MAIN CITY	Las Palmas de Gran Canaria/Santa Cruz de Tenerife
CURRENCY	Euro (EUR)
GOVERNMENT	Regional Autonomous Government
POPULATION	1,995,833
POP. DENSITY	268/km²; 693/mi²
GDP	32.6 Billion US$
LANGUAGE(S)	Spanish
ETHNICITY	Spanish
RELIGION	Roman Catholic 90%
CLIMATE	Maritime, Subtropical

Situated off Morocco's Atlantic coast, the subtropical Canary Islands consist of seven islands, including Tenerife, Fuerteventura, Gran Canaria, and Lanzarote, and numerous islets. The islands form two autonomous provinces of Spain. Known to the Phoenicians and Romans in antiquity, the islands were claimed by the Portuguese during the 1300s, before being ceded to Spain in 1479. The economy of the islands depends mainly on tourism, although farming and fishing are also of importance.

MADEIRA
32°39' N, 16°55' W | 828 KM² | 320 MI² | UTC

FACT FILE
LOCAL NAME	Madeira Autonomous Region
SOVEREIGN STATE	Portugal
MAIN CITY	Funchal
CURRENCY	Euro (EUR)
GOVERNMENT	Autonomous Region
POPULATION	245,806
POP. DENSITY	295/km²; 195/mi²
GDP	5.83 Billion US$
LANGUAGE(S)	Portuguese
ETHNICITY	European
RELIGION	Roman Catholic
CLIMATE	Maritime, Subtropical

Madeira consists of two populated islands, Madeira and Porto Santo, and numerous uninhabited smaller islands. The island group lies in the Atlantic Ocean west of Morocco and about 990 kilometres south of Portugal, of which it is an autonomous region. After settlement by the Portuguese in the fifteenth century, Madeira became a centre for the production of sugarcane and Madeira wine, which remain major exports. Fishing, tourism and textiles are also significant.

NORTHERN AFRICA

WESTERN SAHARA

24° 30' N, 13° 00' W | 266,000KM² | 102,703MI² | UTC

Morocco has occupied the Western Sahara since the 1970s, but its right to do so is disputed.

Consisting almost entirely of open desert, the Western Sahara is hot and dry, with very little rainfall. Between 1884 and 1975 the territory was a Spanish colony known as Spanish Sahara. Following Spanish withdrawal in 1975, Morocco and Mauritania partitioned the territory between them. In the face of a guerrilla war of independence by the nationalist Polisario Front, in 1979 Mauritania relinquished control of its section, which was annexed by Morocco.

A ceasefire between Moroccan forces and Polisario began in 1991, but negotiations over the status of the territory have been stalled since 1996. Although Western Sahara has vast

phosphate deposits, the standard of living is low, with much of the population occupied in fishing and nomadic herding.

FACT FILE

LOCAL NAME	Sahrawi Arab Democratic Republic
CAPITAL/MAIN CITY	Laâyoune
CURRENCY	Moroccan Dirham (MAD)
MEMBERSHIP	Morroccan Administration; Nominal Government supported by Algeria
GOVERNMENT	Nominal Republic (in dispute)
POPULATION	393,831
POPULATION DENSITY	1.5/km²; 4/mi²
GDP	N.A.
LANGUAGE(S)	Hassaniya Arabic, Moroccan Arabic
ETHNICITY	Arab, Berber
RELIGION	Muslim 99%
CLIMATE	Arid

TUNISIA

34° 00' N, 9° 00' E | 163,610 KM² | 63,170 MI² | UTC+2

The smallest country in North Africa, Tunisia is mountainous in the north, with fertile coastal plains, while the centre consists of a large depression containing several salt lakes, and the south is desert.

Occupied over the centuries by the Phoenicians, Carthiginians, Romans, Arabs and Turks, Tunisia became a French protectorate in 1881. Independence was granted in 1956, and in 1957 a one-party republic was established. Unrest in the 1970s led to political liberalization in the 1980s, but the party of government remains unchanged. The economy is diverse, with exports including agricultural products such as cereals, grapes and olive oil, as well as phosphates and textiles. Tourism is also a major source of revenue, the ancient coastal city of Carthage and the Roman amphitheatre at El-Djem being two of the most important attractions. Women make up a relatively large percentage of the workforce in comparison to other Arab countries. In 1995 Tunisia signed a free-trade agreement with the European Union.

FACT FILE

LOCAL NAME	Tunisian Republic
CAPITAL CITY	Tunis
CURRENCY	Tunisian Dinar (TND)
MEMBERSHIP	WTO, LAS, OIC, AU, AFDB
GOVERNMENT	Republic
POPULATION	10,383,578
POP. DENSITY	64/km²; 164/mi²
GDP	78 Billion US$
LANGUAGE(S)	Arabic, Berber, French (commerce)
ETHNICITY	Arab 98%, European 1%
RELIGION	Muslim 98%
CLIMATE	Mediterranean in north, Arid in south

NORTHERN AFRICA

ALGERIA

28° 00' N, 3° 00' E | 2,381,740 KM² | 919,595 MI² | UTC+2

Although blighted by internal conflict in the 1990s, government attempts at reconciliation and a growing economy have brought Algeria relative stability in recent years.

Geography

Algeria is the second largest country in Africa. Most of the population is concentrated in the coastal region, as the Sahara Desert covers around 90 per cent of the land. Most of the territory south of the Atlas Saharien is desert, although the terrain varies from the sand dunes of the Grand Ergs to the sandstone plateaus surrounding the Hoggar mountains.

History

Originally home to the nomadic Berbers, Algeria was successively conquered by the Phoenicians, Romans, Vandals, and Byzantines, before being brought under Arab control during the seventh century. By the sixteenth century, it was part of the Ottoman Empire, with the city of Algiers providing an important base for Barbary pirates. After a campaign beginning with a brutal invasion in 1830, Algeria fell to the French during the nineteenth century. A devastating guerrilla war from 1954 to 1962 resulted in France conceding independence, prompting a mass exodus of European settlers. Virtual civil war erupted between the government and militant Muslims in the 1990s but constitutional reforms and amnesties have since brought relative peace.

Economy

Algeria is one of the richer nations in Africa owing to its vast reserves of natural resources such as oil and gas, which account for over half of GDP, although poverty is still widespread. Agriculture is mostly confined to the coastal plains of the north, where cereals, grapes, olives and citrus fruits are grown and livestock such as sheep and goats are raised.

HOGGAR MOUNTAINS
The Atakor Pinnacles at sunset.

FACT FILE

LOCAL NAME People's Democratic Republic of Algeria

CAPITAL CITY Algiers

CURRENCY Algerian Dinar (DZD)

MEMBERSHIP LAS, OPEC, AU

GOVERNMENT Presidential Republic

POPULATION 33,769,670

POP. DENSITY 14/km²; 37/sq mi²

GDP 224.7 Billion US $

LANGUAGE(S) Arabic, French, Berber

ETHNICITY Arab-Berber 99%

RELIGION Sunni Muslim 99%, Christian and Jewish 1%

CLIMATE Arid, Semi-arid, Mediterranean

REGIONAL DIVISIONS 48 Provinces, named after the main city of each area. Alger contains the capital Algiers.

ECONOMIC ACTIVITIES Agriculture, Petroleum, Natural Gas, Light Industries, Mining, Electrical, Petrochemical, Food Processing

NATURAL RESOURCES Petroleum, Natural Gas, Iron Ore, Phosphates, Uranium, Lead, Zinc

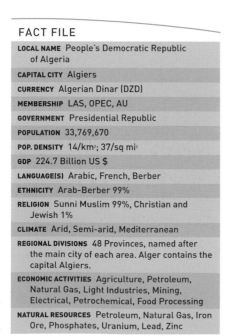

LIBYA

25° 00' N, 17° 00' E | 1,759,540 KM² | 679,359 MI² | UTC+1

Since Colonel Qaddafi came to power in 1969, Libya has been viewed with suspicion by Western governments. However, its international standing has improved in recent years.

Geography

Libya is one of the largest countries in Africa, but the inhospitable Sahara Desert covers over 90 per cent of the country, so most of the population is concentrated along the Mediterranean coastline in the north, where the climate is more temperate, with winters that are warm and relatively wet. Inland, average annual rainfall seldom exceeds 100 mm and average daily temperatures remain above 20°C year round. Apart from a small number of inhabited oases, the desert is largely featureless, although granite massifs rise in the south.

History

Originally inhabited by the Berbers, Libya was successively occupied by the Phoenicians, Carthiginians, Greeks, Romans, Vandals and Byzantines, before being conquered by Arabs in the seventh century. During the sixteenth century, Libya came under Ottoman rule until Italy took control in 1911. The country gained independence in 1951, but in 1969 the monarchy was overthrown by Colonel Muammar al-Qaddafi, who remains in power to this day. Qaddafi's support for militant and revolutionary groups world-wide left Libya internationally isolated until the late 1990s, when Qaddafi began to normalize relations with the West.

SABRATHA, NEAR TRIPOLI
The remains of the Roman theatre at Sabratha.

Economy

Libya was one of the poorest countries in the world until oil was discovered in the 1950s. Today it is one of the richest African nations. Since the lifting of international sanctions in 1999, income from tourism and foreign investment has also increased.

FACT FILE

LOCAL NAME Great Socialist People's Libyan Arab Jamahiriya

CAPITAL CITY Tripoli

CURRENCY Libyan Dinar (LYD)

MEMBERSHIP OIC, LAS, AU, AFDB

GOVERNMENT Authoritarian State

POPULATION 6,173,579

POP. DENSITY 3.5/km²; 9/mi²

GDP 74.75 Billion US$

LANGUAGE(S) Arabic, Italian, English

ETHNICITY Berber and Arab 97%

RELIGION Sunni Muslim 97%

CLIMATE Mediterranean along coast, Arid desert interior

REGIONAL DIVISIONS 32 Municipalities

ECONOMIC ACTIVITIES Petroleum-related, Manufacturing

NATURAL RESOURCES Oil

EGYPT

27° 00' N, 30° 00' E | 1,001,450 KM² | 378,715 MI² | UTC+2

Famed for its ancient civilization and historic monuments, including the Great Pyramid at Giza, today Egypt is regarded as one of the most influential nations in the Arab world.

Geography

Although Egypt is one of Africa's most populous countries, much of the country is covered by the Sahara Desert, so the majority of its people live in the fertile Nile valley and delta and around the Suez Canal, which links the Mediterranean Sea with the Red Sea. The River Nile is undoubtedly Egypt's most significant geographical feature, flowing the length of the country from the Sudan border, through Lake Nasser, which was created by the construction of the Aswân High Dam in the 1960s, to its delta on the Mediterranean coast. To the east of the Nile lie the Eastern or Arabian Desert, the Red Sea Hills and the largely uninhabited Sinai Peninsula, which is generally considered to be part of Asia. To

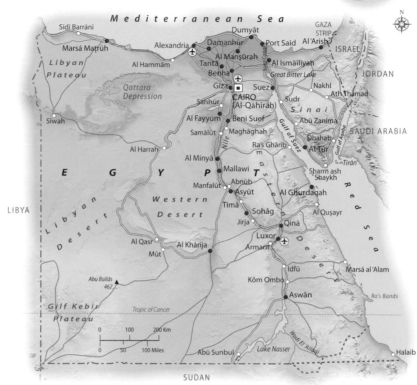

the west is the vast Western and Libyan Desert. Egypt is one of the hottest, sunniest places in the world, and what little rainfall there is tends to occur in the Mediterranean region in winter.

History

The Nile valley became home over 5,000 years ago to one of the earliest civilizations in the world, which flourished for around 3,000 years. Its development was marked by achievements such as irrigated farming, urbanization and literacy, and it left behind some of the largest man-made structures on Earth, the pyramids. Ancient Egypt's gradual decline made it vulnerable to successive conquerors, including the Persians, Greeks and Romans, followed by Arab invaders in the seventh century. During the sixteenth

THE NILE
The Ancient Egyptians based their settlements around the River Nile and farmed on its fertile flood plain. This land is still intensively farmed today.

century it was incorporated into the Ottoman Empire, but British influence increased during the nineteenth century, particularly after the construction of the Suez Canal in 1869, and it became a British protectorate in 1914. Partial independence was gained in 1922, although it was another thirty years before Egypt became an independent republic, by which time the creation of the state of Israel had sparked conflict in the region. Aggression between the two states surfaced again in 1956 in the Suez Crisis; in 1967 with the Six Day War, when the Sinai Peninsula was lost to Israel; and in 1973, when Egypt attempted to recapture the Sinai Peninsula. In 1979 a peace treaty was signed with Israel, attracting fierce criticism from much of the Arab world. Growing Islamic militant activity within Egypt since the 1990s has been met by harsh measures, causing the government to be accused of using anti-terror legislation to suppress human rights and religious freedoms.

Economy

Although Egypt is one of the most industrialized countries in Africa, agriculture continues to represent a significant source of national income, and employs around 30 per cent of the country's workforce. Principal crops include cereals, sugarcane, beans and cotton, which supports a large textile industry. Other major exports include petroleum, natural gas, phosphates and other minerals. Over half of Egypt's GDP comes from tourism and revenues from traffic through the Suez Canal.

FACT FILE

LOCAL NAME	Arab Republic of Egypt
CAPITAL CITY	Cairo
CURRENCY	Egyptian Pound (EGP)
MEMBERSHIP	WTO, LAS, OIC, AU, AFDB
GOVERNMENT	Semi-presidential Republic
POPULATION	81,713,517
POP. DENSITY	82/km²; 216/mi²
GDP	404 Billion US$
LANGUAGE(S)	Arabic, English, French
ETHNICITY	Egyptian 100%
RELIGION	Muslim (mostly Sunni) 90%, Coptic 9%
CLIMATE	Semi-arid, Arid
REGIONAL DIVISIONS	7 geographical Regions divided into 29 Governates
ECONOMIC ACTIVITIES	Agriculture, Textiles, Food processing, Tourism, Chemicals, Pharmaceuticals, Construction, Cement, Metals, Light manufacturing
NATURAL RESOURCES	Petroleum, Natural Gas, Iron Ore, Phosphates, Manganese, Limestone, Gypsum, Talc, Asbestos, Lead, Zinc

GIZA
The pyramids at Giza, just outside modern-day Cairo, are the most famous monuments of Ancient Egypt. The largest of the three was built for King Khufu in about 2528 BC. The other two large pyramids at Giza belong to Khufu's son Khafre and his grandson Menkaure.

SUDAN

15° 00' N | 30° 00' E | 2,505,810 KM2 | 967,499 MI2 | UTC+3

The largest country in Africa, Sudan is also one of the most culturally diverse. This diversity has caused years of division and conflict since independence.

Geography

The terrain ranges from arid desert in the north to the swamps, rain forests and mountains of the equatorial south. The River Nile and its tributaries, the White Nile and the Blue Nile, which converge at the capital Khartoum, flow the length of the country from south to north.

History

The Nubian kingdom of Kush flourished in Sudan from around 1000 BC to AD 350. Coptic Christianity was introduced in the sixth century AD, and Islam in the seventh century. From the eighth century onwards, the north was conquered by a succession of Arab powers before coming under Egyptian rule in the early nineteenth century. Egypt and Britain subdued the whole country in the nineteenth century and ruled until Sudan became independent in 1956. The divisions between the Arab Muslim north and the African Christian and animist south have caused two civil wars (1955–72, 1983–2004) since independence. A fragile peace now exists between north and south, but there has been conflict in the western province of Darfur since 2003.

Economy

The country has prospered through oil exports since 1999, but the disruption of civil conflict has left most Sudanese very poor. About 80 per cent are dependent on agriculture for a living, but persistent droughts and an emphasis on cash crops have caused domestic food shortages in recent years.

GEZIRA
Women trample down a mound of cotton during harvest time at Gezira, in the fertile area between the Blue and White Niles.

FACT FILE

LOCAL NAME Republic of Sudan

CAPITAL CITY Khartoum

CURRENCY Sudanese Pound (SDG)

MEMBERSHIP OIC, LAS, AUC, AFDB

GOVERNMENT Government of National Unity

POPULATION 40,218,455

POP. DENSITY 16/km²; 42/mi²

GDP 80.71 Billion US$

LANGUAGE(S) Arabic, English, Nubian, Ta Bedawie, diverse dialects of Nilotic, Nilo-Hamitic, Sudanic languages

ETHNICITY Black 52%, Arab 39%, Beja 6%

RELIGION Sunni Muslim 70%, Christian 5% , Indigenous beliefs 25%

CLIMATE Tropical in south, Arid Desert in north

REGIONAL DIVISIONS Regions of Northern and Southern Sudan and Darfur comprise 25 States subdivided into 133 Districts

ECONOMIC ACTIVITIES Agriculture, Oil and Electricity Production, Mineral Extraction

NATURAL RESOURCES Oil, Natural Gas, Gold, Silver, Chrome, Asbestos, Manganese, Gypsum, Mica, Zinc, Iron, Lead, Uranium, Copper, Kaolin, Cobalt, Granite, Nickel and Tin

NORTHERN AFRICA

WESTERN AFRICA

**Bounded by the Sahara in the north and the Atlantic Ocean
to the west and south, Western Africa accounts for about one fifth of the continent's area.**

Geographically the terrain is relatively low-lying, being mainly below 300 metres above sea level. At the region's northern boundary is a semi-arid area known as the Sahel, a band of savannah that stretches the width of Africa. The Niger is the third-longest river in Africa and the most important in the region; its basin forms the most significant geographical feature of West Africa. The massive Niger delta empties into the Gulf of Guinea and its many rivulets support fishing, agriculture and trade for the local population.

As well as its own indigenous history, with empires such as Ghana, Mali and Benin, West Africa has been important to the colonial powers of Europe since the sixteenth century as a focus for the slave trade and a staging-point for the long sail east to the Indies. Colonized by Britain, France and Portugal, the country borders in the region have little to do with local demography or natural boundaries. Whether the area would have been more politically stable without the influence of colonial rule is open to debate but the region is notorious for military coups, inter-tribal conflict and civil unrest.

Economically the region is one of Africa's most productive with the economies of Nigeria, Ghana and Côte d'Ivoire being relatively advanced. However, the countries forming this region depend heavily on foreign aid; regular rebellions

COUNTRY	PAGE
Benin	236
Burkina Faso	236
Cape Verde	232
Côte d'Ivoire	239
Ghana	237
Guinea	241
Guinea-Bissau	240
Liberia	238
Mali	233
Mauritania	230
Niger	234
Nigeria	235
Senegal	231
Sierra Leone	240
The Gambia	232
Togo	238

SENEGAL
A group of chimpanzees cool down in a shady pool.

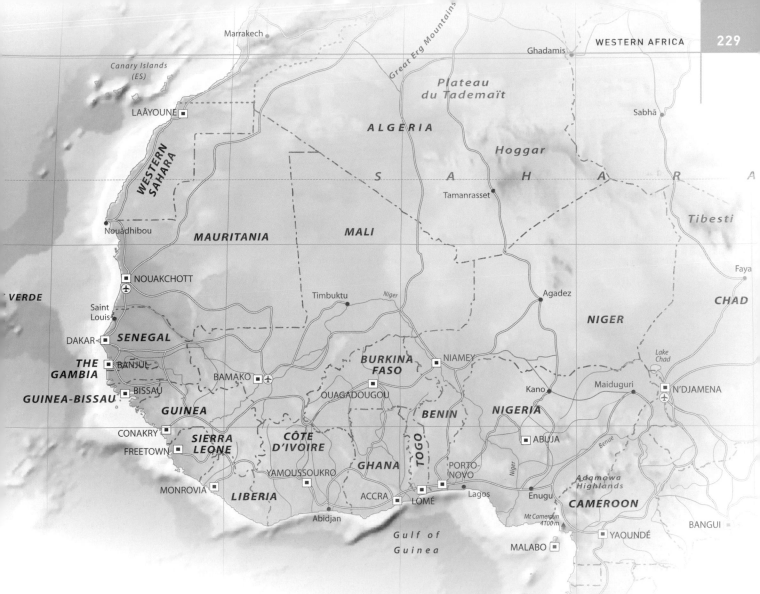

and coups are fuelled by high levels of corruption and the population is in the grip of an AIDS epidemic. Despite unrest and high levels of pollution, this region has many tourist attractions, from beaches to wildlife and, for the adventurous, treks to the interior to explore cities like Timbuktu and countries such as Burkina Faso. More recently the region's economy has benefited from the popularity of its music – especially in Mali and Senegal – and from cacao production in Ghana and Côte d'Ivoire – the world's largest producer.

MALI
A mud village in the Sanga region of Mali.

MAURITANIA

20° 00′ N, 12° 00′ W | 1,030,700 KM² | 397,954 MI² | UTC+1

Mauritania, one of Africa's newest oil producers, stretches from the Arab Maghreb region to sub-Saharan Africa.

Geography

Around 75 per cent of Mauritania is flat desert, with hilly uplands in the centre of the country. The climate is inhospitable, with average daily temperatures in the Sahara ranging from 0°C to 49°C, and the dusty harmattan wind in winter.

History

In the eleventh century Mauritania was the cradle of the Muslim Almoravid dynasty, which spread its religion throughout the region and subjugated the Ghana Empire, North Africa and parts of Spain. European interest in the area began in the sixteenth century, and it came under French control in the course of the nineteenth century. The country became independent as the Islamic Republic of Mauritania in 1960 and annexed part of Western Sahara in 1976, relinquishing it after three years because of guerrilla opposition to its rule. There are ethnic tensions between Mauritania's southern Afro-Mauritanian and northern Arab-Berber populations.

Economy

Mauritania has extensive deposits of iron ore, which accounts for nearly 40 per cent of exports, although exploitation of other mineral resources, including gold and diamonds, has been limited by the poor infrastructure. Offshore oil extraction began in 2006. Around half of the population depends on agriculture and livestock for subsistence. Agriculture is concentrated in the area around the River Senegal, which forms part of the southern border.

ADRAR PLATEAU, NORTHERN MAURITANIA
Archaeologists have found evidence of Neolithic settlements in the Adrar Plateau.

FACT FILE

LOCAL NAME	Islamic Republic of Mauritania
CAPITAL CITY	Nouakchott
CURRENCY	Ouguiya (MRO)
MEMBERSHIP	AU, LAS, AMU, G-77, OIC, WTO
GOVERNMENT	Democratic Republic
POPULATION	3,203,648
POP. DENSITY	3/km²; 8/mi²
GDP	5.95 Billion US$
LANGUAGE(S)	Arabic, Pulaar, Soninke, Wolof, French, Hassaniya
ETHNICITY	Mixed Moor/Black 40%, Moor 30%, Black 30%
RELIGION	Muslim
CLIMATE	Arid
REGIONAL DIVISIONS	12 Regions and 1 Capital District are divided into 44 Departments
DEPENDENCIES	None
ECONOMIC ACTIVITIES	Agriculture, Fish Processing, Mining of Iron Ore and Gypsum
NATURAL RESOURCES	Iron Ore, Gypsum, Copper, Phosphate, Diamonds, Gold, Oil, Fish

SENEGAL

14° 00' N, 14° 00' W | 196,190 KM² | 75,749 MI² | UTC+0

Senegal's capital, Dakar, is located on the Cap-Vert peninsula, the westernmost point of mainland Africa.

Geography

The terrain of low, rolling plains rises to foothills in the southeast; the north of the country is semi-desert. The enclave of The Gambia almost divides Senegal in the south. Senegal's climate is tropical in the south and arid, becoming increasingly dry, in the north. The coasts are cooled by the northern trade winds.

History

Eastern Senegal was once part of the Ghana Empire (c. 750–1076). Later the region came under the influence of the Mandingo empires (c. 1300–1400), and the Wolof Empire dominated northern Senegal from 1350 until 1890. The area around Dakar, colonized in the 1840s, was the the earliest French settlement in sub-Saharan Africa; from here France was able to expand into the Senegalese interior. The French colonies of Senegal and the French Sudan merged in 1959 and became independent as the short-lived Mali Federation in 1960; Senegal seceded a few months later. The Socialist Party dominated post-independence politics for forty years until 2000, when Abdoulaye Wade was elected president.

Economy

Senegal is predominantly rural and has limited resources. Agriculture employs around two-thirds of its population. The main exports are fish, groundnuts and phosphates. Senegal also has one of the most developed tourist industries in Africa, concentrated around Dakar and the beaches of Casamance in the south, which contributes considerably to the economy, along with remittances from abroad. However, it still depends heavily on foreign assistance.

SAINT LOUIS
Fishing boats anchored at Saint Louis.

FACT FILE

LOCAL NAME Republic of Senegal

CAPITAL CITY Dakar

CURRENCY Communauté Financière Africaine Franc (XOF)

MEMBERSHIP AU, ECOWAS, G-15, G-77, OIC, WTO

GOVERNMENT Semi-presidential Republic

POPULATION 12,687,621

POP. DENSITY 65/km²; 168/mi²

GDP 20.6 Billion US$

LANGUAGE(S) French, Wolof, Pulaar, Jola, Mandinka

ETHNICITY Wolof 43%, Pular 24%, Serer 15%, Jola 4%, Mandinka 3%

RELIGION Sunni Muslim 94%, Roman Catholic 5%

CLIMATE Tropical, Arid, Semi-arid

REGIONAL DIVISIONS 11 Regions divided into 34 Departments; each Region capital has the same name as the Region

ECONOMIC ACTIVITIES Agricultural and Fish Processing, Phosphate Mining, Fertilizer Production, Petroleum Refining, Mining (Iron Ore, Zircon and Gold), Construction Materials, Ship Construction and Repair

NATURAL RESOURCES Fish, Phosphates, Iron Ore

THE GAMBIA

13° 28' N, 16° 34' W | 10,300 KM² | 3,977 MI² | UTC+0

The Gambia is a strip of land 322 kilometres long but only 50 kilometres wide. The smallest country on the African continent, it is surrounded by Senegal on three sides.

The country lies mostly in the Gambia river basin and floodplain, with savannah and low hills beyond. The Gambia was part of the Ghana, Mali and Songhai Empires and was later subject to Portuguese and French influences before becoming a British colony in the nineteenth century. Since independence in 1965, the country has enjoyed relative stability, with only two presidents. It has no significant mineral or other natural resources, so around 75 per cent of the population depends on subsistence agriculture. Tourism is a growing source of revenue.

FAJARA
The beach at Fajara, near Bakau, is one of the most beautiful in The Gambia.

FACT FILE

LOCAL NAME Republic of The Gambia
CAPITAL CITY Banjul
CURRENCY Dalasi (GMD)
MEMBERSHIP AU, Commonwealth of Nations, ECOWAS, G-77, OIC, WTO
GOVERNMENT Republic
POPULATION 1,754,068
POP. DENSITY 170/km²; 441/mi²
GDP 2.11 Billion US$
LANGUAGE(S) English, Mandinka, Wolof, Fula
ETHNICITY Mandinka 42%, Fula 18%, Wolof 16%, Jola 10%, Serahuli 9%
RELIGION Muslim 90%, Christian 9%
CLIMATE Tropical

CAPE VERDE

16° 00' N, 24° 00' W | 4,033 KM² | 1,557 MI² | UTC-1

An archipelago of eighteen islands, Cape Verde is located about 500 kilometres west of the coast of Senegal.

The archipelago consists of two groups, Leeward and Windward islands, with

Santiago, location of the capital Praia, being the largest island and part of the Leeward group. Colonized by Portugal in the sixteenth century, Cape Verde's importance grew with the slave trade; its harbours, at the crossroads of Atlantic traffic, retain strategic importance today. The climate is cooler than that of the West African mainland but rainfall is low and the shortage of water affects agriculture. Political rebellion led to independence from Portugal in 1975 although Cape Verde retains strong economic ties with Portugal and its former territories in West Africa. Its economy is stable and supports a higher standard of living than in West Africa. Most food is imported but local fish is

plentiful. The future depends on continuing investment, including development aid, the increasing popularity of tourism and the importance of Praia and Mindelo ports.

FACT FILE

LOCAL NAME Republic of Cape Verde
CAPITAL CITY Praia
CURRENCY Cape Verdean Escudo (CVE)
MEMBERSHIP AU, ECOWAS, G-77, WTO
GOVERNMENT Republic
POPULATION 542,422
POP. DENSITY 135/km²; 348/mi²
GDP 1.60 Billion US$
LANGUAGE(S) Portuguese, Crioulo
ETHNICITY Creole (mulatto) 71%, African 28%
RELIGION Roman Catholic 91%, Muslim 3%
CLIMATE Temperate

WESTERN AFRICA

MALI

17° 00′ N, 4° 00′ W | 1,240,192 KM² | 478,839 MI² | UTC+0

Mali, a landlocked state in the Sahel, has Africa's fastest growing city, Bamako, as its capital.

Geography

Around 65 per cent of Mali is desert or semi-desert, and its terrain is mainly flat, with plains to the north, savannah to the south and rugged hills to the north-east. The climate ranges from arid in the north to subtropical in the south.

History

Formerly known as French Sudan, Mali is a creation of late-nineteenth-century French colonialism. Malians take pride in the heritage of the Mali Empire (c. 1250–1600) and the Songhai Empire (c. 1340–1591), which controlled the trans-Saharan trade in precious materials such as gold, copper and salt. Under the Mali Empire, the ancient city of Timbuktu was a centre of both trans-Saharan trade and Islamic learning. Today it is an entrepôt for rock salt and retains one of the oldest Islamic universities in Africa, the Sankoré Madrasah. The country became independent in 1960 after a brief partnership with Senegal in 1959 in the Federation of Mali. Military or one-party regimes dominated post-independence politics until 1992, when multiparty civilian government was re-established.

DJENNÉ
The Great Mosque at Djenné is the largest mud-brick building in the world.

Economy

Despite being one of the largest gold producers in Africa, Mali is among the poorest countries in the world and is heavily dependent on foreign aid. About 80 per cent of the population supports itself through subsistence agriculture, animal husbandry and fishing.

FACT FILE

LOCAL NAME Republic of Mali
CAPITAL CITY Bamako
CURRENCY Communauté Financière Africaine Franc (XOF)
MEMBERSHIP AU, ECOWAS, G-77, OIC, WTO
GOVERNMENT Republic
POPULATION 12,716,081
POP. DENSITY 10/km²; 27/mi²
GDP 13.47 Billion US$
LANGUAGE(S) French, Bambara
ETHNICITY Mande 50% (Bambara, Malinke, Soninke), Peul 17%, Voltaic 12%, Songhai 6%, Tuareg and Moor 10%
RELIGION Muslim 90%, Indigenous beliefs 9%, Christian 1%
CLIMATE Arid, Semi-arid, Tropical
REGIONAL DIVISIONS 3 natural zones are divided into 8 Regions and 1 Capital district; the regions are divided into 49 Sub-regions
ECONOMIC ACTIVITIES Agriculture, Food Processing, Construction, Phosphate and Gold Mining, Textiles, Fish Processing, Metalworking, Light Manufacturing
NATURAL RESOURCES Gold, Phosphates, Kaolin, Salt, Limestone, Uranium, Gypsum, Granite, Hydropower; Deposits known but not exploited – Bauxite, Iron Ore, Manganese, Tin, Copper

WESTERN AFRICA

NIGER

16° 00' N 8° 00' E | 1,267,000 KM² | 489,678 MI² | UTC+1

Landlocked Niger is the largest country in West Africa, lying in both the Sahara Desert and the semi-arid Sahel region.

Geography

Over 80 per cent of Niger is desert and the remainder, in the south, is savannah. The climate is mostly very hot and dry, with average temperatures ranging from 31° to 41°C. In the extreme south, where most of the population is concentrated, the climate is tropical.

History

Before becoming a French colony in 1922, Niger had long occupied an economically important position on trans-Saharan trade routes. Various West African empires, including the Songhai, Mali and Hausa states, claimed control over parts of the region between the eleventh and the nineteenth centuries. After gaining independence from France in 1960, Niger was under military or single-party rule from the 1970s until 1991. Public agitation brought multiparty elections in 1993, but it was 1999 before stable civilian government was achieved. Present-day Niger is mainly composed of the Hausa, Djerma, Tuareg and Fulani ethnic groups.

Economy

Niger is one of the poorest countries in the world, with minimal government services and a heavy reliance on international aid. The largely agrarian and subsistence-based economy is frequently disrupted by extended droughts, common in the Sahel region and desertification is further reducing the area of land suitable for cultivation. Cowpeas, cotton, peanuts, millet, sorghum and cassava are the main crops. The most important export is uranium, accounting for nearly one-third of the country's exports.

OASIS
Farmers harvest their crop at an oasis in the desert.

FACT FILE

LOCAL NAME Republic of Niger

CAPITAL CITY Niamey

CURRENCY Communauté Financière Africaine Franc (XOF)

MEMBERSHIP AU, ECOWAS, G-77, OIC, WTO

GOVERNMENT Republic

POPULATION 14,730,798

POP. DENSITY 12/km²; 30/mi²

GDP 8.9 Billion US$

LANGUAGE(S) French, Hausa, Djerma

ETHNICITY Hausa 55%, Djerma 21%, Fulani 10%, Tuareg 9%, Peuhl 9%, Kanouri Manga 5%

RELIGION Muslim 80%, Other (includes Indigenous beliefs and Christian) 20%

CLIMATE Arid, Semi-arid, Tropical in extreme south

REGIONAL DIVISIONS 3 natural zones, northern, central and southern, are divided into 8 Administrative Regions and 1 Capital District

ECONOMIC ACTIVITIES Agriculture, Livestock Products, Uranium Mining, Cement, Brick, Textiles, Food Processing, Chemicals, Slaughterhouses, Construction, Production of Soaps, Detergents and Bottled Drinks

NATURAL RESOURCES Uranium, Coal, Iron Ore, Tin, Phosphates, Gold, Molybdenum, Gypsum, Salt, Petroleum

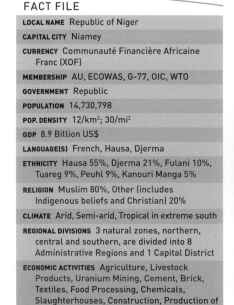

NIGERIA

10° 00' N, 8° 00' E | 923,768 KM² | 356,667 MI² | UTC+1

Nigeria, named after the great River Niger, is Africa's most populous country.

Geography

The coast is composed of mangrove swamps and the vast delta of the Niger where it enters the Gulf of Guinea. The delta covers over 320 kilometres and is the country's main oil-producing region. Inland, tropical forest gradually turns to savannah and then semi-desert. The climate is equatorial in the south, tropical in the centre and arid in the north.

History

The modern state of Nigeria, created in 1914 when Britain united several of its colonies, has more than 250 ethnic groups. The three

that dominate are the Hausa and Fulani in the north, the Yoruba in the west and the Igbo in the southeast. Since independence in 1960, Nigeria has undergone a number of military coups and conflicts between, and within, these three ethnocentric regions, including a civil war (1967–70) when Igbos in the eastern region attempted to secede as the Republic of Biafra. However, in 1999 a new constitution was adopted, ending almost sixteen years of military rule, and the state is now experiencing its longest period of civilian government since independence. Government is based in the city of Abuja, built in the centre of the country after the civil war.

Economy

The economy has been heavily dependent on oil since the 1970s, when it experienced its first oil boom. Successive governments have attempted to diversify but progress has been undermined by corruption and mismanagement. Lagos, the economic and financial capital, is the largest conurbation in Africa, with about 9 million inhabitants, and Port Harcourt is the centre of the oil industry.

NIGER DELTA
Oil is extracted in the delta of the River Niger.

FACT FILE

LOCAL NAME Federal Republic of Nigeria

CAPITAL CITY Abuja

CURRENCY Naira (NGN)

MEMBERSHIP AU, C, D-8, ECOWAS, G-15, G-77, OAS (observer), OIC, OPEC, WTO

GOVERNMENT Federal Republic

POPULATION 151,478,125

POP. DENSITY 164/km²; 425/mi²

GDP 292.7 Billion US$

LANGUAGE(S) English, Hausa, Yoruba, Igbo (Ibo), Fulani

ETHNICITY Hausa and Fulani 29%, Yoruba 21%, Igbo (Ibo) 18%, Ijaw 10%, Kanuri 4%, Ibibio 4%, Tiv 3%

RELIGION Muslim 50%, Christian 40%, Indigenous beliefs 10%

CLIMATE Equatorial, Tropical, Arid, Semi-arid

REGIONAL DIVISIONS 36 States and 1 Territory further subdivided into 774 Local Government Areas (LGAs)

ECONOMIC ACTIVITIES Coal, Tin, Columbite Mining, Agriculture: Palm Oil, Peanuts, Cotton, Rubber, Wood, Hides and Skins, Textiles, Cement and other Construction Materials, Food Products, Footwear, Chemicals, Fertilizer, Printing, Ceramics, Steel, Small Commercial Ship Construction and Repair, Beverages

NATURAL RESOURCES Natural Gas, Petroleum, Tin, Iron Ore, Coal, Limestone, Niobium, Lead, Zinc, Arable Land

BENIN

9° 30' N, 2° 15' E | 112,620 KM² | 43,483 MI² | UTC+1

Benin, now one of Africa's most stable democracies, was known as Dahomey until 1975, when the country was renamed after a coup.

The climate is tropical in the south and semi-arid in the north, with relatively little rain. Most of Benin's population lives on the southern coastal plains. In the seventeenth and eighteenth centuries, slave-trading flourished in the kingdom of Dahomey, causing the area to be labelled the Slave Coast; by 1700, some 20,000 slaves were exported annually. After independence in 1960, the country experienced several coups and seventeen years of one-party rule,

returning to multi-party democracy in 1991. While Benin has recently experienced steady economic growth, its rapid population

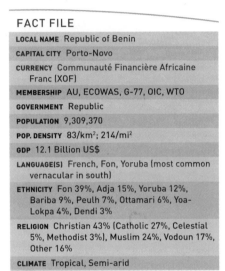

FACT FILE

LOCAL NAME Republic of Benin

CAPITAL CITY Porto-Novo

CURRENCY Communauté Financière Africaine Franc (XOF)

MEMBERSHIP AU, ECOWAS, G-77, OIC, WTO

GOVERNMENT Republic

POPULATION 9,309,370

POP. DENSITY 83/km²; 214/mi²

GDP 12.1 Billion US$

LANGUAGE(S) French, Fon, Yoruba (most common vernacular in south)

ETHNICITY Fon 39%, Adja 15%, Yoruba 12%, Bariba 9%, Peulh 7%, Ottamari 6%, Yoa-Lokpa 4%, Dendi 3%

RELIGION Christian 43% (Catholic 27%, Celestial 5%, Methodist 3%), Muslim 24%, Vodoun 17%, Other 16%

CLIMATE Tropical, Semi-arid

increase has offset much of this expansion and the economy remains underdeveloped.

BURKINA FASO

13° 00' N, 2° 00' W | 274,200 KM² | 105,869 MI² | UTC+0

Landlocked Burkina Faso (meaning 'land of honest men') was known as Upper Volta until 1984.

Burkina Faso is partly located in the Sahel and although the country has three major rivers (the Black Volta, the Red Volta and the White Volta), most of the terrain is arid and the soil infertile. The Mossi make up nearly half of the population, but the country has over sixty other ethnic groups. Independence from France in 1960 was followed by three decades of instability and several coups, concluding with Blaise Compaoré's seizure of power in 1987; he has remained president since the return to multiparty civilian government in 1991. Burkina Faso has few

natural resources and a weak industrial base. About 90 per cent of the population is engaged in subsistence agriculture, which is vulnerable to periodic drought.

FACT FILE

LOCAL NAME Burkina Faso

CAPITAL CITY Ouagadougou

CURRENCY Communauté Financière Africaine Franc (XOF)

MEMBERSHIP AU, ECOWAS, OIC, WTO

GOVERNMENT Parliamentary Republic

POPULATION 15,213,314

POP. DENSITY 56/km²; 144/mi²

GDP 17.2 Billion US$

LANGUAGE(S) French, native African languages

ETHNICITY Mossi over 40%, Other approximately 60% (includes Gurunsi, Senufo, Lobi, Bobo, Mande, Fulani)

RELIGION Muslim 50%, Indigenous beliefs 40%, Christian (mainly Roman Catholic) 10%

CLIMATE Tropical, Semi-arid

FALAGOUNTOU, NORTH-EAST OF DORI
Women and children at a water pump.

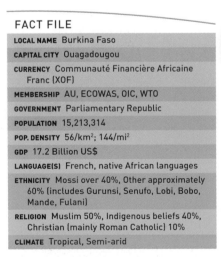

WESTERN AFRICA

GHANA

8° 00' N, 2° 00' W | 239,460 KM² | 92,456 MI² | UTC+0

Ghana, the first of Britain's African colonies to be granted independence, lies on the Gulf of Guinea.

Geography

The terrain is mostly low plains, with rain forest in the south-west and savannah in the north. The Black Volta and White Volta Rivers flow into Lake Volta, the largest artificial lake in the world, covering almost 8,500 square kilometres. The climate is warm and humid in the south, and hot and dry in the north.

FACT FILE

LOCAL NAME Republic of Ghana

CAPITAL CITY Accra

CURRENCY Ghana Cedi (GHC)

MEMBERSHIP AU, C, ECOWAS, G-24, G-77, OAS (observer), WTO

GOVERNMENT Constitutional Democracy

POPULATION 23,946,816

POP. DENSITY 100/km²; 259/mi²

GDP 31.33 Billion US$

LANGUAGE(S) Asante, Ewe, Fante, Boron (Brong), Dagomba, Dangme, Dagarte (Dagaba), Akyem, Ga, Akuapem, English

ETHNICITY Akan 45%, Mole-Dagbon 15%, Ewe 12%, Ga-Dangme 7%, Guan 4%, Gurma 4%, Grusi 3%

RELIGION Christian 69% (Pentecostal/Charismatic 24%, Protestant 19%, Roman Catholic 15%, Other 11%), Muslim 16%, Indigenous beliefs 9%

CLIMATE Tropical

REGIONAL DIVISIONS 5 geographical regions are divided into 10 Regions and further into 138 Districts

ECONOMIC ACTIVITIES Agriculture, Mining, Fishing; Forestry, Light Manufacturing, Aluminium Smelting, Food Processing, Cement, Steel Industry, Small Commercial Shipbuilding, Refining, Car, Truck and Bus Assembly, Tourism

NATURAL RESOURCES Gold, Timber, Industrial Diamonds, Bauxite, Manganese, Fish, Rubber, Hydropower, Petroleum, Silver, Salt, Limestone

ELMINA
St George castle in the colonial gold- and slave-trading centre of Elmina, near Cape Coast.

History

Ghana is a British colonial creation, an amalgamation of the British Gold Coast colony (established in 1874) and British Togoland that takes its name from the Ghana Empire in West Africa (c. 750–1240). There are numerous ethnic groups, the three largest being the Akan, Mole-Dagbon and Ewe, and seventy-five spoken languages. After independence from Britain in 1957, Ghana experienced long periods of military rule interspersed with short-lived civilian government until 1992, when multiparty politics and civilian government were restored.

Economy

Ghana is one of the world's largest producers of cocoa, which, along with gold, diamonds, other minerals and timber, is a major export. However, despite its abundant natural resources and a per capita output roughly twice that of the poorest countries in West Africa, it remains dependent on international financial and technical assistance. The domestic economy continues to revolve around agriculture, which employs over half of the country's workforce.

TOGO
8° 00' N, 1° 10' E | 56,785 KM² | 21,925 MI² | UTC+0

Togo, a narrow strip of sub-Saharan land, was governed by Gnassingbé Eyadéma, Africa's longest-ruling dictator, from 1967 until 2005.

Togo's terrain varies from coastal plains with lagoons and marshes in the south to savannah in the north, divided by a central mountain range. The climate is tropical in the south and semi-arid in the north. A German colony until 1914 and then administered by the French for half a century, Togo gained independence in 1960. Under one-party rule for much of Gnassingbé Eyadéma's presidency, since his death in 2005 political pluralism has gained ground, allowing Togo to hold its first relatively free and fair elections in 2007. The economy, damaged by the long-term suspension of international aid over Togo's human rights record, is heavily dependent on both commercial and subsistence agriculture, although phosphates are a major export.

FACT FILE
LOCAL NAME Togolese Republic
CAPITAL CITY Lomé
CURRENCY Communauté Financière Africaine Franc (XOF)
MEMBERSHIP AU, ECOWAS, G-77, OIC, WTO
GOVERNMENT Republic under transition to multi-party democratic rule
POPULATION 6,762,421
POP. DENSITY 119/km²; 308/mi²
GDP 5.208 Billion US$
LANGUAGE(S) French (commerce), Ewe and Mina (in south), Kabye and Dagomba (in north)
ETHNICITY African (37 tribes; largest: Ewe, Mina, and Kabre) 99%
RELIGION Christian 29%, Indigenous beliefs 51%, Muslim 20%
CLIMATE Tropical

TOGOLESE VILLAGE
A mud wall surrounding a village in Togo.

LIBERIA
6° 30' N, 9° 30' W | 111,370 KM² | 43,000 MI² | UTC+0

Liberia, Africa's oldest republic, was created in 1847 by freed American slaves, Americo-Liberians, who had begun to settle in the area in 1822.

Liberia has a tropical climate and is one of the wettest countries in the world, with an average annual rainfall of over 500 cm. Its coastline is composed of lagoons and mangrove swamps, with rain forest and grassy plateaux inland. Liberia, rich in timber, gold, diamonds and iron ore and with extensive rubber plantations, was renowned for its political stability and well-run economy until 1980, when a coup introduced a corrupt regime that brought about economic collapse. Attempts to overthrow the regime led to a civil war that raged almost continuously from 1990 to 2003. The conflict devastated Liberia's infrastructure and economy but the country is recovering and exports are growing again.

FACT FILE
LOCAL NAME Republic of Liberia
CAPITAL CITY Monrovia
CURRENCY Liberian Dollar (LRD)
MEMBERSHIP AU, ECOWAS, G-77, WTO (observer)
GOVERNMENT Republic
POPULATION 3,942,212
POP. DENSITY 35/km²; 92/mi²
GDP 1.34 Billion US$
LANGUAGE(S) English, Pidgin English, Kpelle, Bassa, Mano, Dan
ETHNICITY Indigenous African 95%, Americo-Liberians 3%, Congo people 2%
RELIGION Christian 40%, Indigenous beliefs 40%, Muslim 20%
CLIMATE Tropical Monsoon

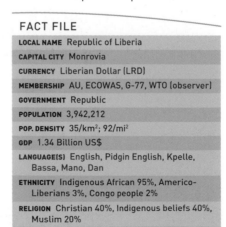

WESTERN AFRICA

CÔTE D'IVOIRE

8° 00' N, 5° 00' W | 322,460 KM² | 124,502 MI² | UTC+0

Côte d'Ivoire, or the Ivory Coast, was once home to thousands of savannah and forest elephants, but hunting and the destruction of their habitat have decimated their numbers.

Geography

The coastal plain gradually rises to a forested plateau, turning to wet savannah in the north. The climate is tropical along the coast, with heavy rainfall. The far north is semi-arid.

History

Côte d'Ivoire's major ethnic groups, the Akan, Gur and Mandes, arrived from neighbouring areas from the seventeenth century onwards. In the 1840s France took an interest in the region, making it a colony in 1893. Ties between the two countries remain strong today and French is the official state language. After independence in 1960, Côte d'Ivoire was ruled for over thirty years as a one-party state by its first president, Felix Houphouet-Boigny. Following his death in 1993, the country experienced political and social turmoil, with two coups (1999 and 2001) and a civil war (2002–3), although a peace agreement was finally signed in 2007.

Economy

Once one of West Africa's most prosperous states, Côte d'Ivoire's economy has been damaged by its recent political instability. It is the world's largest producer and exporter of cocoa beans, and a significant exporter of coffee and palm oil. The economy is still heavily dependent on agriculture, which engages nearly 70 per cent of the population, although since 2006 oil and gas production has become increasingly important.

IROBO
A palm oil plantation at Irobo, between Abidjan and Fresco.

FACT FILE

LOCAL NAME Republic of Côte d'Ivoire

CAPITAL CITY Yamoussoukro

CURRENCY Communauté Financière Africaine Franc (XOF)

MEMBERSHIP AU, ECOWAS, G-24, G-77, OIC, WTO

GOVERNMENT Republic; Multiparty Presidential Regime established 1960

POPULATION 19,624,236

POP. DENSITY 61/km²; 158/mi²

GDP 32.18 Billion US$

LANGUAGE(S) French, Dioula

ETHNICITY Akan 42%, Voltaiques or Gur 18%, Northern Mandes 17%, Krous 11%, Southern Mandes 10%

RELIGION Muslim 39%, Christian 33%, Indigenous beliefs 12%

CLIMATE Tropical

REGIONAL DIVISIONS 19 Regions divided into 58 Departments which are further divided into 197 Communes

ECONOMIC ACTIVITIES Agriculture, Cocoa, Food Processing, Beverages, Wood Products, Oil Refining, Truck and Bus Assembly, Textiles, Fertilizer, Building Materials, Electricity, Ship Construction and Repair

NATURAL RESOURCES Petroleum, Natural Gas, Diamonds, Manganese, Iron Ore, Cobalt, Bauxite, Copper, Gold, Nickel, Tantalum, Silica Sand, Clay, Hydropower

SIERRA LEONE

8° 30′ N, 11° 30′ W | 71,740 KM² | 27,699 MI² | UTC+0

The former British colony of Sierra Leone was once a point of transit for thousands of slaves. Its capital, Freetown, was founded as a haven for freed slaves in 1787.

The coastal terrain is composed of mangrove swamps and beaches. Inland, there are rain-forested plains and a mountain plateau rising to a height of nearly 2,000 metres. Following independence in 1961, Sierra Leone enjoyed three decades of relative political stability until 1991, when the country became embroiled in a civil war that lasted until 2002. In 2007 the country held elections that

were deemed free and fair. Diamonds are the cornerstone of the economy, accounting for 50 per cent of exports. Although the

FACT FILE

LOCAL NAME Republic of Sierra Leone
CAPITAL CITY Freetown
CURRENCY Leone (SLL)
MEMBERSHIP AU, Commonwealth of Nations, ECOWAS, G-77, OIC, WTO
GOVERNMENT Constitutional Democracy
POPULATION 5,968,523
POP. DENSITY 83/km²; 216/mi²
GDP 3.97 Billion US$
LANGUAGE(S) English, Mende, Temne, Krio
ETHNICITY African ethnic groups 90% (Temne 30%, Mende 30%, other 30%), Creole (Krio) 10%
RELIGION Muslim 60%, Indigenous beliefs 30%, Christian 10%,
CLIMATE Tropical Monsoon

economy is recovering from the civil war, around half of government revenue comes from international donors.

GUINEA-BISSAU

12° 00′ N, 15° 00′ W | 36,120 KM² | 13,946 MI² | UTC+0

Guinea-Bissau, one of the smallest states in mainland Africa, is one of the world's ten poorest countries.

Predominantly low-lying, Guinea-Bissau's highest point reaches only 300 metres. Much of the country is coastal plain, with many creeks and mangrove swamps,

although there is savannah in the east. The Portuguese colonized the coast and established Portuguese Guinea in 1630, granting independence in 1974. Guinea-Bissau subsequently experienced political upheaval, with several military coups and a short civil war (1998–9), until the restoration of constitutional government in 2004. Over 80 per cent of the workforce is employed in

BIJAGÓS ISLANDS
A fisherman empties water from his wooden boat.

subsistence agriculture, and cashew nuts, fish and peanuts are the main exports. Reserves of offshore oil have yet to be exploited.

FACT FILE

LOCAL NAME Republic of Guinea-Bissau
CAPITAL CITY Bissau
CURRENCY Communauté Financière Africaine Franc (XAF)
MEMBERSHIP AU, ECOWAS, G-77, OIC, WTO
GOVERNMENT Republic
POPULATION 1,745,838
POP. DENSITY 48/km²; 125/mi²
GDP 0.80 Billion US$
LANGUAGE(S) Portuguese, Crioulo
ETHNICITY Balanta 30%, Fula 20%, Manjaca 14%, Mandinga 13%, Papel 7%
RELIGION Indigenous beliefs 50%, Muslim 45%, Christian 5%
CLIMATE Tropical

GUINEA

11° 00' N, 10° 00' W | 245,857 KM² | 94,926 MI² | UTC+0

The Guinea highlands are the source of twenty-two West African rivers, including the Niger, the Gambia and the Senegal.

Geography

Guinea's coastal areas consist mainly of flat plains and mangrove swamps, with hills and mountains in the interior, including the Guinea highlands in the south-east. The climate is mostly tropical, with a rainy season from April to November. The capital, Conakry, records an average annual rainfall of 4,300 mm.

History

The region fell under the influence of four African empires between c. 900 and the end of the sixteenth century: the Ghana Empire, the Sosso kingdom, the Mali Empire and the Songhai Empire. Although discovered by Portugal in the fifteenth century, the area came under French influence, becoming a colony in 1890. Since independence in 1958, Guinea has had only two presidents. Although one-party rule ended in 1993, elections since then have been hampered by irregularities.

Economy

Although Guinea possesses considerable mineral, hydro-electric and agricultural resources, the economy remains under-developed. Inflation, mismanagement and the suspension of international aid have been serious problems. An influx of refugees from conflicts in neighbouring countries has created an additional economic burden. Around 80 per cent of the workforce is employed in agriculture, mostly at subsistence level. The country has almost half of the world's bauxite (aluminium ore) reserves and is the second largest bauxite producer. Mining provides nearly 80 per cent of foreign exchange earnings.

RAIN FOREST
Much of the interior of Guinea is densely forested.

FACT FILE

LOCAL NAME Republic of Guinea

CAPITAL CITY Conakry

CURRENCY Guinean Franc (GNF)

MEMBERSHIP AU, ECOWAS, G-77, OIC, WTO

GOVERNMENT Republic

POPULATION 9,572,039

POP. DENSITY 39/km²; 101/mi²

GDP 10.69 Billion US$

LANGUAGE(S) French

ETHNICITY Peuhl 40%, Malinke 30%, Soussou 20%

RELIGION Muslim 85%, Christian 8%, Indigenous beliefs 7%

CLIMATE Tropical

REGIONAL DIVISIONS 7 Administrative Regions divided into 33 Prefectures, and 1 Special Zone (Capital Conakry)

ECONOMIC ACTIVITIES Agriculture, Mining (Bauxite, Gold, Diamonds, Iron), Alumina Refining, Light Manufacturing, Agricultural Processing, Construction

NATURAL RESOURCES Bauxite, Iron Ore, Diamonds, Gold, Uranium, Hydropower, Fish, Salt

WESTERN AFRICA

CENTRAL AFRICA

The native vegetation of this vast area is tropical rainforest;

its dense jungle earned Africa the soubriquet of the Dark Continent.

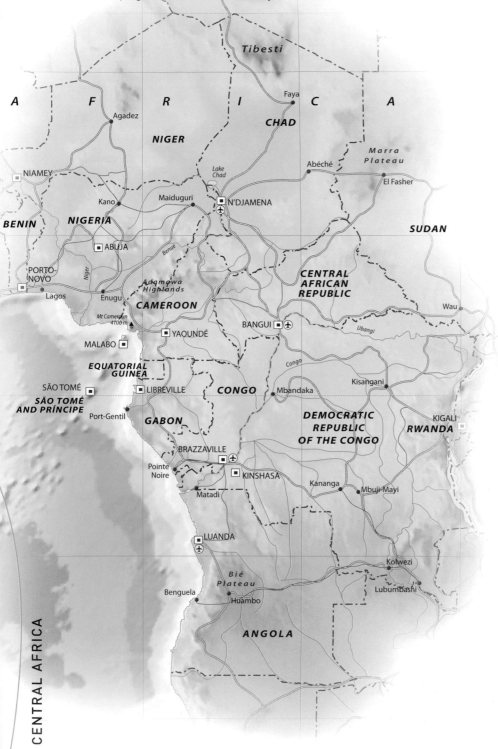

Of the nine countries that comprise the UN subregion of Central Africa, only two, Chad and the Central African Republic, are entirely landlocked. The remainder, from Cameroon to Angola, all possess stretches of Atlantic coastline, whilst São Tomé and Príncipe make up an island group off the coast of Gabon. The region straddles the Equator, extending over 3,000 kilometres from Chad in the north to Angola in the south, and although large parts of these two countries are covered by arid desert, Central Africa is dominated by the heavily forested Congo River Basin, which drains an area of over 4 million square kilometres, making it the world's second largest after the Amazon. The river itself is the second longest in Africa, flowing for around 4,700 kilometres. In an area where road and rail communications are largely inadequate the Congo River remains an important trading route and a reliable means of transport.

Home to numerous tribes and kingdoms since ancient times, European exploration of Central Africa, and in particular that of the Congo Basin, began with the arrival of the Portuguese during the fifteenth century, and from the sixteenth to the nineteenth centuries the region was subjected to some of the worst excesses of the Atlantic slave trade, as forays were made into the interior to secure African slaves for transport to European colonies in the Americas. Following the navigation of the Congo River by the Anglo-American explorer Henry Morton Stanley in 1877, European powers recognized the significance of the river as an arterial route for the transport of such commodities as ivory, copper, palm kernels and latex rubber to the western coast, whilst countries such as Portugal, Belgium and France continued to exercise control over the region through their territorial acquisitions.

Having gained their independence in the twentieth century, many Central African nations were blighted by conflict, as local warlords filled the vacuum created by the withdrawal of colonial governments, and

although countries such as the Democratic Republic of the Congo, the Central African Republic and Angola possess vast resources of mineral wealth, these have frequently been exploited by corrupt regimes and their sponsors in the industrial countries of the

THE CONGO RIVER
An aerial view of the Congo winding through mangrove swamps near the mouth of the river.

world. As a result, little of this wealth has percolated to the poverty-stricken people of the region, which remains amongst the most impoverished in Africa.

Despite many problems, some Central African nations have begun to see their economic fortunes improved by the recent discovery of oil. The rapids and waterfalls that dominate the lower reaches of the River Congo also offer significant potential for the generation of hydroelectric power.

HIPPOPOTAMUSES
A large group of Hippopotamuses wallow in a river in the Viruguna National Park in the Democratic Republic of the Congo.

CHAD

0° 00' N, 25° 00' E | 2,345,410 KM² | 905,568 MI² | UTC+1

The landlocked republic takes its name from Lake Chad, the most significant body of water in the Sahel region, and is located in the eastern part of this lake's vast basin.

Geography

Apart from fertile lowlands in the south, where more than half the population lives, the country is predominantly arid in the centre and largely desert in the mountainous north. The Emi Koussi, a dormant volcano in the Tibesti Mountains, reaches 3,415 metres above sea level and is the highest point in the Sahara. Chad's climate is tropical in the south and arid in the north.

History

The Chadian Basin has been inhabited for more than 2,000 years, the earliest people being the Sao. The Sao fell to the Kanem Empire, which developed in Chad's Sahelian belt by controlling the trans-Saharan trade routes that crossed the region. Colonized by France from the 1890s, by 1920 the area had become part of French Equatorial Africa. Following independence in 1960, the country endured three decades of instability and civil war, as well as invasions by Libya, before a nominal peace was restored in 1990, although insurgency continues.

Economy

Chad's economic fortunes have improved since 2004, when oil production started, leading to a 38 per cent growth in GDP in the same year. Despite this, Chad remains one of the poorest countries in the world and at least 80 per cent of its population is dependent on agriculture and livestock. The main exports apart from oil are cotton, cattle and gum arabic.

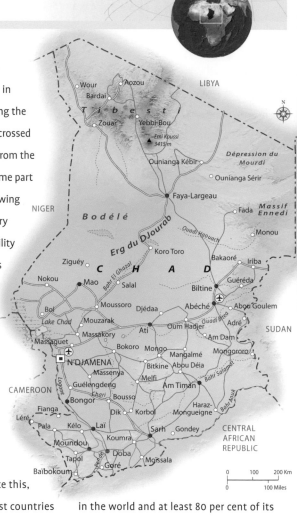

FACT FILE

LOCAL NAME Republic of Chad

CAPITAL CITY N´Djamena

CURRENCY Communauté Financière Africaine Franc (XAF)

MEMBERSHIP AU, CEMAC, G-77, OIC, WTO

GOVERNMENT Republic

POPULATION 11,087,698

POP. DENSITY 9/km²; 22/mi²

GDP 15.9 Billion US$

LANGUAGE(S) French, Arabic, Sara (in south)

ETHNICITY Sara 28%, Arab 12%, Mayo-Kebbi 12%, Kanem-Bornou 9%, Ouaddai 9%, Hadjarai 7%, Tandjile 7%, Gorane 6%, Fitri-Batha 5%

RELIGION Muslim 53%, Roman Catholic 20%, Protestant 14%, Animist 7%

CLIMATE Tropical, Arid, Semi-arid

REGIONAL DIVISIONS 3 Climate-Vegetative zones are divided into 18 Administrative Regions and further into 51 Departments

ECONOMIC ACTIVITIES Agriculture, Oil, Cotton Textiles, Meatpacking, Brewing, Natron (Sodium Carbonate) Mining, Soap, Cigarettes, Construction Materials

NATURAL RESOURCES Petroleum, Uranium, Natron, Kaolin, Fish, Gold, Limestone, Sand and Gravel, Salt, Bauxite, Tin, Tungsten, Titanium, Iron Ore

ARCHEI CANYON
Camels bathe in the cool water in the base of the Archei Canyon in the Ennedi Massif.

CAMEROON

6° 00' N, 12° 00' E | 475,440 KM² | 183,568 MI² | UTC+1

Cameroon is sometimes called 'Africa in miniature', because it possesses all the major geographical features of the continent, including a coastal plain, desert, savannah, mountains and rain forest.

Cameroon's climate varies between tropical on the coast and semi-arid in the north. Its longest continuous inhabitants are pygmy groups such as the Baka. It became the German colony of Kamerun in 1884 but following the First World War the territory was administered by France and Britain. By 1961 both areas had secured independence and been unified. Cameroon has since enjoyed relative stability and in 1992 it reintroduced multiparty politics. The economy relies on oil, timber and agriculture, including cocoa and rubber, for its export earnings.

FACT FILE

LOCAL NAME Republic of Cameroon

CAPITAL CITY Yaoundé

CURRENCY Communauté Financière Africaine Franc (XAF)

MEMBERSHIP AU, CEMAC, C, G-77, OIC, WTO

GOVERNMENT Republic; Multiparty Presidential Regime

POPULATION 18,920,236

POP. DENSITY 40/km²; 103/mi²

GDP 39.37 Billion US$

LANGUAGE(S) English, French

ETHNICITY Cameroon Highlanders 31%, Equatorial Bantu 19%, Kirdi 11%, Fulani 10%, Northwestern Bantu 8%, Eastern Nigritic 7%, Other African 13%

RELIGION Indigenous beliefs 40%, Christian 40%, Muslim 20%

CLIMATE Tropical, Semi-arid

CENTRAL AFRICAN REPUBLIC

7° 00' N, 21° 00' E | 622,984 KM² | 240,534 MI² | UTC+1

One of the poorest countries in the world, the landlocked Central African Republic is located almost at the precise centre of the continent of Africa.

The country lies on a plateau between the basins of the Chad and Congo Rivers, with dry savannah in the north and equatorial forest in the south, and a tropical climate. Less than 5 per cent of the population lives in the arid north of the country. The former French colony of Ubangi-Shari – named after the country's two main rivers – became the Central African Republic upon independence in 1960. A coup in 1966 brought to power Jean-Bédel Bokassa, who renamed the country the Central African Empire in 1976 and declared himself emperor, but was deposed in 1979. There have been further periods of political instability and military government. Diamond and gold mining and forestry are among the major activities, but agriculture, mostly at a subsistence level, remains the mainstay of the economy. Cassava, peanuts, maize, sorghum, millet and plantains are among the most important crops.

FACT FILE

LOCAL NAME Central African Republic

CAPITAL CITY Bangui

CURRENCY Communauté Financière Africaine Franc (XAF)

MEMBERSHIP AU, CEMAC, G-77, OIC (observer), WTO

GOVERNMENT Republic

POPULATION 4,424,292

POP. DENSITY 7/km²; 18/mi²

GDP 3.10 Billion US$

LANGUAGE(S) French, Sangho (lingua franca and national language)

ETHNICITY Baya 33%, Banda 27%, Mandjia 13%, Sara 10%, Mboum 7%, M'Baka 4%, Yakoma 4%

RELIGION Indigenous beliefs 35%, Protestant 25%, Roman Catholic 25%, Muslim 15%

CLIMATE Tropical

CENTRAL AFRICA

DEMOCRATIC REPUBLIC OF THE CONGO

62° 00' N, 10° 00' E | 323,802 KM² | 125,021 MI² | UTC+1

The Democratic Republic of the Congo (DRC), known as Zaire between 1971 and 1997, is Africa's third largest country by area. It has vast natural resources and the world's second largest area of rain forest.

Geography

The country straddles the Equator, lying mostly in the Congo river basin, which is covered by dense rain forest. The terrain rises in the east to a forested plateau, with a range of volcanic mountains and a chain of lakes beyond. The climate is equatorial, with different climatic cycles on either side of the Equator.

History

Bantu migrants had settled most of the area by AD 1000. European contact was first made by the Portuguese in the late fifteenth century but was limited in the interior until the 1870s. The territory was acquired by King Leopold II of Belgium, whose claim was recognized in 1885, and he exploited the region for personal profit. In 1908 the Belgian state took control, granting the country independence in 1960. The corrupt regime of Mobutu Sese Seko (1965–97) was overthrown in 1996–7 by a rebel army led by Laurent Kabila, who became president. However, rebellion against Kabila's government led to further conflict. A ceasefire was achieved in 2001 by Joseph Kabila (who became president after his father's assassination), followed by a peace accord in 2003 and elections in 2006. A fragile peace has held, although the government has little control over large areas of the country, especially in the east, where rebel incursions continue.

Economy

Decades of mismanagement, corruption and conflict have left the economy devastated. With improved security, exploitation of its natural resources, particularly diamonds, copper, oil and hydro-electric power, has begun.

VIRUNGA NATIONAL PARK
Elephants cross a river in the Virunga park, Africa's first national park. Virunga is home to more than 200 species of mammal and 700 birds.

FACT FILE

LOCAL NAME Democratic Republic of the Congo

CAPITAL CITY Kinshasa

CURRENCY Congolese Franc (CDF)

MEMBERSHIP AU, CEPGL, COMESA, G-24, G-77, SADC, WTO

GOVERNMENT Republic

POPULATION 64,703,617

POP. DENSITY 28/km²; 72/mi²

GDP 18.84 Billion US$

LANGUAGE(S) French, Lingala (trade), Kingwana, Kikongo, Tshiluba

ETHNICITY Luba 18%, Kongo (all Bantu) 16%, Mongo 14%, and the Mangbetu-Azande (Hamitic) 6%, Rwanda 10%, Bangi and Ngale 6%, Rundi 4%, Teke 3%, Boa 2%

RELIGION Roman Catholic 50%, Protestant 20%, Kimbanguist 10%, Muslim 10%

CLIMATE Tropical, Subtropical

REGIONAL DIVISIONS 10 Provinces and 1 City

ECONOMIC ACTIVITIES Agriculture, Mining (Diamonds, Gold, Copper, Cobalt, Coltan Zinc), Forestry, Mineral Processing, Consumer Products (including Textiles, Footwear, Cigarettes, Processed Foods and Beverages), Cement, Commercial Ship Repair, Textiles, Oil Refining

NATURAL RESOURCES Cobalt, Copper, Niobium, Tantalum, Petroleum, Industrial and Gem Diamonds, Gold, Silver, Zinc, Manganese, Tin, Uranium, Coal, Hydropower, Timber

CONGO

1° 00' S, 15° 00' E | 342,000 KM² | 132,047 MI² | UTC+1

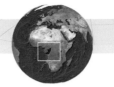

The Republic of the Congo was the first African nation to declare itself a communist state.

FACT FILE

LOCAL NAME	Republic of the Congo
CAPITAL	Brazzaville
CURRENCY	Communauté Financière Africaine Franc (XAF)
MEMBERSHIP	AU, CEMAC, G-77, WTO
GOVERNMENT	Republic
POPULATION	3,847,191
POP. DENSITY	11/km²; 29/mi²
GDP	13.23 Billion US$
LANGUAGE(S)	French, Lingala (trade), Monokutuba (trade), Kikongo
ETHNICITY	Kongo 48%, Sangha 20%, Teke 17%, M'Bochi 12%
RELIGION	Christian 50%, Animist 48%, Muslim 2%
CLIMATE	Tropical

The republic lies mostly on mountainous plateaux covered with rain forest or savannah and cut by river valleys, including that of the River Congo. The climate is equatorial. Congo's earliest inhabitants were pygmy and Bantu peoples. In 1880, the explorer Pierre de Brazza secured the territory for France; the capital, Brazzaville, is named after him. Independence was achieved in 1960, but heralded political instability. A Marxist state was proclaimed in 1970, but Marxism and one-party rule were abandoned in 1990. Further instability in the 1990s led to civil war from 1997 to 2003, and the current

peace is fragile. The economic mainstays are oil (although reserves are falling), forestry, diamond mining and subsistence agriculture.

GABON

1° 00' S, 11° 45' E | 267,667 KM² | 103,347 MI² | UTC+1

Gabon, located on the Equator, is one of the most mineral-rich nations on the continent of Africa.

Gabon's climate is hot and tropical, and about 85 per cent of the terrain is covered with rain forest. The area came under French control from 1839, with Libreville, the capital, founded by freed slaves in 1849. Since independence in 1960, Gabon has had only two presidents, the current one has held the presidency for four decades. Gabon is one of the more stable African countries and has a

FACT FILE

LOCAL NAME	Gabonese Republic
CAPITAL CITY	Libreville
CURRENCY	Communauté Financière Africaine Franc (XAF)
MEMBERSHIP	AU, CEMAC, G-24, G-77, OIC, WTO
GOVERNMENT	Republic; Multiparty Presidential regime
POPULATION	1,350,156
POP. DENSITY	5/km²; 13/mi²
GDP	20.18 Billion US$
LANGUAGE(S)	French, Fang, Myene, Nzebi, Bapounou/Eschira, Bandjabi
ETHNICITY	Fang 29%, Punu 10%, Nzebi 9%, French 7%, Mpongwe 4%, Teke 4%
RELIGION	Christian 91% (Roman Catholic 57%, Protestant, 18%), Muslim 3%, Indigenous beliefs 6%
CLIMATE	Tropical

relatively high per capita income owing to its small population and abundance of natural resources. Oil accounts for nearly 80 per cent of exports, but manganese and uranium mining, forestry and agriculture are also important.

LIBREVILLE
The port of Libreville is situated on the Komo River.

CENTRAL AFRICA

EQUATORIAL GUINEA

2° 00' N, 10° 00' E | 28,051 KM² | 10,828 MI² | UTC+1

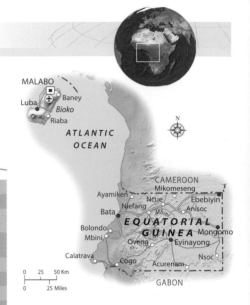

Equatorial Guinea comprises two main islands off the Cameroon coast and a small area of the African mainland called Rio Muni.

The islands of Bioko and Annobon (some 200 kilometres west of São Tomé) are volcanic, while the mainland rises from a narrow coastal plain to a densely forested mountainous plateau inland. The climate is hot and humid. The islands were colonized by the Portuguese in the 1470s and ceded to Spain, along with Rio Muni, in 1788, although Spain only took control in 1844. The colony of Spanish Guinea won independence under its present name in 1968 and has since had only two leaders, the first president being overthrown by his nephew in 1979. Oil has

FACT FILE

LOCAL NAME	Republic of Equatorial Guinea
CAPITAL CITY	Malabo
CURRENCY	Communauté Financière Africaine Franc (XAF)
MEMBERSHIP	AU, CEMAC, G-77, OAS (observer), WTO (observer)
GOVERNMENT	Republic
POPULATION	519,697
POP. DENSITY	19/km²; 48/mi²
GDP	15.54 Billion US$
LANGUAGE(S)	Spanish, French, Fang, Bubi
ETHNICITY	Fang 86%, Bubi 7%, Mdowe 4%
RELIGION	Roman Catholic 80%, Other Christian 7%, Muslim 4%
CLIMATE	Tropical Monsoon

transformed the economy since the 1990s but most of the population, who depend on agriculture, fishing and forestry, have benefited little because of corruption.

SÃO TOMÉ AND PRÍNCIPE

1° 00' N, 7° 00' E | 1,001 KM² | 386 MI² | UTC+0

São Tomé and Príncipe, a group of two main islands and a number of islets formed from a chain of extinct volcanoes off the coast of Gabon, is one of Africa's smallest nations.

The volcanic mountains, covered by dense rain forest, have a tropical climate. The uninhabited islands were discovered and settled in the late fifteenth century by the Portuguese, who established cocoa and sugar plantations worked by slave labour. Agitation for independence began in the 1950s and independence was achieved in 1975 as a one-party state under a Marxist

FACT FILE

LOCAL NAME	Democratic Republic of São Tomé and Príncipe
CAPITAL CITY	São Tomé
CURRENCY	Dobra (STD)
MEMBERSHIP	AU, G-77, WTO (observer)
GOVERNMENT	Republic
POPULATION	160,174
POP. DENSITY	160/ km²; 415/mi²
GDP	0.26 Billion US$
LANGUAGE(S)	Portuguese
ETHNICITY	Mestico 80%, Fang 10%, Angolares 8%, Portuguese 2%
RELIGION	Roman Catholic 70%, Other Christian 7%
CLIMATE	Tropical

regime. Political and economic liberalization was introduced in 1990 and democracy has brought a degree of instability. The economy is still dominated by the cocoa production, but this is likely to change when offshore oil production starts in about 2010.

BON BALM
A plantation house at Bon Balm. At the time of independence Portuguese-owned plantations covered some 90 per cent of the cultivated land.

ANGOLA

12° 30' S, 18° 30' E | 1,246,700 KM² | 481,354 MI² | UTC+1

Angola, sub-Saharan Africa's second largest oil producer, is potentially one of the continent's wealthiest countries, but since independence it has suffered almost continuous conflict.

Geography

Angola's narrow coastal plain rises abruptly to a vast interior plateau. The south is desert. The country includes Cabinda, a mineral-rich enclave separated from the rest of the country by the Democratic Republic of the Congo and lying between the DRC and the Republic of the Congo. The north of Angola has a tropical climate and the south is arid. Temperatures in the north vary with altitude, and coastal areas are cooled by the Benguela current.

History

The first inhabitants of the region were the Khoisan, who were largely replaced by Bantu tribes from around 1500 BC. Portuguese control of the region began in the fifteenth century and ended, after an anti-colonial war from the early 1960s, with the country's independence in 1975. Shortly after independence, a civil war broke out between three nationalist groups and conflict continued until 2002. However, violence continues in the enclave of Cabinda, where separatists have conducted a low-level guerilla war for over thirty years.

Economy

Although ruined by the decades of conflict and corruption, the economy has grown recently owing to increased production of oil, which contributes nearly 50 per cent of GDP. Mining of metal and mineral resources, particularly diamonds, forestry and fishing are the other key industries. Subsistence agriculture, however, still provides a livelihood for over 80 per cent of the workforce.

CATUMBELA, NEAR BENGUELA
A church rises above the village of Catumbela.

FACT FILE

LOCAL NAME Republic of Angola

CAPITAL CITY Luanda

CURRENCY Kwanza (AOA)

MEMBERSHIP AU, G-77, OAS (observer), OPEC, SADC, WTO

GOVERNMENT Republic; Multiparty Presidential Regime

POPULATION 17,499,406

POP. DENSITY 14/km²; 36/mi²

GDP 91.29 Billion US$

LANGUAGE(S) Portuguese, Bantu

ETHNICITY Ovimbundu 37%, Kimbundu 25%, Bakongo 13%, Mestico 2%

RELIGION Indigenous beliefs 47%, Roman Catholic 38%, Protestant 15%

CLIMATE Tropical, Subtropical, Arid, Semi-arid

REGIONAL DIVISIONS 18 Provinces further divided into 163 Municipalities

ECONOMIC ACTIVITIES Petroleum, Mining (Diamonds, Iron Ore, Phosphates, Feldspar, Bauxite, Uranium, Gold), Cement, Basic Metal Products, Fish Processing, Food Processing, Brewing, Tobacco Products, Sugar, Textiles, Ship Repair

NATURAL RESOURCES Petroleum, Diamonds, Iron Ore, Phosphates, Copper, Feldspar, Gold, Bauxite, Uranium, Granite; Hydropower Potential

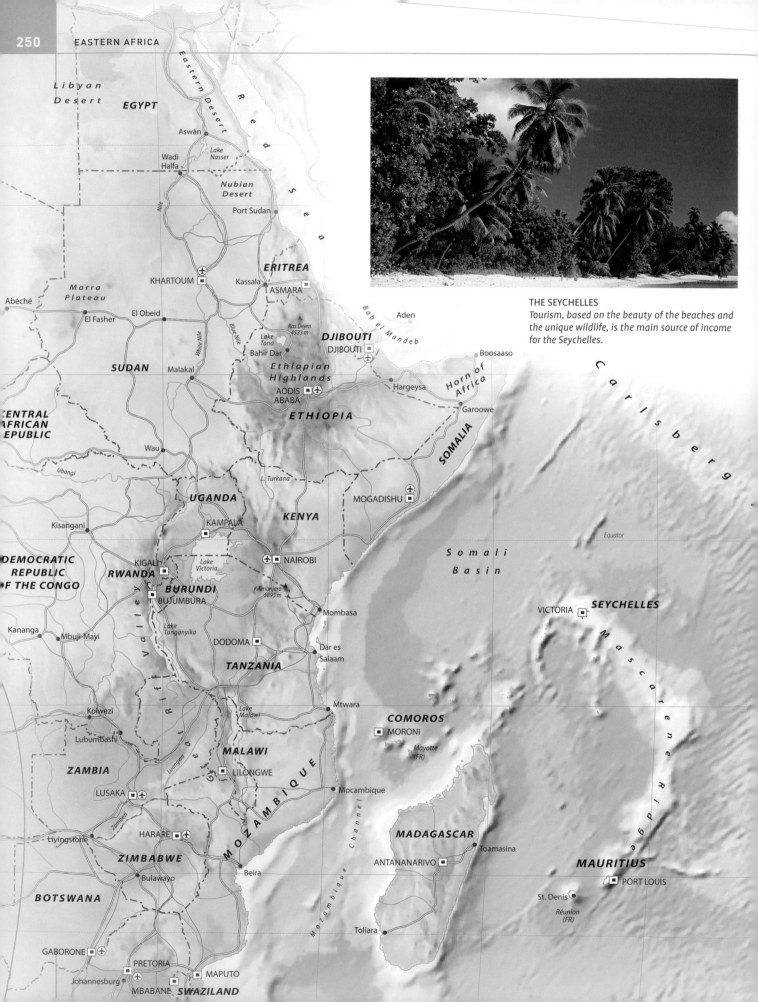

EGYPT
Libyan Desert

Aswān

Wadi Halfa

Lake Nasser

Nubian Desert

Port Sudan

ERITREA

Abéché

Marra Plateau

KHARTOUM

Kassala

ASMARA

El Fasher

El Obeid

Aden

DJIBOUTI

Ras Dejen 4533 m

DJIBOUTI

Bab el Mandeb

Boosaaso

SUDAN

Malakal

Lake Tana

Bahir Dar

Ethiopian Highlands

CENTRAL AFRICAN REPUBLIC

AODIS ABABA

ETHIOPIA

Hargeysa

Horn of Africa

Garoowe

Wau

L. Turkana

SOMALIA

Ubangi

UGANDA

Kisangani

KAMPALA

KENYA

MOGADISHU

DEMOCRATIC REPUBLIC OF THE CONGO

KIGALI

RWANDA

Lake Victoria

NAIROBI

Somali Basin

Equator

VICTORIA

SEYCHELLES

BURUNDI

BUJUMBURA

Kananga

Mbuji-Mayi

Lake Tanganyika

Killmanjaro 3895 m

Mombasa

DODOMA

Dar es Salaam

TANZANIA

Kolwezi

Mtwara

COMOROS

MORONI

Lubumbashi

Lake Malawi

Mayotte (FR)

MALAWI

ZAMBIA

LILONGWE

LUSAKA

Mocambique

MADAGASCAR

Livingstone

Zambezi

HARARE

MAURITIUS

ZIMBABWE

Beira

Toamasina

PORT LOUIS

Bulawayo

ANTANANARIVO

BOTSWANA

St. Denis

Réunion (FR)

GABORONE

Toliara

PRETORIA

MAPUTO

Johannesburg

MBABANE **SWAZILAND**

Red Sea

Carlsberg

Mascarene Ridge

Mozambique Channel

MOZAMBIQUE

Luangwa

THE SEYCHELLES

Tourism, based on the beauty of the beaches and the unique wildlife, is the main source of income for the Seychelles.

EASTERN AFRICA

Stretching from Eritrea in the north to Zimbabwe in the south, nineteen territories make up the region of Eastern Africa according the the United Nations scheme. The region is bordered to the east by the Red Sea and, south of the Gulf of Aden, by the Indian Ocean.

The great East African Rift Valley is the primary geographical feature of the region, containing deep lakes which are among the largest in the world. The local equatorial climate is moderated by the altitude of the highland topography and the rain shadow that protects the region from monsoonal excesses. The agreeable climate, fertile soil and teeming wildlife made it attractive to European colonists who congregated there in the nineteenth century to exploit the riches of the land by hunting or agriculture in vast farms and then plantations when it was discovered that coffee and tea thrived in the environment.

Prior to colonial settlement by English and Germans the dominant colonial powers were Arab and Portuguese, whose activities were mainly confined to the coast where they plied the slave trade and traded spices transported from the Indian Ocean. The balance of power pushed Portugal and the Arabs out when Britain and the Dutch made the East Indies their domain; the final nail in the coffin for the Arab slavers was when Britain enforced its anti-slavery legislation using its naval power. The Omani Arabs retreated to the Arabian Gulf while the remains of the Portuguese power settled in the country known in modern times as Mozambique. In the north, Italy made Ethiopia and Somalia a colonial target whilst to the south England and France traded territories to give the French Madagascar, Mauritius and other Indian Ocean territories in exchange for the spice-rich island of Zanzibar.

Despite possessing a wealth of natural resources, in post-colonial times the prosperity of many of Eastern Africa's nations has been adversely affected by civil wars and poorly-run and highly corrupt regimes. Kenya, traditionally the primary destination for East African tourism and home to the safari, is currently regarded as too volatile for safe holidays while Zimbabwe, once the grain store of the region, is bankrupt and its people are starving and ravaged by disease. Africa's future prosperity will very much depend on this region returning to its past standards of production and wealth.

KENYA
African elephants travel across the Serengeti Plain after a thunderstorm.

EASTERN AFRICA

ERITREA

15° 00' N, 39° 00' E | 121,320 KM² | 46,842 MI² | UTC+3

Ravaged by years of war and drought, the small state of Eritrea faces the daunting task of reconstructing its economy.

Eritrea, on the western edge of the Red Sea, has highlands in the north and a narrow coastal plain that forms part of the Danakil Desert in the south. The majority of the population lives in settlements in the central highlands, such as the capital city Asmara, where the air is cooled by breezes and the average rainfal is 1,150 mm a year. Eritrea was occupied by Italy from 1884 to 1941 and then by Britain until 1952, when it was federated with Ethiopia. A campaign for independence began in the 1950s and developed in 1962 into a guerrilla war that became part of a wider rebellion against Ethiopia's Mengistu regime. The regime's overthrow in 1991 resulted in Eritrea gaining its independence in 1993. Relations with Ethiopia are still poor, with several serious border clashes since 1993. Decades of war, drought and famine have ruined Eritrea's fragile economy. Eighty per cent of the workforce is involved in subsistence agriculture and herding, but around three-quarters of Eritreans rely on food aid to survive.

FACT FILE

LOCAL NAME State of Eritrea
CAPITAL CITY Asmara (Asmera)
CURRENCY Nakfa (ERN)
MEMBERSHIP AU, LAS (observer), COMESA, G-77
GOVERNMENT Transitional Government
POPULATION 5,005,678
POP. DENSITY 41/km²; 107/mi²
GDP 3.26 Billion US$
LANGUAGE(S) Tigrinya, English, Arabic, Tigre, Kunama, Afar, Saho, Bega, Bilen, Nara
ETHNICITY Tigrinya 50%, Tigre and Kunama 40%, Afar 4%, Saho 3%
RELIGION Christian 51% (Eritrean Orthodox 46%, Roman Catholic and Protestant 4%), Muslim 45%
CLIMATE Arid, Semi-arid

DJIBOUTI

11° 30' N, 43° 00' E | 23,000 KM² | 8,880 MI² | UTC+3

The location of the tiny country of Djibouti ensures its importance in East Africa.

Situated on the Bab al Mandab Strait, between the Red Sea and the Gulf of Aden, linking the Red Sea to the Indian Ocean, Djibouti is one of the hottest countries on Earth and, with the exception of a narrow coastal plain, is almost entirely desert. It was colonized by France as French Somaliland in the nineteenth century, and became independent in 1977, although ties between the two countries remain strong. Tensions between the Issa and Afar ethnic groups have destabilized the country at times, underlying a brief civil war in the 1990s. Although agriculture supports around three-quarters of the population, Djibouti generates most of its revenue from its strategic location as a regional transit port and free-trade zone, and a military base for French troops. It is also the site of the only American miltary base in sub-Saharan Africa.

FACT FILE

LOCAL NAME Republic of Djibouti
CAPITAL CITY Djibouti
CURRENCY Djiboutian Franc (DJF)
MEMBERSHIP AU, LAS, G-77, OIC, WTO
GOVERNMENT Republic
POPULATION 847,715
POP. DENSITY 37/km²; 96/mi²
GDP 1.74 Billion US$
LANGUAGE(S) French, Arabic, Somali, Afar
ETHNICITY Issa 60%, Afar 35%, Other 5% (includes French, Arab, Ethiopian and Italian)
RELIGION Muslim 94%, Christian 6%
CLIMATE Arid

ETHIOPIA

8° 00' N, 38° 00' E | 1,127,127 KM² | 435,186 MI² | UTC+3

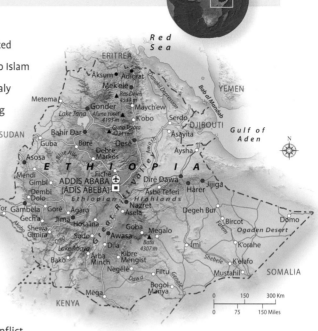

Formerly known as Abyssinia, Ethiopia has been ravaged by years of war and famine and is making slow progress on the road to recovery.

Geography

Ethiopia is largely mountainous, with over half of its area occupied by a high central plateau, divided by the Great Rift Valley from the desert plains that lie to the south and east. The climate varies considerably with altitude, from the arid lowlands through tropical and subtropical hills to a cooler, wetter temperate zone.

History

Home to the ancient Aksum Kingdom, Ethiopia adopted Coptic Christianity during the fourth century, and later resisted attempts to convert the country to Islam and Roman Catholicism. In 1935 Italy invaded the territory, incorporating it into Italian East Africa. Ethiopia was liberated with British assistance in 1941, and the emperor Haile Selassie was restored to power. In 1962 Ethiopia annexed Eritrea, sparking a guerrilla war that would last for almost thirty years, and, despite the fact that Eritrea regained independence in 1993, conflict between the two states has continued. In 1974 Emperor Haile Selassie was deposed in a military coup leading to a devastating civil war, the effects of which were compounded by severe droughts and acute famine during the 1970s and 1980s. Since that time political reforms and international aid have brought some improvements in conditions, although Ethiopia has recently clashed with Islamist forces across the Somali border.

Economy

Ethiopia is one of the world's poorest countries, with around 80 per cent of the workforce engaged in agriculture. Owing to the lasting effects of war and drought Ethiopia continues to rely on foreign aid.

BLUE NILE FALLS
The Blue Nile Falls, one of Ethiopia's major tourist attractions, are about 40 metres high.

FACT FILE

LOCAL NAME Federal Democratic Republic of Ethiopia

CAPITAL CITY Addis Ababa

CURRENCY Birr (ETB)

MEMBERSHIP AU, COMESA, G-24, G-77, WTO (observer)

GOVERNMENT Federal Republic

POPULATION 85,219,109

POP. DENSITY 76/km²; 196/mi²

GDP 62.19 Billion US$

LANGUAGE(S) Amharic, Tigrigna, Oromifa, English

ETHNICITY Oromo 32%, Amara 30%, Tigraway 6%, Somalie 6%, Guragie 4%, Sidama 4%

RELIGION Christian 61% (Orthodox 51%, Protestant 10%), Muslim 33%, Indigenous beliefs 5%

CLIMATE Arid, Semi-arid, Tropical, Mediterranean, Maritime

REGIONAL DIVISIONS 9 ethnically based Regions and 2 Self-governing Administrations (chartered cities) further divided into 68 Zones

ECONOMIC ACTIVITIES Agriculture, Food Processing, Coffee Export, Textiles, Leather, Chemicals, Metals Processing, Cement Industries, Construction, Flower Export

NATURAL RESOURCES Small reserves of Gold, Platinum, Copper, Potash, Natural Gas, Hydropower

SOMALIA

10° 00' N, 45° 00' E | 637,657 KM² | 246,201 MI² | UTC+3

Since independence Somalia has been devastated by tribal war, drought, famine and floods, which have devastated the country's economy and infrastructure.

Geography

Situated on the Horn of Africa, Somalia possesses over 3,000 kilometres of coastline. Beyond the narrow coastal plain on the Gulf of Aden, mountains dominate the north, while the south consists of a lower plateau and broad plains stretching along the Indian Ocean. The climate is mainly arid or semi-arid, with an average annual rainfall of around 280 mm.

History

Once part of Ethiopia's ancient Aksum Kingdom, this land saw Somali people begin arriving from Yemen during the ninth century. Between the seventeenth and nineteenth centuries the area was part of the Omani Sultanate. The region was then divided into protectorates within British and Italian Somaliland until Somalia was reunified at independence in 1960. Nine years later the government was overthrown in a military coup. Attempts at economic reform were hampered during the 1970s by both famine and a conflict for control of Ethiopia's Ogaden region, while political wrangling sparked an internal tribal war that led to the deaths of thousands during the 1980s and 1990s. The north of the country declared itself independent as Somaliland in 1991, while a peace agreement and transitional government were put in place in the south in 2004. Two years later Islamic militants attempted to seize power, leading Ethiopia to send thousands of troops across the border to help reclaim the capital, Mogadishu.

Economy

Although seriously disrupted by the civil war, Somalia's economy is gradually recovering. The rearing of livestock is the principal economic activity and crops are grown in the south of the country, with bananas as the chief export.

SOMALI DESERT
Somali herders drive their cattle past their village.

FACT FILE

LOCAL NAME Somalia

CAPITAL CITY Mogadishu

CURRENCY Somali Shilling (SOS)

MEMBERSHIP AU, LAS, G-77, OIC

GOVERNMENT No permanent national government; Transitional, parliamentary federal government

POPULATION 8,956,006

POP. DENSITY 14/km²; 36/mi²

GDP 5.57 Billion US$

LANGUAGE(S) Somali, Arabic, Italian, English

ETHNICITY Somali 85%, Bantu and other non-Somali 15%

RELIGION Sunni Muslim 100%

CLIMATE Arid, Semi-arid

REGIONAL DIVISIONS Four quasi-independent States are divided into 27 de facto Regions

ECONOMIC ACTIVITIES Agriculture, Few Light Industries including Sugar Refining, Textiles, Telecommunication, Fishing

NATURAL RESOURCES Uranium and largely unexploited reserves of Iron Ore, Tin, Gypsum, Bauxite; Copper, Salt, Natural Gas; Likely Oil Reserves

KENYA

1° 00' N, 38° 00' E | 582,650 KM² | 224,962 MI² | UTC+3

Kenya's beautiful and diverse landscapes make it one of the most visited countries in Africa.

Geography

Straddling the Equator, Kenya has a varied topography, from the shores of Lake Victoria in the west to the narrow coastal plains of the east, the arid grasslands of the north and the Great Rift Valley and highlands of the interior, including Africa's second highest peak, Mount Kenya. The climate is generally tropical, although temperatures are moderated by altitude, with summer temperatures in Nairobi averaging 10°C lower than in the coastal area of Mombasa.

History

Cited as one of the possible birthplaces of modern man, Kenya is known to have been inhabited for millennia and became an important Arab trading centre around the eighth century. The Portuguese attempted to gain a foothold in the region between 1505 and 1698, but by the late nineteenth century the coast was under British control. However, as Kenya's white population rapidly swelled and moved inland, nationalist sentiment grew and, in 1953, the underground Mau Mau group launched an armed rebellion. The uprising was violently suppressed by the British, but by 1963 Kenya had gained its independence. Since that time the country has prospered, but tribal factionalism, political corruption and Islamic terrorism have at times threatened the nation's stability.

Economy

Kenya's economy is relatively stable and productive, with well-developed service and manufacturing industries and a significant revenue from tourists who visit the national parks and beaches. However, around 80 per cent of the population are engaged in agriculture. Most are subsistence farmers, although tea and coffee are important exports.

FACT FILE

LOCAL NAME Republic of Kenya

CAPITAL CITY Nairobi

CURRENCY Kenyan Shilling (KES)

MEMBERSHIP AU, COMESA, Commonwealth of Nations, EAC, G-15, G-77, WTO

GOVERNMENT Republic

POPULATION 38,549,711

POP. DENSITY 66/km²; 171/mi²

GDP 58.88 Billion US$

LANGUAGE(S) English, Kiswahili

ETHNICITY Kikuyu 22%, Luhya 14%, Luo 13%, Kalenjin 12%, Kamba 11%, Kisii 6%, Meru 6%, Other African 15%

RELIGION Protestant 45%, Roman Catholic 33%, Muslim 10%, Indigenous beliefs 10%

CLIMATE Tropical, Arid, Semi-arid

REGIONAL DIVISIONS 7 Provinces and 1 Area further divided into 71 Districts; Districts are sub-divided into 262 Divisions

ECONOMIC ACTIVITIES Agriculture, Small-scale Consumer Goods (Plastic, Furniture, Batteries, Textiles, Clothing, Soap, Cigarettes, Flour), Agricultural Products, Horticulture, Oil Refining, Aluminium, Steel, Lead, Cement, Commercial Ship Repair, Tourism

NATURAL RESOURCES Limestone, Soda Ash, Salt, Gemstones, Fluorspar, Zinc, Diatomite, Gypsum, Wildlife, Hydropower

NAKURU
Thousands of flamingos gather at the alkali lake at Nakuru, north west of Nairobi.

UGANDA

1° 00' N, 32° 00' E | 236,040 KM² | 91,136 MI² | UTC+3

Once known as 'the pearl of Africa', today Uganda is struggling to recover from the dictatorial regimes of Idi Amin and Milton Obote that blighted the country in the 1970s and 1980s.

Geography

Situated on a plateau which increases in height from north to south, Uganda's landscape is extremely varied, with semi-desert regions in the north, central savannah and marshlands, and lush forests and farmland in the south. The southeast is occupied by part of Lake Victoria, the main source of the Nile, and Lakes Edward and Albert lie in the Rift Valley along the western border. Although equatorial, Uganda's climate is moderated by altitude.

History

Prior to Europeans' arrival in the nineteenth century, Uganda was divided into various kingdoms, including that of Buganda, which prospered after it became a British protectorate in 1894. Independence was granted in 1962, with the Bugandan king Mutesa as head of state. In 1967 Prime Minister Milton Obote seized power but was overthrown four years later by General Idi Amin, who began a reign of terror during which thousands of Ugandans perished. With the aid of Tanzanian forces, Obote returned to power in 1978, but his own bloody regime prompted a coup in 1985, leading to the appointment of Yoweri Museveni as president. Museveni made significant economic, political and social reforms during the 1990s, including easing tensions with Rwanda, Kenya and Sudan.

Economy

Shattered during the 1970s and 1980s, Uganda's economy has gradually recovered, and strong links with Kenya and Tanzania have been forged. Although most people are engaged in subsistence farming, coffee is a major export and wildlife tourism is growing.

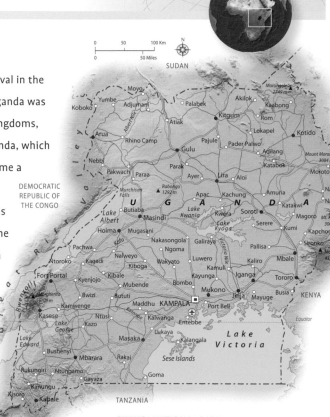

BWINDI NATIONAL PARK
A baby gorilla with an adult male.

FACT FILE

LOCAL NAME Republic of Uganda

CAPITAL Kampala

CURRENCY Ugandan Shilling (UGX)

MEMBERSHIP AU, COMESA, Commonwealth of Nations, EAC, G-77, OIC, WTO

GOVERNMENT Republic

POPULATION 31,902,609

POPULATION DENSITY 135/km²; 350/mi²

GDP 29.04 Billion US$

LANGUAGE(S) English, Ganda/Luganda, Niger-Congo languages, Nilo-Saharan languages, Swahili, Arabic

ETHNICITY Baganda 17%, Banyakole 10%, Basoga 8%, Bakiga 7%, Iteso 6%, Langi 6%, Acholi 5%, Bagisu 5%, Lugbara 4%

RELIGION Protestant 42%, Roman Catholic 42%, Muslim 12%

CLIMATE Equatorial

REGIONAL DIVISIONS Four Administrative Divisions, Northern, Eastern, Central and Western, are divided into 80 Districts

ECONOMIC ACTIVITIES Agriculture, Agroprocessing, Sugar, Brewing, Tobacco, Cotton Textiles, Cement, Steel Production, Light Consumer Goods

NATURAL RESOURCES Copper, Cobalt, Hydropower, Limestone, Salt, Arable Land, Phosphate, Untapped Reserves of Oil and Natural Gas

EASTERN AFRICA

RWANDA

2° 00′ S, 30° 00′ E | 26,338 KM² | 10,169 MI² | UTC+2

One of the most densely populated countries in Africa, Rwanda was torn apart by ethnic conflict and civil war during the 1990s.

Eastern and central Rwanda are dominated by hills and plateaux, divided by a mountainous ridge from Lake Kivu and the River Ruzizi in the west. Rwanda was absorbed into German East Africa in the nineteenth century and later came under Belgian administration. Tension between the Hutu majority and the dominant Tutsi minority, who migrated to the area in the fourteenth century, has surfaced frequently since independence in 1962. The worst outbreak, which was in 1994, resulted in over 800,000 deaths. Political reforms under a new multiracial government have maintained calm since, but despite economic reconstruction the country is poor and most survive by subsistence farming.

FACT FILE

LOCAL NAME	Republic of Rwanda
CAPITAL CITY	Kigali
CURRENCY	Rwandan Franc (RWF)
MEMBERSHIP	AU, CEPGL, COMESA, EAC, G-77, WTO
GOVERNMENT	Republic; Presidential, Multiparty system
POPULATION	10,008,622
POP. DENSITY	380/km²; 984/mi²
GDP	8.44 Billion US$
LANGUAGE(S)	Kinyarwanda, French, English, Kiswahili (Swahili)
ETHNICITY	Hutu (Bantu) 84%, Tutsi (Hamitic) 15%, Twa (pygmy) 1%
RELIGION	Roman Catholic 57%, Other Christian 27%, Muslim 5%
CLIMATE	Tropical

CYANGUGU
Women wait to sell produce at a market in south-west Rwanda.

BURUNDI

3° 30′ S, 30° 00′ E | 27,830 KM² | 10,745 MI² | UTC+2

Like its neighbour Rwanda, Burundi's recent history has been blighted by ethnic violence.

Located partly in the Great Rift Valley, Burundi is dominated by mountainous central highlands, with lower-lying areas in the east and in the west, where Lake Tanganyika forms much of its western border. The predominantly Hutu population of the area came under Tutsi domination in the sixteenth century, sowing the seeds of modern intercommunal tension. A German colony from 1890, Burundi came under Belgian administration from 1919 until independence in 1962. In 1993 intercommunal tension led to a coup that left 100,000 dead. Violence in 1994 degenerated into a civil war that lasted until

FACT FILE

LOCAL NAME	Republic of Burundi
CAPITAL CITY	Bujumbura
CURRENCY	Burundi Franc (BIF)
MEMBERSHIP	AU, CEPGL, COMESA, EAC, G-77, WTO
GOVERNMENT	Republic
POPULATION	8,856,221
POP. DENSITY	318/km²; 824/mi²
GDP	2.90 Billion US$
LANGUAGE(S)	Kirundi, French, Swahili
ETHNICITY	Hutu (Bantu) 81%, Tutsi (Hamitic) 16%, Lingala 2%, Twa (pygmy) 1%
RELIGION	Roman Catholic 62%, Protestant 5%, Indigenous beliefs 23%, Muslim 10%
CLIMATE	Tropical

2000. The country is one of the poorest nations on Earth, dependent on agriculture for subsistence and exports.

EASTERN AFRICA

TANZANIA

6° 00' S, 35° 00' E | 945,087 KM² | 364,898 MI² | UTC+3

The largest country in eastern Africa, Tanzania possesses a huge range of habitats and wildlife.

Geography

Over a third of Tanzania's land is occupied by national parks and conservation areas, encompassing such habitats as rain forest, swampland, desert scrub, the Serengeti grasslands, vast lakes and volcanic peaks, including Africa's highest mountain, Mount Kilimanjaro. The climate is tropical, becoming temperate at higher altitudes.

History

One of the earliest inhabited regions in Africa, by the eighth century Tanzania's coast and the island of Zanzibar were established as important Arab trading centres, giving rise to the distinctive Swahili culture. The Portuguese seized power during the sixteenth century but by the early eighteenth century they had been expelled, leaving Omani Arabs to consolidate their power through slave trading. During the late nineteenth century Britain took control of Zanzibar, while the mainland was incorporated into German East Africa, but from 1922 the whole area became a British possession, known as Tanganyika. Independence was granted in 1961, although Britain would not relinquish Zanzibar until 1963. The Republic of Tanzania was created the following year. Since that time Tanzania's development has been hindered by a war with Uganda in 1978 and its one-party, socialist regime. However, progress has been made since democratic reform in the 1990s.

Economy

Over half of Tanzania's GDP and most of the country's export revenue is provided by agriculture, forestry and fishing, with coffee being the most significant cash crop. Service industries, including tourism, are also of major importance, but Tanzania remains one of the world's poorest nations.

FACT FILE

LOCAL NAME United Republic of Tanzania

CAPITAL Dodoma (legislative), Dar es Salaam (commercial)

CURRENCY Tanzanian Shilling (TZS)

MEMBERSHIP AU, LAS, Commonwealth of Nations, EAC, G-77, OIC, SADC, WTO

GOVERNMENT Republic

POPULATION 41,463,922

POPULATION DENSITY 44/km²; 114/mi²

GDP 48.94 Billion US$

LANGUAGE(S) Kiswahili, English (commerce, administration), Arabic (widely spoken in Zanzibar)

ETHNICITY Mainland: African 99% (of which 95% are Bantu)

RELIGION Mainland: Muslim 35%, Indigenous beliefs 35%, Christian 30%, Zanzibar: Muslim 99%

CLIMATE Tropical, Temperate

REGIONAL DIVISIONS 26 Administrative Regions (21 mainland, 5 Zanzibar), 130 Administrative Districts (210 Mainland, 10 Zanzibar)

ECONOMIC ACTIVITIES Agriculture, Agricultural Processing (Sugar, Beer, Cigarettes, Sisal Twine), Diamond, Gold and Iron Mining, Salt, Soda Ash, Cement, Oil Refining, Shoes, Apparel, Wood Products, Fertilizer, Textiles

NATURAL RESOURCES Hydropower, Tin, Phosphates, Iron Ore, Coal, Diamonds, Gemstones, Gold, Natural Gas, Nickel

KILIMANJARO
The snow-covered cone of Kilimanjaro, the highest mountain in Africa.

ZAMBIA

15° 00′ S, 30° 00′ E | 752,614 KM² | 290,586 MI² | UTC+2

Although Zambia is highly urbanized by African standards, and with rich mineral deposits, the country continues to strive for economic and political stability.

Geography

Situated on a high plateau interspersed with mountains, lakes and swamps, Zambia's altitude gradually decreases from north to south, where the Zambezi River plunges over the Victoria Falls at the border with Zimbabwe. The climate is essentially subtropical, with a rainy season between November and April.

History

Although the area was first settled around the fourth century, migration into the region from surrounding areas was still occurring when the British arrived during the nineteenth century. It was claimed as a protectorate in

1889, and renamed Northern Rhodesia in 1911. European settlement increased following the discovery of copper reserves in the 1920s, and in 1953 the region was incorporated into a federation with Southern Rhodesia and Nyasaland (present-day Zimbabwe and Malawi). Ten years later, at the dissolution of the federation, Zambia gained its independence. Between 1964 and 1991 the country was ruled as a one-party state by President Kaunda, and despite attempts to diversify the economy and reduce its reliance on copper, the country suffered a decline, enduring soaring crime rates and widespread rioting in the 1980s. Multiparty elections brought hope of political reform during the early 1990s, although the decade was blighted by allegations of corruption, which are only now being resolved. The prevalence of AIDS is also a major issue.

Economy

Although copper remains Zambia's chief export commodity, around 70 per cent of the country's workforce is employed in agriculture, with coffee, tobacco and cotton grown as cash crops.

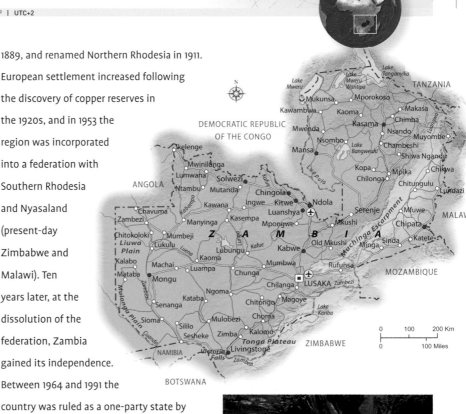

VICTORIA FALLS
Victoria Falls, on the Zambezi River on the border of Zambia and Zimbabwe.

FACT FILE

LOCAL NAME Republic of Zambia

CAPITAL CITY Lusaka

CURRENCY Zambian Kwacha (ZMK)

MEMBERSHIP AU, COMESA, C, G-77, SADC, WTO

GOVERNMENT Republic

POPULATION 12,154,058

POP. DENSITY 16/km²; 42/mi²

GDP 15.92 Billion US$

LANGUAGE(S) English, Bemba, Kaonda, Lozi, Lunda, Luvale, Nyanja, Tonga

ETHNICITY African 99% (Bemba, Tonga, Retse and others), European 1%

RELIGION Christian 53%, Hindu 24%, Muslim 5%

CLIMATE Humid Subtropical

REGIONAL DIVISIONS 9 Provinces divided into 72 Districts; most populous province is Lusaka, location of the national capital

ECONOMIC ACTIVITIES Agriculture, Copper Mining and Processing, Construction, Foodstuffs, Beverages, Chemicals, Textiles, Fertilizer, Horticulture, Transport

NATURAL RESOURCES Copper, Cobalt, Zinc, Lead, Coal, Emeralds, Gold, Silver, Uranium, Hydropower

EASTERN AFRICA

ZIMBABWE

20° 00' S, 30° 00' E | 390,580 KM² | 150,804 MI² | UTC+2

The former seat of an ancient trading empire, Zimbabwe has been blighted in recent times by the repressive regime of President Robert Mugabe.

Geography

Much of Zimbabwe is situated on a plateau, covered in woodland and savannah, which lies between the Limpopo and Zambezi Rivers. The spectacular Victoria Falls are on the Zambezi, on the border between Zimbabwe and Zambia. The climate is generally tropical, with hot wet summers and cooler, drier winters, although average temperatures vary considerably according to altitude.

History

Once the seat of a Shona trading empire, which was founded around the ninth century, the civilization of Great Zimbabwe gradually declined and the region came under the influence of Ndebele migrants. In 1890 Cecil Rhodes of the British South Africa Company arrived in search of gold, and by the early twentieth century the British had colonized the area, renaming it Southern Rhodesia. Between 1953 and 1963 the country was absorbed into the Central African Federation until, in 1965, Prime Minister Ian Smith declared independence under white minority rule. International and internal pressure finally forced the formation of a multiracial government in 1980. Since that time Zimbabwe has been led by President Mugabe, who has been accused of vote-rigging and widespread human rights abuses. There are hopes that a power-sharing agreement signed with the opposition in 2008 will improve the situation.

Economy

After 1965 international sanctions forced Zimbabwe to become self-sufficient, but the country has endured economic collapse under Mugabe's regime, with inflation spiralling out of control. Most farming operates at subsistence level, although important exports include tobacco, sugarcane and cotton.

GREAT ZIMBABWE
The stone ruins of Great Zimbabwe, estimated to have had a population of 18,000 at its peak.

FACT FILE

LOCAL NAME Republic of Zimbabwe

CAPITAL Harare

CURRENCY Zimbabwean Dollar (ZWD)

MEMBERSHIP AU, COMESA, G-15, G-77, SADC, WTO

GOVERNMENT Parliamentary Democracy

POPULATION 13,481,234

POP. DENSITY 35/km²; 89/mi²

GDP 2.21 Billion US$

LANGUAGE(S) English, Shona, Sindebele

ETHNICITY African 98% (Shona 82%, Ndebele 14%, other 2%), Mixed and Asian 1%, White less than 1%

RELIGION Syncretic 50%, Christian 25%, Indigenous beliefs 24%

CLIMATE Subtropical

REGIONAL DIVISIONS 8 Provinces and 2 Cities with provincial status divided into 59 Districts and further into 1,200 Municipalities

ECONOMIC ACTIVITIES Agriculture, Mining (Coal, Gold, Platinum, Copper, Nickel, Tin, Clay, Metallic and Non-metallic Ores), Steel, Wood Products, Cement, Chemicals, Fertilizer, Clothing and Footwear, Foodstuffs, Beverages, Transport, Communication

NATURAL RESOURCES Coal, Chromium Ore, Asbestos, Gold, Nickel, Copper, Iron Ore, Vanadium, Lithium, Tin, Platinum-group Metals

MOZAMBIQUE

18° 15' S, 35° 00' E | 801,590 KM² | 309,496 MI² | UTC+2

Since independence in 1975, Mozambique has endured civil war, famine and floods. However, in recent years the country has demonstrated its remarkable resilience, enjoying peace and relative prosperity.

Geography

Bisected by the Zambezi River, Mozambique is divided into two main regions, with a narrow coastal plain rising inland to the northern highlands, and wide lowlands of forest and savannah to the south. The climate is generally tropical, with hot, wet summers and dry winters, although most rainfall is concentrated in the north.

History

Originally settled by tribes from North and West Africa, by the eighth century Arab trading posts had sprung up along Mozambique's extensive coastline. However, following Vasco da Gama's arrival in 1498, Portugal began to establish itself in the region, and over the next 300 years strengthened its claims by trading in ivory and slaves. Portugal attempted to further consolidate control in the late nineteenth and early twentieth centuries, but following a ten-year guerrilla war waged by the liberation movement FRELIMO, Mozambique eventually gained independence in 1975. Two years later, civil war erupted, as the resistance group RENAMO fought to destabilize the government, with hostilities continuing until 1992, but since 1994's multiparty elections, Mozambique has experienced increased stability and economic growth.

Economy

Destabilized by war, drought and flooding, Mozambique's economy had effectively collapsed by the early 1990s, and although significant progress had been made by the end of the decade, flooding brought renewed challenges in 2000. Agriculture and fishing are the principal economic activities, and cashews, sugar and shrimps are the main exports.

NIASSA RESERVE, NORTHERN MOZAMBIQUE
Inselbergs rise from the surrounding flat land.

FACT FILE

LOCAL NAME Republic of Mozambique

CAPITAL CITY Maputo

CURRENCY Metical (MZM)

MEMBERSHIP AU, C, G-77, OIC, SADC, WTO

GOVERNMENT Republic

POPULATION 21,812,551

POP. DENSITY 27/km²; 71/mi²

GDP 17.02 Billion US$

LANGUAGE(S) Portuguese, Emakhuwa, Xichangana, Elomwe, Cisena, Echuwabo

ETHNICITY African 100% (Makhuwa, Tsonga, Lomwe, Sena and others)

RELIGION Roman Catholic 24%, Other Christian 18%, Muslim 18%,

CLIMATE Tropical, Subtropical

REGIONAL DIVISIONS 10 Provinces and 1 City further divided into 128 Districts; Zambézia is the most populous province

ECONOMIC ACTIVITIES Agriculture, Fishing, Food, Beverages, Chemicals (Fertilizer, Soap, Paints), Aluminium, Petroleum Products, Textiles, Cement, Glass, Asbestos, Tobacco

NATURAL RESOURCES Coal, Titanium, Natural Gas, Hydropower, Tantalum, Graphite, Titanium Ore, Iron Ore, Semi-precious Stones

EASTERN AFRICA

MALAWI

13° 30' S, 34° 00' E | 118,480 KM² | 45,745 MI² | UTC+2

Landlocked Malawi is perhaps best known for its lake, the most ecologically diverse in the world, containing hundreds of species of cichlid fish.

Although much of Malawi is hilly and mountainous, almost a fifth of its surface area is occupied by the 568-kilometre-long Lake Malawi, or Nyasa, which lies in the Rift Valley and forms the eastern border with Tanzania and Mozambique. The climate tends to be hot and humid at lower elevations, becoming more temperate with altitude. Settled by Bantu peoples over 2,000 years ago, the area became the British protectorate of Nyasaland in 1891, later joining with Rhodesia. In 1964 the country gained independence as Malawi and although its first prime minister, Dr Hastings Banda, instituted a programme of economic reform, he effectively ruled the country as a dictatorship. Multiparty elections were held in 1994 and since that time Malawi has begun to tackle health issues, such as AIDS, political corruption and education. More than 80 per cent of Malawi's population lives in rural areas and is engaged in agriculture, with tobacco, sugar, tea and coffee comprising the main exports.

FACT FILE

LOCAL NAME Republic of Malawi
CAPITAL CITY Lilongwe
CURRENCY Malawian Kwacha (MWK)
MEMBERSHIP AU, COMESA, C, G-77, SADC, WTO
GOVERNMENT Multiparty Democracy
POPULATION 14,288,374
POP. DENSITY 121/km²; 312/mi²
GDP 10.51 Billion US$
LANGUAGE(S) Chichewa, Chinyanja, Chiyao, Chitumbuka, Chisena, Chilomwe, Chitonga
ETHNICITY Chewa 35%, Maravi 12%, Ngoni 9%, Tumbuka 8%, Yao 8%, Lomwe 8%, Ngonde 4%
RELIGION Christian 80%, Muslim 13%
CLIMATE Subtropical

COMOROS

12° 10' S, 44° 15' E | 2,170 KM² | 838 MI² | UTC+3

Formerly a French protectorate, today the Comoros Islands form a republic, although Mayotte remains under French administration.

Situated between northern Madagascar and the Mozambique coast, Comoros consists of four principal volcanic islands, Njazidja, Nzwani, Mwali and Mayotte, as well as a number of coral islets. The main islands are all mountainous, with the highest peak being the active volcano of Karthala on Njazidja. The climate is tropical, with heavy monsoon rains between November and March. The majority of the population is involved in subsistence farming, although a great deal of food has to be imported. Flowers and spices are grown as cash crops.

FACT FILE

LOCAL NAME Union of Comoros
CAPITAL CITY Moroni
CURRENCY Comoran Franc (KMF)
MEMBERSHIP AU, LAS, COMESA, G-77, OIC, WTO (observer)
GOVERNMENT Republic
POPULATION 860,100
POP. DENSITY 396/km²; 1026/mi²
GDP 1.26 Billion US$
LANGUAGE(S) Arabic, French, Shikomoro
ETHNICITY Comorian 97%, Makoa 2%
RELIGION Sunni Muslim 98%, Roman Catholic 2%
CLIMATE Tropical Wet

EASTERN AFRICA

MADAGASCAR
20° 00' S, 47° 00' E | 587,040 KM² | 226,657 MI² | UTC+3

Isolated from the African mainland for over 160 million years, Madagascar is one of the world's most unique wildlife habitats, with around 75 per cent of its plants and animals found nowhere else on Earth.

Geography

Sometimes known as 'the Great Red Island' because of its iron-rich soils, Madagascar is the fourth largest island in the world. It is dominated by a mountainous central plateau, with coastal plains in the east and west. Coastal areas tend to be hot all year, with the east coast receiving high rainfall, while the interior is drier and more temperate. The island's rain forests attract tourists who come to see the many species found only on Madagascar, including lemurs, and numerous types of chameleons and frogs.

History

As with its wildlife, Madagascar's location has led to the development of a culture that is unique within Africa. It was first settled by people from southeast Asia, before the arrival of Arabs, Africans, and later, Europeans. The Portuguese, English and French all made attempts to colonize the island from the 1600s, with France finally claiming the territory in 1896. Against a backdrop of growing nationalism, Madagascar became independent in 1960. During the 1970s, public disorder and political unrest led to the imposition of military rule, but the country's instability continued until the election of the Tiako I Madagasikara party in 2002. Since that time there have been significant improvements in the country's infrastructure, health and education systems.

MORONDAVA
An alley of baobab trees, which are indigenous to the island.

Economy

Despite recent progress, Madagascar remains one of the world's poorest nations, with a primarily agricultural economy. Almost 80 per cent of the workforce is involved in farming, with coffee, cotton, cloves, vanilla and tobacco as the main exports.

FACT FILE

LOCAL NAME Republic of Madagascar

CAPITAL CITY Antananarivo

CURRENCY Ariary (MGA)

MEMBERSHIP AU, LAS, C, COMESA, G-77, SADC, OIC, WTO

GOVERNMENT Republic

POPULATION 20,215,199

POP. DENSITY 34/km²; 89/mi²

GDP 18.2 Billion US$

LANGUAGE(S) English, French, Malagasy

ETHNICITY Malagasay 96%, Makua 1%

RELIGION Indigenous beliefs 52%, Christian 41%, Muslim 7%

CLIMATE Tropical, Temperate, Semi-arid

REGIONAL DIVISIONS 5 geographical Regions are divided into 6 Provinces, further divided into 22 Regions

ECONOMIC ACTIVITIES Agriculture, Meat Processing, Seafood, Soap, Breweries, Tanneries, Sugar, Textiles, Glassware, Cement, Automobile Assembly Plant, Paper, Petroleum, Tourism, Clothing, Mining, Construction

NATURAL RESOURCES Graphite, Chromite, Coal, Bauxite, Salt, Quartz, Tar Sands, Semi-precious Stones, Mica, Fish, Hydropower

MAYOTTE

12° 50′ S, 45° 10′ E | 374 KM² | 144 MI² | UTC+3

Despite some international criticism, Mayotte has remained a French territorial collectivity since referendums were held during the 1970s.

Located within the Comoros island group in the Mozambique Channel, Mayotte consists of the main volcanic island called Grande Terre (or Mahoré), the smaller Petite Terre and several islets. The climate is tropical, with monsoon rains and cyclones experienced between November and April. During the early nineteenth century, Mayotte was ruled by the Malagasy chief Andriansouli, who

would cede Dzaoudzi to the French in 1843; by 1912 France had exerted its control over the entire archipelago.When the Comoros

gained independence in 1975, Mayotte opted to remain a French dependency, although the Comoros continue to claim sovereignty over the islands. Mayotte's economy is heavily subsidized by France; exports include vanilla, coffee and ylang-ylang essence.

FACT FILE

LOCAL NAME	Departmental Collectivity of Mayotte
SOVEREIGN STATE	France
CAPITAL/MAIN CITY	Mamoudzou
CURRENCY	Euro (EUR)
GOVERNMENT	Departmental Collectivity of France
POPULATION	216,306
POP. DENSITY	578/km²;1,502/mi²
GDP	953.6 Million US$
LANGUAGE(S)	Mahorian (a Swahili dialect), French
ETHNICITY	Comorian (Mauri, Mahorais) 92%, Swahili 3%, White (French) 2%
RELIGION	Muslim 97%, Christian (mostly Roman Catholic) 3%
CLIMATE	Tropical Maritime

SEYCHELLES

4° 35′ S, 55° 40′ E | 455 KM² | 176 MI² | UTC+4

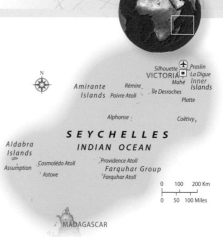

Despite political turmoil in the period following independence, tourism and foreign investment have enabled the Seychelles to prosper in recent years.

Comprising four main islands in the Mahé group, as well as numerous coral islets, the Seychelles are located in the Indian

Ocean, to the northeast of Madagascar. Uninhabited until the eighteenth century, the Seychelles were first settled by the French in 1768, although by 1794 they had been annexed by Britain, becoming a British dependency in 1814. The islands became independent in 1976, but from 1978 to 1990 they were ruled as a one-party state, leading to social unrest and numerous attempted coups during the 1980s. Multiparty democracy was introduced in 1992, but the ruling party has continued to hold power. Tourism is of major economic importance, as are fishing and fish processing.

FACT FILE

LOCAL NAME	Republic of Seychelles
CAPITAL CITY	Victoria
CURRENCY	Seychelles Rupee (SCR)
MEMBERSHIP	AU, COMESA, C, G-77, WTO
GOVERNMENT	Republic
POPULATION	82,247
POP. DENSITY	181/km²; 467/mi²
GDP	1.38 Billion US$
LANGUAGE(S)	Creole, English
ETHNICITY	Seychellois Creole (mixed African, Asian, European) 93%, British 3%, French 2%
RELIGION	Roman Catholic 82%, Other Christian 11%, Hindu 2%, Muslim 1%
CLIMATE	Tropical Maritime

COUSIN ISLAND
A secluded beach on Cousin Island, near Praslin Island.

RÉUNION

21° 5' S, 55° 29' E | 2,512 KM² | 970 MI² | UTC+4

Formerly known as Bourbon, Réunion has been a French possession since 1638, and a French overseas department since 1946.

The largest island in the Mascerene group, around 200 kilometres south of Mauritius, Réunion is an actively volcanic island, with a rugged, mountainous interior. Settled by the French from around the mid-seventeenth century, Réunion was developed as an agricultural centre, producing coffee, cereals, cotton and spices, with the aid of African slaves. However, in 1810 the island fell to the British, who introduced sugarcane as the principal cash crop. Réunion was retuned to the French in 1815, and following the abolition of slavery, labourers were introduced from India to work on the plantations. Sugar is still of huge economic importance, while the growing tourism industry has been adversely affected by a recent epidemic of the Chikungunya virus.

FACT FILE

LOCAL NAME Overseas Department of Réunion
SOVEREIGN STATE France
CAPITAL/MAIN CITY St-Denis
CURRENCY Euro (EUR)
GOVERNMENT Overseas Department of France
POPULATION 793,000
POP. DENSITY 316/km²; 818/mi²
GDP 19.5 Billion US$
LANGUAGE(S) French, Réunion French Creole, Tamil
ETHNICITY Mixed race (black-white-South Asian) 43%, Local white 26%, South Asian 23% (including Tamil 20%), Chinese 3%, East African 3%
RELIGION Christian 88% (including Roman Catholic 82%, Pentecostal 4%), Hindu 5%, Muslim 4%
CLIMATE Tropical Maritime

MAURITIUS

20° 17' S, 57° 33' E | 2,040 KM² | 787 MI² | UTC+4

Famed as the home of the now-extinct dodo, today Mauritius is developing a name for itself as an exclusive tourist destination.

Consisting of Mauritius, Rodrigues and a number of smaller islands, the Republic of Mauritius lies in the Indian Ocean, around 800 kilometres east of Madagascar. The climate is tropical, with high rainfall in the highland areas. Although previously known to Arab traders, Mauritius was first settled by the Dutch during the early seventeenth century, before being colonized by the French, and later the British, who brought African and Indian labour to the islands. Independence was granted in 1968, although Mauritius did not become a republic until 1992. Formerly centred on the growth of sugarcane, Mauritius has successfully diversified its economy, with textiles and tourism comprising important industries. However, the Creole population remains comparatively impoverished, leading to occasional conflicts with the Indian majority.

FACT FILE

LOCAL NAME Republic of Mauritius
CAPITAL CITY Port Louis
CURRENCY Mauritian Rupee (MUR)
MEMBERSHIP AU, C, SADC, WTO
GOVERNMENT Parliamentary Democracy
POPULATION 1,271,538
POP. DENSITY 623/km²; 1616/mi²
GDP 14.06 Billion US$
LANGUAGE(S) English, Creole, Bhojpuri, French
ETHNICITY Indo-Mauritian 68%, Creole 27%, Sino-Mauritian 3%, Franco-Mauritian 2%
RELIGION Hindu 48%, Roman Catholic 24%, Muslim 17%, Other Christian 9%
CLIMATE Tropical

BAMBOU MOUNTAIN RANGE
An aerial view of the Bambou mountain range in the south-east of Mauritius.

EASTERN AFRICA

Benguela
Bié Plateau
Huambo
Lubumbashi

ANGOLA
ZAMBIA
MALAWI
LILONGWE
LUSAKA

MOZAMBIQUE
Mocambique

Luangwa
Zambezi
HARARE

Livingstone
ZIMBABWE
Beira

Tsumeb
NAMIBIA
Bulawayo

MADAGA
ANTANANARIVO

Mozambique Channel

Swakopmund
WINDHOEK
BOTSWANA

Toliara

Keetmanshoop
Kalahari Desert
GABORONE

PRETORIA
MAPUTO

Orange
Johannesburg
MBABANE
SWAZILAND

Kimberley
MASERU
LESOTHO

Bloemfontein
Durban

Drakensberg

SOUTH AFRICA

Great Karoo

Cape Town
Cape of Good Hope
Port Elizabeth

COUNTRY	PAGE
Ascension Island (UK)	273
Botswana	268
Lesotho	272
Namibia	268
Saint Helena (UK)	273
South Africa	269
Swaziland	272
Tristan da Cunha (UK)	273

STELLENBOSCH
The vineyards at Stellenbosch, which is around 55 kilometres east of Cape Town.

SOUTHERN AFRICA

According to the United Nations scheme of geographic regions, Southern Africa comprises the countries of Botswana, Lesotho, Namibia, Swaziland and South Africa. Of these, South Africa is by far the largest and, as the most highly developed country on the continent, it dominates the region in terms of its geography, economy and politics.

Geographically Southern Africa is dominated by a vast plateau that includes the arid and semi-arid territory of the Kalahari Desert, which occupies much of Botswana and parts of Namibia and South Africa, and the folded mountain chain of the Drakensberg, which lies to the south and east. Despite this, the region's terrain varies considerably, encompassing such habitats as the subtropical woodlands of the Bushveld, savannah grasslands and the extensive inland waterways of the Okavango Delta, all of which are inhabited by a diverse range of flora and fauna.

Southern Africa is also home to numerous peoples and cultures. Although it was once dominated by indigenous San bushmen, the expansion of Bantu peoples saw groups such as the Zulu, Xhosa, Ndebele and Shona spread across the region. European colonial powers such as the Dutch and British would follow in their wake, establishing staging posts on their route to the East Indies before turning inland to carve up the land for farming and to exploit Southern Africa's great mineral wealth, which includes gold and diamonds, as well as the world's largest platinum reserves.

NAMIBIA
Rippled sand in the Namib Desert, which occupies an area of around 80,900 square kilometres.

Following the end of colonial rule, Southern Africa has attempted to unite its economic ambitions, perhaps most notably with the formation of the South African Development Community (SADC) in 1980. While countries such as Botswana and South Africa have begun to enjoy a greater level of prosperity, the region shares many of the problems common to Africa as a whole, including widespread poverty, political corruption and the ravages brought by the HIV and AIDS epidemic. South Africa was also blighted by decades of racial segregation under the system of apartheid and its refusal to relinquish control of Namibia led to conflict between the two nations until the late 1980s. Today, however, the efforts of the SADC have brought the promise of increased political and economic stability to the Southern African region as a whole.

KALAHARI GEMSBOK NATIONAL PARK
A camelthorn tree in the veld at sunset. Grasses, thorny shrubs and Acacia trees, all of which can survive the long drought periods of more than ten months every year, are the dominant forms of vegetation in the Kalahari.

SOUTHERN AFRICA

NAMIBIA

22° 00' S, 17° 00' E | 825,418 KM² | 318,696 MI² | UTC+1

One of the least densely populated countries in the world, Namibia's terrain is one of the most inhospitable in Africa.

Namibia's central plateau is bordered by the Kalahari Desert in the east and by a series of mountains in the west that fall to the Namib Desert along the Atlantic coast. The Namib Desert is one of the world's oldest and driest deserts, with an annual rainfall of less than 10 mm a year, and the sand dunes are among the highest in the world. The territory was annexed in 1884 by Germany, which crushed the indigenous Bantu and San peoples. The territory was administered from 1920 by South Africa, which refused to terminate its mandate in 1961. This led the independence movement to wage a guerrilla war that lasted until 1988, and independence was granted in 1990. The economy is based primarily on

FACT FILE

LOCAL NAME Republic of Namibia
CAPITAL CITY Windhoek
CURRENCY Namibian dollar (NAD); South African Rand (ZAR)
MEMBERSHIP AU, C, G-77, SADC, WTO
GOVERNMENT Republic
POPULATION 2,102,140
POP. DENSITY 3/km²; 7/mi²
GDP 10.72 Billion US$
LANGUAGE(S) English, Afrikaans, German, Oshivambo, Herero, Nama
ETHNICITY Black 88%, White 6%, Mixed 7%
RELIGION Protestant (mostly Lutheran) 48%, Roman Catholic 18%, African Christian 11%, Indigenous beliefs 6%
CLIMATE Arid, Semi-arid

the export of diamonds and other minerals such as uranium, zinc and silver, although around half of the population are subsistence farmers. Fishing and cattle-ranching are also of economic importance.

BOTSWANA

22° 00' S, 24° 00' E | 600,370 KM² | 224,606 MI² | UTC+2

Botswana has bucked the regional trend in HIV/AIDS infection rates, reducing levels that were the world's highest a few years ago through prevention and treatment programmes.

Over half of Botswana lies in the arid Kalahari Desert, but to the north and east are subtropical grasslands. To the north and north-west are the swamps of the vast Okavango Delta, which covers an area of almost 16,000 square kilometres and is home to hundreds of species of animals and birds including rare species such as the African fish eagle and the red lechwe antelope. In 1885 Britain responded to Tswana requests for assistance by founding the protectorate of Bechuanaland. The country gained independence in 1966 as Botswana, and has since maintained a

FACT FILE

LOCAL NAME Republic of Botswana
CAPITAL CITY Gaborone
CURRENCY Pula (BWP)
MEMBERSHIP AU, C, G-77, SADC, WTO
GOVERNMENT Parliamentary Republic
POPULATION 1,905,516
POP. DENSITY 3/km²; 9/mi²
GDP 25.68 Billion US$
LANGUAGE(S) Setswana, English, Kalanga, Sekgalagadi
ETHNICITY Tswana (or Setswana) 79%, Kalanga 11%, Basarwa 3%, Other (including Kgalagadi and White 7%)
RELIGION Christian 72%, Badimo 6%
CLIMATE Arid, Semi-arid

stable democracy and developed into one of the most prosperous economies in Africa, with some of the highest literacy rates in the continent, owing to its mineral resources, especially diamonds.

SOUTHERN AFRICA

SOUTH AFRICA
29° 00′ S, 24° 00′ E | 1,219,912 KM² | 471,011 MI² | UTC+2

South Africa is the most developed country on the African continent, but it has not yet recovered from the effects of centuries of colonial rule and decades of apartheid.

Geography

Africa's southernmost country, South Africa is divided into three principal geographic areas: the vast interior plateau, the narrow, fertile coastal plains, and the mountainous Great Escarpment, which forms a barrier between the two. The interior is dominated by the Orange River, which rises in Lesotho and flows west to enter the Atlantic Ocean at the border with Namibia. In the north-west the plateau extends into the arid Kalahari Desert, while the north-east is mostly grassland and is home to the Kruger National Park. South Africa has several major cities, including the commercial centre of Johannesburg, the legislative capital Cape Town, the administrative capital Pretoria, the judicial capital Bloemfontein and the port of Durban.

The climate is one of the most temperate in Africa, being generally warm and sunny with little rainfall, although it is typically cooler and drier in winter and hotter and wetter in summer. However, there are also widespread climatic variations because of the topography and maritime influences.

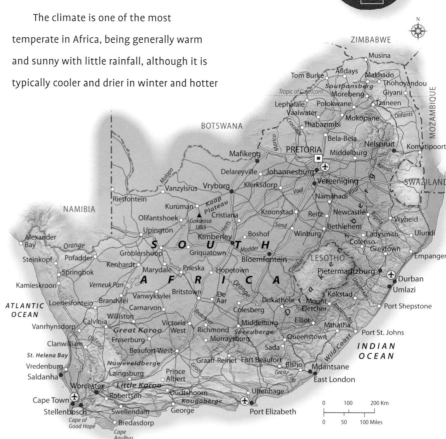

CAPE TOWN
Table Mountain and Cape Town below it. The plateau at the top of the mountain measures approximately 3 kilometres across.

History

The San people (Bushmen) were well established in the area by 8000 BC. About 2,000 years ago, Bantu tribes began to spread throughout the region from the north-east, reaching the south coast by the eighteenth century. Europeans, especially the Dutch, established settlements in the Cape Town area from the seventeenth century, and these came under British rule after Britain annexed the Cape in 1814. In response, many Dutch settlers, or Boers, began to migrate northwards, founding their own independent states and developing Afrikaner culture. However, the discovery of diamonds and gold in these states in the 1860s and 1880s led to friction between the British and the Boers, which resulted in the Anglo-Boer Wars of 1880–1 and 1899–1902. Britain emerged victorious, and united the four provinces in 1910 to form the Union of South Africa, which became a sovereign state in 1931 and a republic in 1961. In 1948, the National Party came to power, and began to implement its policy of racial segregation, or apartheid, prompting a campaign of defiance led by the African National Congress (ANC). As unrest escalated throughout the 1960s and 1970s, South Africa came under increasing international pressure to reform the apartheid system. Although some concessions were made during the 1980s, the gradual dismantling of apartheid did not begin until 1990, when the ban on the ANC was lifted and its former deputy president, Nelson Mandela, was released from prison after almost thirty years. Despite further civil conflict, in 1994 the country's first multiracial elections were held, resulting in the establishment of an ANC-led multiracial government and Nelson Mandela's election as South Africa's first black president.

CAPE TOWN
Nelson Mandela, South Africa's first black president, shakes hands with is predecessor F. W. de Klerk at the parliament building in Cape Town.

FACT FILE

LOCAL NAME Republic of South Africa

CAPITAL CITY Pretoria (administrative capital), Cape Town (legislative), Bloemfontein (judicial capital)

CURRENCY South African Rand (ZAR)

MEMBERSHIP AU, C, G-20, G-24, G-77, SADC, WTO

GOVERNMENT Parliamentary Republic

POPULATION 48,832,133

POP. DENSITY 40/km²; 104/mi²

GDP 467.1 Billion US$

LANGUAGE(S) Afrikaans, English, IsiNdebele, IsiXhosa, IsiZulu, Sesotho Sa Leboa, Sesotho, Setswana, SiSwati, Tshivenda, Xitsonga

ETHNICITY Black African 79%, White 10%, Coloured 9%, Indian/Asian 3%

RELIGION Christian 78% (73% Protestant, 7% Roman Catholic) , Muslim 2%, Hinduism 1%

CLIMATE Semi-arid, Subtropical, Mediterranean, Maritime

REGIONAL DIVISIONS 9 Provinces further divided into 52 Districts (6 Metropolitan and 46 District Municipalities)

ECONOMIC ACTIVITIES Agriculture, Mining, Automobile Assembly, Machinery, Clothing, Textiles, Chemicals, Iron and Steel, Metal working, Fertilizer, Agroprocessing, Financial Services, Commercial Ship Repairing, Pulp and Paper

NATURAL RESOURCES Gold, Chromium, Antimony, Coal, Iron Ore, Manganese, Nickel, Phosphates, Tin, Uranium, Gem Diamonds, Platinum, Copper, Vanadium, Salt, Natural Gas

SOUTHERN AFRICA

KRUGER NATIONAL PARK
A giraffe grazes in the Kruger park. Nearly 150 species of mammal can be found there.

A Truth and Reconciliation Commission began hearings in 1996 on human rights abuses during the apartheid era.

Despite increased political stability and trade expansion since the 1990s, a vast economic divide remains between whites and blacks. Over half of South Africa's population lives below the poverty line, and the overwhelming majority are the black urban and rural poor. HIV/AIDS infection continues to ravage the black population and, along with poverty, accounts for the relatively low life expectancy and high infant mortality rates of such an industrialized nation.

Economy

The discovery of precious minerals in the nineteenth century stimulated the transformation of South Africa's economy from an agricultural to an industrial one. Today it is the world's leading producer of gold and platinum and a major source of diamonds, with one of the world's most advanced deep-level mining industries. Although industry continues to generate around 30 per cent of GDP, service industries account for around 65 per cent and employ a similar percentage of the country's workforce. Agriculture has steadily declined in significance, although it continues to

occupy around 10 per cent of the workforce, who are engaged in the production of cotton, grains, sugarcane, fruit and vegetables, and the rearing of livestock. Tourism has increased since the end of apartheid, some of the principal attractions being the Kruger National Park, the largest game reserve in South Africa covering 18,989 square kilometres of the north-east of the country, the Kirstenbosch botanical garden at Cape Town and wine production centres such as Stellenbosch, located close to Cape Town.

SWAZILAND

26° 30′ S, 31° 30′ E | 17,363 KM² | 6,704 MI² | UTC+2

Encircled almost entirely by South Africa apart from a short border with Mozambique in the north-east, Swaziland is a small landlocked kingdom with a varied topography and climate.

The Swazi kingdom was founded in the nineteenth century, and in 1894 the area came under joint British and Boer control, before becoming a British protectorate in 1903. Since independence in 1968, Swaziland has remained in effect an absolute monarchy, despite calls for greater democracy. The economy is relatively stable, with over three quarters of the population employed in agriculture. But the country's future looks bleak, as nearly 40 per cent of adults are infected with HIV/AIDS, the world's highest incidence of the disease.

FACT FILE

LOCAL NAME	Kingdom of Swaziland
CAPITAL CITY	Mbabane
CURRENCY	Lilangeni (SZL)
MEMBERSHIP	AU, COMESA, C, G-77, SADC, WTO
GOVERNMENT	Monarchy
POPULATION	1,148,255
POP. DENSITY	66/km²; 171/mi²
GDP	5.63 Billion US$
LANGUAGE(S)	English, Siswati
ETHNICITY	African 97%, European 3%
RELIGION	Zionist 40%, Roman Catholic 20%, Muslim 10%, Other (includes Anglican, Bahai, Methodist, Mormon, Jewish) 30%
CLIMATE	Varies from Tropical to near-Temperate

LESOTHO

29° 30′ S, 28° 30′ E | 30,355 KM² | 11,717 MI² | UTC+2

The mountainous kingdom of Lesotho is one of only a handful of states completely surrounded by another country.

Lesotho lies within South Africa, and its entire terrain is above 1,000 metres. The high altitude means that winter temperatures can fall below freezing and summers tend to be mild. Originally inhabited by San people, the region's population was swollen during the nineteenth century by native peoples fleeing Zulu and Boer expansion. In 1868 the area became the British protectorate of Basutoland, which refused to join the Union of South Africa in 1910 and eventually gained independence as Lesotho in 1966. It is a very poor agricultural country whose only natural resource is the water that enables it to export water and hydro-electric power to South Africa. Drought, soil erosion and the high levels of HIV/AIDS infection are serious problems.

KATSE DAM
The Katse Dam is Africa's biggest dam project.

FACT FILE

LOCAL NAME	Kingdom of Lesotho
CAPITAL CITY	Maseru
CURRENCY	Loti (LSL); South African Rand (ZAR)
MEMBERSHIP	AU, C, G-77, SADC, WTO
GOVERNMENT	Parliamentary Constitutional Monarchy
POPULATION	2,020,076
POP. DENSITY	67/km²; 172/mi²
GDP	3.09 Billion US$
LANGUAGE(S)	Sesotho, English, Zulu, Xhosa
ETHNICITY	Sotho
RELIGION	Christian 80%, Indigenous beliefs 20%
CLIMATE	Temperate

SOUTHERN AFRICA

SAINT HELENA

15° 57′ S, 5° 42′ W | 413 KM² | 159 MI² | UTC +1

The British Overseas Territory of Saint Helena and Dependencies, comprising the island of Saint Helena, Ascension island and the Tristan da Cunha group, is situated in the South Atlantic Ocean between Africa and South America.

Saint Helena, the largest of the islands, lies approximately 1,900 kilometres west of Angola and is of volcanic origin. It is one of the most remote places on earth. The terrain is largely rugged and mountainous, with rocky islets around the coast. The island was uninhabited when the Portuguese navigator Joao de Nova discovered it in 1502 and it was not until the middle of the seventeenth century that the East India Company established the first settlement there. As a part of the British Empire Saint Helena was used as a place of exile, most famously of Napoleon Bonaparte following his defeat at Waterloo but also of several thousand prisoners captured during the Boer War.

Ascension Island, with an area of 88 square kilometres, lies about 1,100 kilometres north-west of Saint Helena. This dry, barren volcanic island was uninhabited until 1815, when a garrison was established to help ensure that Napoleon did not escape from Saint Helena. Ascension Island has never had an established indigenous population but is home to military and civilian personnel who maintain the Widewake airfield and military base.

Five small volcanic islands make up the territory of Tristan da Cunha, which lies 2,430 kilometres south of Saint Helena, some 2,820 kilometres from South Africa and 3,360 kilometres from South America. The islands were first sighted in 1506 by a Portuguese sailor, Tristão da Cunha, although he did not land, and were annexed by the United Kingdom in 1816, in part as a measure to block any attempt by France to rescue Napoleon Bonaparte. The main Island of Tristan da Cunha is the only one with a permanent though very small population, almost all of whom are farmers. The isolation of the islands has created a unique ecology and this has led one of the group, Gough Island, to become a UNESCO World Heritage Site.

FACT FILE

LOCAL NAME British Overseas Territory of Saint Helena and Dependencies

SOVEREIGN STATE United Kingdom

CAPITAL/MAIN CITY Jamestown

CURRENCY Saint Helenian Pound (SHP)

GOVERNMENT British Overseas Territory

POPULATION 6,646

POP. DENSITY 16/km²; 42/mi²

GDP 18 Million US$

LANGUAGE(S) English

ETHNICITY African descent 50%, White 25%, Chinese 25%

RELIGION Anglican (majority), Baptist, Seventh-day Adventist, Roman Catholic

CLIMATE Tropical Marine

REGIONAL DIVISIONS 1 Administrative Area and 2 Dependencies (Ascension and Tristan da Cunha)

ECONOMIC ACTIVITIES Construction, Crafts (Furniture, Lacework, Fancy Woodwork), Fishing, Philatelic Sales

NATURAL RESOURCES Fish

SOUTHERN AFRICA

VIETNAM
CAMBODIA

Philippine
Basin

Luzon

Philippine
Sea

MANILA

PHILIPPINES

Mindoro
Panay
Samar

Spratly Islands
Palawan

Sulu
Sea

Moro
Gulf
Mindanao

Celebes
Sea

Halmahera

Gorontalo

Molucca Sea

Sulawesi
(Celebes)

Taliabu
Mangole
Buru
Obi

Seram
Ambon

Banda
Sea

West
Mariana
Basin

Pagan

Saipan
Rota
Guam (US)

Northern Mariana Islands (US)

Mariana Trench

East
Mariana
Basin

MARSHALL ISLANDS

Chuuk
Pohnpei
PALIKIR
Kosrae

Kwajalein
Maloelap
MAJURO
Jaluit
Mili

Ralik Chain

Ratak Chain

Gilbert
Islands

MELEKEOK
PALAU

West
Caroline
Basin

East
Caroline
Basin

FEDERATED STATES
OF MICRONESIA

Caroline Islands

Melanesian
Basin

YAREN
NAURU

Regunungan Maoke
Mt. Wilhelm
4509 m

New Guinea

New
Ireland

PAPUA

New Britain

NEW GUINEA

Bougainville

Choiseul

SOLOMON
ISLANDS

TUV

Santa
Isabel
Malaita

New Georgia
Islands

HONIARA

Guadalcanal
San Cristobal

MALAYSIA
BANDAR SERI
BEGAWAN
BRUNEI
Kuching
SINGAPORE
SINGAPORE

Borneo

Bangka
Belitung

Balikpapan

Makassar

Makassar Strait

INDONESIA

JAKARTA
Java
Surabaya
Madura
Bali
Lombok
Sumbawa
Sumba

Java Sea
Bali
Sea
Flores Sea
Flores
Savu
Sea
Timor

DILI
EAST TIMOR

Kepulauan
Aru

Kepulauan
Tanimbar

Arafura
Sea

Torres Strait

PORT
MORESBY

Gulf
of Papua

Tagula

Solomon Sea

Coral
Basin

Coral Sea

Ashmore and
Cartier Islands
(AU)

Timor Sea

Melville
Bathurst
Beagle Gulf
Darwin

Joseph
Bonaparte
Gulf

Daly

Arnhem
Land

Cape Arnhem

Groote
Eylandt

Mornington

Gulf
of
Carpentaria

Cape York

Cape
York
Peninsula

Cairns

Great Barrier Reef

Coral Sea
Islands
Territory
(AU)

Banks Islands

Espiritu Santo
VANUATU
Malakula

Luganville

PORT VILA
Efate

North Australian
Basin

Exmouth
Plateau

Barrow

North West Cape

Dirk Hartog

Perth
Basin

Perth

Cape Leeuwin

Eighty Mile
Beach

King Leopold Ranges

Kimberley
Plateau

L. Argyle

Chichester Range

Ashburton

Gascoyne

Murchison

Great Sandy Desert

L. Mackay

Gibson Desert

Great
Victoria Desert

Tanami
Desert

Barkly Tableland

Alice Springs
Macdonnell Ranges

Musgrave Ranges

Simpson
Desert

Gilbert

Diamantina

Townsville

Grey Range

AUSTRALIA

L. Eyre
(North)

L. Eyre (South)

Sturt
Stony
Desert

Great Dividing Range

Brisbane

New Caledonia
(FR)
Iles
Loyauté
Nouméa

Anatom

Sou
Fi
Bas

Lord Howe
(AU)

Lord Howe Rise

Nullarbor Plain

Great
Australian Bight

Cape Catastrophe

Kangaroo
Island

Cape
Jaffa

Spencer Gulf

L. Gairdner

L. Torrens

Flinders Ranges

L. Frome

Adelaide

Murray
Darling

Melbourne

Sydney

CANBERRA

Mount
Kosciuszko
2229 m

Norfolk
(AU)

Tasman Abyssal Plain

South
Australian
Basin

King

Bass Strait

Furneaux
Group

Tasmania

Hobart

South East
Cape

Tasman Sea

Tasman
Basin

North Cape

Auckland
Hamilton

North Island

Mt. Ruapehu
2797 m

Napi

Tasman
Bay

Cape Farewell
Nelson

WELLINGT

NEW ZEAL

Mt. Cook
3754 m

Southern Alps

South Island

Christchurch

Cape Providence

Foveaux Strait
Stewart

INDIAN OCEAN

South Tasman Rise

Indian-Antarctic Ridge

Auckland Islands
(NZ)

Campbell
Plateau

OCEANIA

OCEANIA

Spread out across the Pacific Ocean, the continent of Oceania is composed of more than 25,000 islands and islets as well as the massive landmass of Australia and the relatively large islands of New Guinea and New Zealand.

Oceania covers a vast area and its islands vary in size from the near-continental landmass of Australia to some of the world's smallest and lowest coral islands. Some are independent nation-states, others are parts of larger countries, such as the USA, and a few retain links with the former colonial powers of the United Kingdom and France.

This extensive region is subdivided into four areas: Melanesia, Micronesia, Polynesia and Australasia. These divisions are based on a combination of the location of the islands and the culture of their inhabitants. The indigenous peoples of Oceania comprise many different ethnic groups speaking more than 1,000 languages. Over the last few centuries, the migration of large numbers of people from Europe and Asia has added to the ethnic mix. Although many areas of Oceania are remote from other parts of the world, some of the islands have gained global significance: because of their strategic location, such as Guam; as the focus of public debate on the testing of nuclear weapons, the Marshall Islands; or, more recently, because of the perilous future shared by many of them as a result of climate change.

OCEANIA

AUSTRALIA

27° 00' S, 133° 00' E | KM² 7,686,850 | MI² 2,967,909 | UTC+10

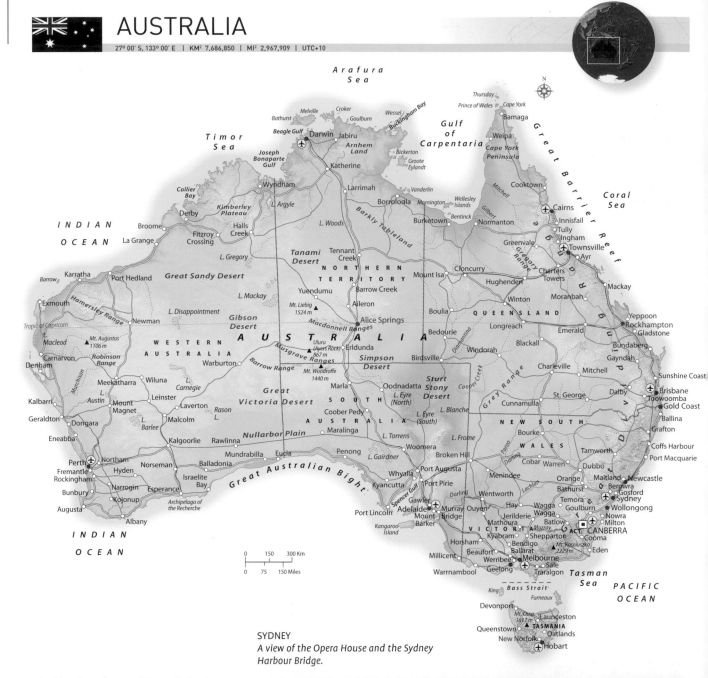

Arafura Sea

Timor Sea

Gulf of Carpentaria

Coral Sea

INDIAN OCEAN

Thursday
Prince of Wales
Cape York
Bamaga
Weipa
Cape York Peninsula

Melville
Croker
Goulburn
Wessel
Buckingham Bay

Bathurst
Beagle Gulf
Darwin
Jabiru
Arnhem Land
Bickerton
Groote Eylandt

Joseph Bonaparte Gulf
Katherine
Vanderlin
Mornington
Wellesley Islands
Bentinck

Collier Bay
Wyndham
Larrimah
Borroloola
Burketown
Normanton
Gilbert
Mitchell
Cooktown

Derby
Kimberley Plateau
L. Argyle
L. Woods
Barkly Tableland
Cairns
Innisfail
Tully
Ingham
Greenvale

Broome
Halls Creek
Tennant Creek
Greenvale
Townsville
Ayr

Fitzroy Crossing
L. Gregory
Tanami Desert
NORTHERN TERRITORY
Mount Isa
Cloncurry
Hughenden
Charters Towers

La Grange
Great Sandy Desert
Yuendumu
Barrow Creek
Boulia
Winton
Moranbah
Mackay

Karratha
Port Hedland
L. Mackay
Mt. Liebig 1524 m
Aileron
Alice Springs
Bedourie
Longreach
QUEENSLAND
Emerald
Yeppoon
Rockhampton
Gladstone

Exmouth
Hamersley Range
L. Disappointment
Gibson Desert
Macdonnell Ranges
Erldunda
Windorah
Blackall
Bundaberg
Gayndah

Tropic of Capricorn
Mt. Augustus 1106 m
Robinson Range
AUSTRALIA
Uluru (Ayers Rock) 867 m
Simpson Desert
Birdsville
Charleville
Mitchell
Sunshine Coast

L. Macleod
Carnarvon
Denham
WESTERN AUSTRALIA
Warburton
Barrow Range
Mt. Woodroffe 1440 m
Marla
Oodnadatta
Sturt Stony Desert
Windorah
Charleville
Dalby
Brisbane
Toowoomba
Gold Coast

Meekatharra
Wiluna
L. Carnegie
Leinster
Great Victoria Desert
SOUTH AUSTRALIA
Coober Pedy
L. Eyre (North)
St. George
Cunnamulla
Ballina
Grafton

Kalbarri
L. Austin
Mount Magnet
Laverton
Rason L.
Maralinga
L. Eyre (South)
L. Blanche
NEW SOUTH WALES
Bourke
Coffs Harbour

Geraldton
Dongara
L. Barlee
Malcolm
Kalgoorlie
Rawlinna
Nullarbor Plain
L. Torrens
L. Frome
Cobar
Tamworth
Port Macquarie

Eneabba
Perth
Northam
Norseman
Balladonia
Eucla
Penong
Woomera
Broken Hill
Menindee
Warren
Dubbo
Maitland
Newcastle

Fremantle
Rockingham
Hyden
Narrogin
Esperance
Israelite Bay
Mundrabilla
Great Australian Bight
L. Gairdner
Whyalla
Port Augusta
Orange
Berowra
Gosford
Sydney

Bunbury
Kojonup
Archipelago of the Recherche
Kyancutta
Port Pirie
Wentworth
Hay
Wagga Wagga
Goulburn
Wollongong

Augusta
Albany
Port Lincoln
Adelaide
Mount Barker
Murray Bridge
Ouyen
Jerilderie
Batlow
Temora
Nowra
Milton

INDIAN OCEAN
Kangaroo Island
Gawler
Mathoura
Kyabram
Shepparton
ACT
CANBERRA
Cooma
Eden

Horsham
Beaufort
Ballarat
Bendigo
VICTORIA
Mt. Kosciuszko 2229 m

Millicent
Werribee
Geelong
Melbourne
Sale
Traralgon
Tasman Sea
PACIFIC OCEAN

Warrnambool
Bass Strait
King
Furneaux

Devonport
Launceston
Mt. Ossa 1617 m
TASMANIA
Oatlands

Queenstown
New Norfolk
Hobart

0 150 300 Km
0 75 150 Miles

SYDNEY
A view of the Opera House and the Sydney Harbour Bridge.

The island continent of Australia is the sixth largest country in the world, and has one of the strongest and best developed economies on the globe.

Geography

Although the majority of Australia's landscape is arid desert, it actually has a highly diverse environment. The western half of the country is given over to the Western

Plateau, a generally flat region which is punctuated by mountains such as the Hamersley and Macdonnell Ranges. Much of the territory is inhospitable, with drought a particular challenge, and consequently is sparsely populated. Towards the east are the central lowlands where the river systems which drain into Lake Eyre create a more fertile environment for Australia's agricultural needs. The densely populated eastern coast is separated from the central lowlands by the Great Dividing Mountain Range, or Eastern Highlands, some of which is covered with tropical forest. To the northeast, the coast is home to the world's largest coral formation, the Great Barrier Reef comprising over 2,900 individual reefs. Australia is divided into six states (including the island of Tasmania), two major and several minor territories. It also governs a number of islands, including Norfolk Island, a small inhabited territory in the Pacific and Christmas Island, a rainforested territory in the Indian Ocean. The capital of Australia is Canberra, although Sydney is larger with a population of 4.28 million.

History

Australia's indigenous peoples are believed to have settled on the island some 50,000 years ago, remaining almost undisturbed until the seventeenth century. Today, their descendants, including both Torres Strait Islanders and Aborigines, make up just over two per cent of Australia's total population and generally endure social and economic marginalization. Their numbers were depleted mainly by imported diseases and mistreatment by the white colonists.

The first Europeans to settle Australia were British, following the charting of the islands by Captain James Cook in 1770. Colonization was initially driven by the British establishment of penal colonies in New South Wales, the first being at Port Jackson in 1788. Australia eventually became a popular destination for British and Irish migrants, particularly following the gold rush of the 1850s. Although for many decades Australia employed a strict whites-only immigration law, in the 1960s this changed and the majority of immigrants now are from Asian countries. In 1901, the six established colonies federated, becoming

ULURU
Uluru, situated in the centre of Australia, is sacred to the Aboriginal people.

FACT FILE

LOCAL NAME Commonwealth of Australia

CAPITAL CITY Canberra

CURRENCY Australian Dollar (AUD)

MEMBERSHIP APEC, ASEAN (dialogue partner), C, CP, G20, OECD, PIF, SPC, WTO

GOVERNMENT Parliamentary Democracy and Constitutional Monarchy

POPULATION 20,950,604

POP. DENSITY $3/km^2$; $7/mi^2$

GDP 773 Billion US$

LANGUAGE(S) English, Italian, Greek, Cantonese, Arabic, Chinese, Australian Aboriginal languages

ETHNICITY Australian 37%, Australian aboriginal 0.6%, English 32%

RELIGION Christian 64% (Catholic 26%, Anglican 19%, Other Christian 19%), Aboriginal indigenous beliefs 0.03%

CLIMATE Arid and Semi-arid, Temperate in south and east, Tropical in north

REGIONAL DIVISIONS 6 States and 2 Territories; The largest city in the country, Sydney, is the capital of New South Wales, the oldest and most populous State

DEPENDENCIES Ashmore and Cartier Islands, Christmas Island, Cocos Keeling Islands, Coral Sea Islands, Heard Island and McDonald Islands, Macquarie Island, Norfolk Island (External Territories)

ECONOMIC ACTIVITIES Agriculture (Wool, Sugar and Beef Export, Horticulture, Dairy), Mining, Forestry and Wood Products, Industrial and Transportation Equipment, Food Processing, Wine, Chemicals, Steel, Tourism

NATURAL RESOURCES Bauxite, Coal, Iron Ore, Copper, Tin, Gold, Silver, Uranium, Nickel, Tungsten, Mineral Sands, Lead, Zinc, Diamonds, Natural Gas, Petroleum.

the Commonwealth of Australia, although it effectively remained part of the British Empire until 1942. The current states are all self-governing with their own legislature, or parliament, each with an elected Premier. At a national level, the Commonwealth Parliament is the governing body, led by the Australian Prime Minister and with Queen Elizabeth II as Head of State. Because of its history and language, Australian culture is greatly influenced by European, particularly British traditions; however Asian and American influences are becoming more apparent, from cuisine to pastimes such as surfing. In addition, Aboriginal traditions such as the dreamtime and the sacred site Uluru, or Ayers Rock, are important elements of the Australian identity.

Economy

Australia's economy is one of the strongest in the world and it has significant trading links with both Japan and China. Natural resources feed the agricultural and industrial sectors and key exports include iron ore, gold, coal, wheat and wool. The largest feature of the Australian economy is the services sector, which accounts for almost 70 per cent of the GDP. Relatively low unemployment and low inflation have also contributed to the 16-year period of growth that the country has enjoyed. Australia has a global outlook, maintaining good relations with both the United States and with its Asian neighbours; it is a member of the OECD, the World Trade Organization, a founder-member of the United Nations and part of the Commonwealth of Nations. Australia's currency, the Australian Dollar, is also used by its overseas territories.

THE GREAT BARRIER REEF
Situated between 50 and 150 kilometres off the north-east coast of Australia, the Great Barrier Reef is the world's largest known coral reef, measuring about 2,000 kilometres long. The reef is a World Heritage Site.

NEW ZEALAND

41° 00' N, 174° 00' E | KM² 268,680 | MI² 103,738 | UTC+12

The island country of New Zealand is located 1600 kilometres southeast of Australia, in the Pacific Ocean, at the heart of the world's 'water hemisphere', the half of the globe that is dominated by water rather than land.

Geography

Consisting of two main islands and a number of smaller islands, the archipelago of New Zealand is geographically isolated, with the Tasman Sea to the west and the Pacific Ocean stretching out to the east, north and south. The two major islands, North and South form a long narrow sweep of land separated by the Cook Strait which is only 20 kilometres at its narrowest. Of the two, North Island is the smaller and more populous. It has a rugged, mountainous landscape which includes several active volcanoes and hot springs. It is also the location of New Zealand's largest city, Auckland and its capital, Wellington. South Island is home to only one quarter of the total population of over four million people. It is dominated by the Alpine ridge of mountains, and the highest peak is Mount Cook at 3,754 metres. Both islands are largely grassland, although there is a variety of distinctive flora and fauna unique to New Zealand because of its isolation. The length of the country results in different climatic regions; in the far north the Northland Peninsula reaches into the tropics, while the southernmost parts of South Island are exposed to colder air currents and southerly winds. Some 70 per cent of New Zealand's electrical energy comes from renewable resources, such as hydroelectricity and geothermal power.

History

First sighted by the Dutch explorer Abel Tasman in 1642, New Zealand was named after the Dutch province of Zeeland. It was already home to the indigenous Maori peoples, Polynesian tribes who had populated

WHIRINAKI
Subtropical vegetation in the Whirinaki Forest, which is close to the Bay of Plenty on the North Island.

OCEANIA

FACT FILE

LOCAL NAME	New Zealand
CAPITAL CITY	Wellington
CURRENCY	New Zealand Dollar (NZD)
MEMBERSHIP	APEC, ASEAN (dialogue partner), C, CP, OECD, PIF, SPC, WTO
GOVERNMENT	Parliamentary Democracy and Constitutional Monarchy
POPULATION	4,214,814
POP. DENSITY	16/km²; 41/mi²
GDP	112.4 Billion US$
LANGUAGE(S)	English, Maori, Samoan, Sign Language
ETHNICITY	European 67%, Maori 15%, Asian 9%, Pacific islander 7%
RELIGION	Christian 50% (Anglican 14%, Roman Catholic 13%, Presbyterian 10%)
CLIMATE	Temperate
REGIONAL DIVISIONS	16 Regions and 1 Territory; Auckland region is largest by population and Canterbury by area
DEPENDENCIES	Cook Islands, Niue (self-governing territories in free association with New Zealand), Tokelau (non self-governing territory)
ECONOMIC ACTIVITIES	Agriculture (Dairy, Meat), Food Processing, Wine, Fishing, Wood and Paper Products, Textiles, Machinery, Transportation Equipment, Banking and Insurance, Tourism, Mining
NATURAL RESOURCES	Natural Gas, Iron Ore, Sand, Coal, Timber, Hydropower, Gold, Limestone

the islands and developed their own culture and traditions. The British explorer James Cook was the first European to formally map the coastline and the country soon became popular for trading rather than for colonizing. Christian missionaries were the first to settle and in 1840 the British negotiated a formal claim to sovereignty with the Maori; New Zealand remains a member of the British Commonwealth today, with Queen Elizabeth II acting as Head of State. During the 1860s and 70s a series of Land Wars saw the Maoris loose large swathes of territory to the mainly British settlers; the consequences are still seen as the present government continues to negotiate Maori land claims. A highly developed democracy, New Zealand was the first to enfranchise women, who won the right to vote in 1893.

MARLBOROUGH SOUNDS
Situated at the north-eastern tip of the South Island, the Marlborough Sounds are one of New Zealand's principal tourist attractions.

Economy

The country has a dynamic free-market economy; although agriculture remains the chief export industry it has developed a highly industrialized manufacturing industry with food products, textiles, transportation equipment and mining all increasing in importance. The banking, insurance and services sectors are also growing as is tourism, particularly in the wake of New Zealand's recent popularity as a location for films. Important trading partners include Australia, China and the United States. New Zealand is a member of the United Nations, OECD and the World Trade Organization.

MELANESIA

Ninigo Group
Pelleluhu
Wuvulu
Hermit
St. Matthias Group
Lumi
Schouten
Admiralty
Manus
Lorengau
Kavieng
New Ireland
Tanga
Nuguria
Sepik
Wewak
Manam
Karkar
Tanga
Feni
Green
Nukumanu
Bismarck Sea
Madang
Long
Rabaul
Takuu
Ontong Java Atoll
Mt. Wilhelm
Umboi
Hoskins
New Britain
Bougainville
PACIFIC
Mount Hagen
Goroka
Lae
Arawa
Choiseul
SOLOMON ISLANDS
OCEAN
Mendi
PAPUA
Wau
Morobe
Lusancay Islands and Reefs
New Georgia Sound
Santa Isabel
NEW GUINEA
Kerema
Woodlark
Gizo
Buala
Stewart
Balimo
Gulf of Papua
Bereina
New Georgia Islands
HONIARA
Malaita
Daru
Popondetta
Guadalcanal
Nupani
Duff Islands
Torres Strait
PORT MORESBY
D'Entrecasteaux Islands
San Cristobal (Makira)
Kirakira
Swallow Islands
Abau
Alotau
Ndeni
Utupua
Samarai
Rennell
Vanikoro
Tikopia
Tagula
M E L A N E S I A
Rotuma (FJ)
Torres
Urèparapara
AUSTRALIA
Coral Sea
Banks Islands
Santa Maria
Maéwo
Espíritu Santo
VANUATU
Luganville
Cikobia
Vetauua
Norsup
Malakula
Lamen Bay
Yasawa Group
FIJI
Labasa
Qele Levu
Lautoka
Vanua Levu
Somosomo
Viti Levu
Levuka
PORT VILA
Éfaté
Sigatoka
SUVA
Lau Group
Îles Chesterfield (FR)
Erromango
Potnarvin
Kadavu
Vatoa
Tanna
Futuna
Lénakel
Anatom
Ouvéa
Îles Loyauté
Koumac
Houailu
Bourail
NEW CALEDONIA (FR)
Yaté
Matthew
0 125 250 Km
Nouvelle Calédonie
NOUMÉA
Le Mont-Dore
Hunter
0 100 Miles

The Oceania sub-region of Melanesia covers an area across the western Pacific, from the island of New Guinea to the archipelagos which extend to the north-east of Australia.

Melanesian peoples are considered to be of New Guinean descent – during the passage of 30,000 years the inhabitants of New Guinea are believed to have migrated across the area, developing shared languages and cultural practises. However, Melanesia today is no longer classified as an anthropological region, but rather a geopolitical one with shared trade agreements and economic ties between the islands which it encompasses.

NEW CALEDONIA
A row of wooden totems on the beach in New Caledonia.

PAPUA NEW GUINEA

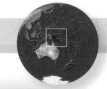

6° 00' S, 147° 00' E | KM² 462,840 | MI² 178,704 | UTC+10

Papua New Guinea occupies the eastern portion of the island of New Guinea, the second largest island in the world.

Geography

Mainland Papua New Guinea is rugged and mountainous and most of this terrain is covered in thick rainforest. There are several active volcanoes inland while on the highest peaks snowfall is common, unusual for a tropical country. The 5,152 kilometres of coastline provides lowlands where the country's few urban areas are situated. A huge area of swampland lies to the southwest. The capital, Port Moresby, is on the south coast; the majority of the population, however, live in the highlands.

FACT FILE

LOCAL NAME Independent State of Papua New Guinea

CAPITAL CITY Port Moresby

CURRENCY Kina (PGK)

MEMBERSHIP APEC, ASEAN (observer), C, CP, G77, PIF, SPC, WTO

GOVERNMENT Constitutional Parliamentary Democracy

POPULATION 6,458,059

POP. DENSITY 14/km²; 119/mi²

GDP 12.05 Billion US$

LANGUAGE(S) Tok Pisin, Hiri Motu, English

ETHNICITY New Guinea Papuan 84%, New Guinea Melanesian 15%

RELIGION Roman Catholic 27%, Evangelical Lutheran 20%, United Church 12%, Seventh-day Adventist 10%, Pentecostal 9%, Evangelical Alliance 5%, Anglican 3%, Other Protestant 11%

CLIMATE Tropical

REGIONAL DIVISIONS 4 Regions are divided into 20 Provinces; Southern Highlands is the most populous province

ECONOMIC ACTIVITIES Agriculture, Copra Crushing, Palm Oil processing, Coffee, Tea, Rubber, Cocoa, Forestry (Plywood Production, Wood Chip Production), Fishing (Tuna Industry), Mining, Crude Oil Production, Petroleum Refining, Construction, Tourism

NATURAL RESOURCES Gold, Copper, Silver, Natural Gas, Timber, Oil, Fisheries

The territory also includes a number of smaller inhabited and uninhabited islands, the most significant being Bougainville, New Ireland and New Britain.

History

Noted for the predominance of traditional tribal communities in the highland region, Papua New Guinea has a population of over six million with some 800 different languages being spoken. Only 18 per cent of the population actually lives in urban areas, the rest have preserved very traditional and rural societies. In 1884 Northern New Guinea became German; the south was taken by the British who in 1902 transferred administration to Australia. During the First World War, the German portion was annexed by Australia, but in 1975, PNG regained its independence. The now autonomous island of Bougainville saw a bloody secessionist revolt in 1988 that lasted until 1997.

Economy

Despite its wealth of natural resources, particularly minerals and natural gas, the economy of Papua New Guinea still relies upon agriculture. Copper, gold and oil significantly contribute to export earnings.

However, the lack of modern infrastructures hampers progress, as does the difficulty of establishing land ownership. Aid from Australia accounts for 20 per cent of the national budget.

BOUGAINVILLE
Mount Bagana, on the island of Bougainvillle, is an active volcano.

SOLOMON ISLANDS

8° 00' S, 159° 00' E | KM² 28,450 | MI² 10,985 | UTC+11

An archipelago of hundreds of coral islands in the South Pacific, the Solomon Islands is a Commonwealth nation that became independent from the UK in 1976.

The majority of the Melanesian population of the Solomons lives on the main islands of Guadalcanal, New Georgia, Choiseul, Santa Isabel and San Christobal, all of which are mountainous, volcanic and thickly forested. The islands were declared a Protectorate of the British Empire in 1893 to curb the illegal recruitment and enslaving practised by Australian plantation owners. They were then the focus of fierce fighting during the War of the Pacific in the Second World War. Since independence, ethnic tensions, civil unrest and lawlessness have escalated; in

FACT FILE

LOCAL NAME	Solomon Islands
CAPITAL CITY	Honiara
CURRENCY	Solomon Islands dollar (SBD)
MEMBERSHIP	C, G77, PIF, SPC, WTO
GOVERNMENT	Parliamentary democracy
POPULATION	507,321
POP. DENSITY	18/km²; 46/mi²
GDP	948 Million US$
LANGUAGE(S)	Melanesian Pidgin, English
ETHNICITY	Melanesian 94%, Polynesian 3%, Micronesian 1%
RELIGION	Church of Melanesia 33%, Roman Catholic 19%, South Seas Evangelical 17%, Seventh-day Adventist 11%, United Church 10%, Other Christian 7%
CLIMATE	Tropical Monsoon

2003 an Australian-led taskforce invaded in order to restore order. Undeveloped, despite rich natural resources, the unstable economy relies upon agriculture and fishing.

VANUATU

16° 00' S, 167° 00' E | KM² 12,200 | MI² 4,710 | UTC+11

The New Hebridean archipelago of Vanuatu consists of around eighty islands, some sixty of which are inhabited.

Situated in the South Pacific, the generally small volcanic islands of the Republic of Vanuatu were first discovered by Europeans in 1606 when Portuguese explorers landed on Espíritu Santo. Named the New Hebrides by James Cook, the islands became the focus of waves of colonizers and missionaries until the English and French agreed to co-administer the islands in 1906. The island of Tanna became the centre of a cargo cult in which the mythical figure of John Frum is revered; possibly a vestige of the period during the Second World War when the islands were occupied by American servicemen. In 1980 the independent Vanuatu was established. The relatively stable parliamentary republic has since developed its agricultural and fishing sectors and encouraged Vanuatu's status as a tourist destination and offshore financial services centre.

FACT FILE

LOCAL NAME	Republic of Vanuatu
CAPITAL CITY	Port Vila (on Éfaté)
CURRENCY	Vatu (VUV)
MEMBERSHIP	C, G77, PIF, SPC, WTO (observer)
GOVERNMENT	Parliamentary Republic
POPULATION	231,592
POP. DENSITY	19/km²; 49/mi²
GDP	897 Million US$
LANGUAGE(S)	Bislama, English, French
ETHNICITY	Ni-Vanuatu 99%
RELIGION	Presbyterian 31%, Anglican 13%, Roman Catholic 13%, Seventh-day Adventist 11%, Other Christian 14%, Indigenous beliefs 6%
CLIMATE	Tropical

OCEANIA

NEW CALEDONIA

21° 30′ S, 165° 30′ E | KM² 19,060 | MI² 7,359 | UTC+11

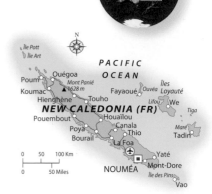

A possession of France since 1893, New Caledonia is currently undergoing the process of transferring to independence, with a referendum due in 2014.

The main island of Grande Terre is accompanied by the smaller Loyalty Islands to the east, the Île des Pins to the south and a number of smaller coral islands. Grande Terre has a mineral-rich mountainous interior surrounded by coastal plains and is the location for the capital and only New Caledonian city, Nouméa. Other islands are rugged with dense forests and woodland. Under French control New Caledonia became a penal colony in 1864; the islands now benefit from rich mineral deposits,

FACT FILE

LOCAL NAME	Territory of New Caledonia and Dependencies
SOVEREIGN STATE	France
CAPITAL/MAIN CITY	Nouméa
CURRENCY	Comptoirs Français du Pacifique Franc (XPF)
MEMBERSHIP	PIF (associate member), SPC
GOVERNMENT	Territorial collectivity of France
POPULATION	245,487
POP. DENSITY	13/km²; 33/mi²
GDP	3.158 Billion US$
LANGUAGE(S)	French, Melanesian-Polynesian dialects
ETHNICITY	Melanesian 44%, European 34%, Wallisian & Futunian 9%, Tahitian 3%
RELIGION	Roman Catholic 60%, Protestant 30%
CLIMATE	Tropical

exporting a quarter of the world's nickel. Only half of New Caledonia's population of over 240,000 is of Melanesian descent, the rest being a mixture of European and Southeast Asian origin.

FIJI

18° 00′ S, 175° 00′ E | KM² 18,270 | MI² 7,054 | UTC+12

A volcanic archipelago in the southern Pacific, Fiji consists of two main islands, Viti Levu and Vanua Levu, 322 smaller islands and numerous islets.

FACT FILE

LOCAL NAME	Republic of the Fiji Islands
CAPITAL CITY	Suva
CURRENCY	Fijian Dollar (FJD)
MEMBERSHIP	C (suspended), CP, G77, PIF, SPC, WTO
GOVERNMENT	Republic Under Military Rule
POPULATION	844,046
POP. DENSITY	46/km²; 120/mi²
GDP	5.079 Billion US$
LANGUAGE(S)	English, Fijian, Hindustani (Fijian Hindi)
ETHNICITY	Fijian 57%, Indian 38%
RELIGION	Christian 64% (including Methodist 34%, Roman Catholic 9%, Seventh-day Adventist 4%), Hindu 28%, Muslim 6%
CLIMATE	Tropical Maritime

A territory within the British Empire from 1874 until independence in 1970, Fiji has since experienced political instability with a series of military coups. Persistent ethnic tensions between the indigenous Fijians and the descendants of Indian labourers brought to Fiji in the late nineteenth century are the major cause of social instability. Fiji is one of the most developed and economically diverse of the southern Pacific islands. The forested islands have abundant natural resources; timber, gold mining and fishing all support the dominant sugar industry, and about half of the labour force is employed in agriculture. The tourism sector continues to grow, despite the most recent coup in 2006, and is also a major source of employment.

MICRONESIA

6° 55' N, 158° 15' E | KM² 702 | MI² 271 | UTC +11

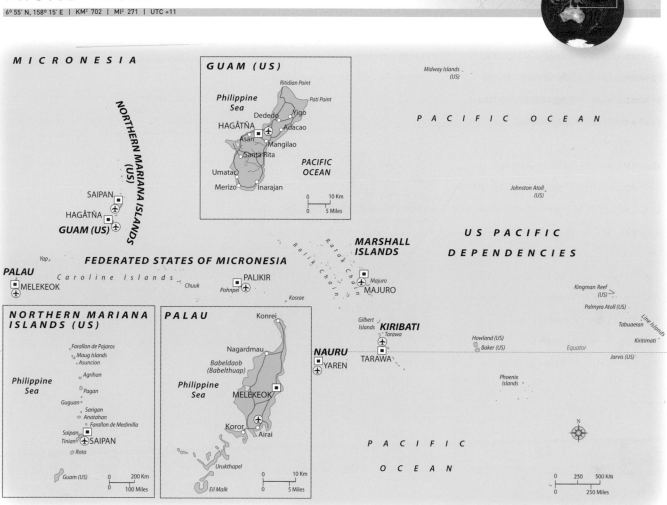

The collection of small islands and atolls in the western Pacific that make up Micronesia are organized into five independent nation states – Kiribati, Nauru, Palau, the Federated States of Micronesia and the Marshall Islands – and several territories that are linked to the United States of America.

 The indigenous peoples of Micronesia were traditionally maritime explorers and fishermen and the area was home to the Yap Empire until European colonizers arrived in the early nineteenth century. During the twentieth century, the islands came under the control of the United States, Germany and Britain and the wars in Europe led to German territories being handed over to Australia and Japan. War in the Pacific ended the Japanese Mandate, control of the islands being assumed by the United Nations. The southernmost stretch of the Marianas Trench, the deepest part of any of the world's oceans (estimated at 11,033 metres), is situated in Micronesia.

BABELDAOB ISLAND
A large number of stone megalithic monuments are arranged in lines at Badrulchau, at the north end of the island of Babeldaob, one of the more populated of the islands making up Palau.

OCEANIA

GUAM

13° 28' N, 144° 47' E | KM² 541 | MI² 209 | UTC+10

The island of Guam is an unincorporated, insular territory of the United States; islanders are US citizens but do not vote in US elections, having instead their own government.

The largest island in Micronesia, Guam is of volcanic origin. To the north the terrain is a forested limestone plateau; the less populated south is dominated by dormant volcanic peaks covered in woodland and grass. Spanish explorers arriving in 1668 were greeted by the indigenous Chamorros peoples who remain the majority population. The island was ceded to the United States by Spain following the war of 1898, and with the exception of a brief period of Japanese occupation during the Second World War, has remained under US control. It is an important strategic base, and nearly 30 per cent of the island is given over to US military installations. Tourists, mainly from Japan, provide much of the island's income.

HAGÅTÑA
The Dulce Nombre de Maria Church in Hagåtña.

FACT FILE

LOCAL NAME Territory of Guam
SOVEREIGN STATE United States
CAPITAL Hagåtña (Agana)
CURRENCY US Dollar (USD)
MEMBERSHIP SPC
GOVERNMENT Unincorporated territory of the US
POPULATION 175,553
POP. DENSITY 325/km²; 840/mi²
GDP 2.5 Billion US$
LANGUAGE(S) English, Chamorro
ETHNICITY Native Hawaiian and other Pacific Islander (including Chamorro 37%, Chuukese 4%) 45%, Asian (including Filipino 26%) 33%, White 7%
RELIGION Roman Catholic 85%
CLIMATE Tropical Maritime

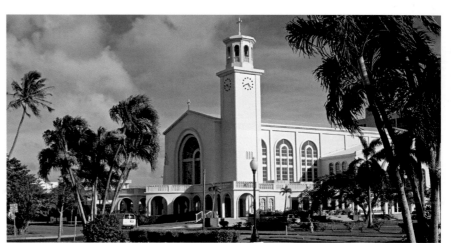

NORTHERN MARIANA ISLANDS

15° 12' N, 145° 45' E | KM² 477 | MI² 184 | UTC+10

Stretching across almost 650 kilometres, the Northern Marianas Islands form an independent commonwealth, which is in close political union with the United States (similar in status to Puerto Rico), and whose head of state is the President of the US.

Of the fourteen islands that make up the Northern Marianas only Saipan, Tinian and Rota have a significant population. All the islands are volcanic, with active volcanoes on Anatahan, Pagan and Agrihan. The islands are surrounded by coral reefs, consequently the main economic sectors are tourism and fishing. Income from these sectors is supplemented by support from the United States. The islands were violently annexed by the Spanish in 1521 and the indigenous Chamorro population came under greater suppression than on other Pacific territories. Today the islands are populated by a mix of Chamorros and Europeans along with large Asian and Chinese communities.

FACT FILE

LOCAL NAME Commonwealth of the Northern Mariana Islands
SOVEREIGN STATE United States
CAPITAL/MAIN CITY Saipan
CURRENCY US Dollar (USD)
MEMBERSHIP SPC
GOVERNMENT Commonwealth
POPULATION 86,616
POP. DENSITY 182/km²; 471/mi²
GDP 900 Million US$
LANGUAGE(S) English, Chamorro, Carolinian, Chinese
ETHNICITY Native Hawaiian and other Pacific Islander 32% (including Chamorro 21%, Carolinian 4%), Asian 56% (including Filipino 26%, Chinese 22%)
RELIGION Christian 89% (Roman Catholic 73%, Independent Christian 7%, Protestant 7%), Buddhist 5%
CLIMATE Tropical Maritime

OCEANIA

PALAU

7° 30' N, 134° 30' E | KM² 458 | MI² 177 | UTC+9

This archipelago of some 300 islands in the western Pacific became independent from US administration in 1994.

FACT FILE

LOCAL NAME	Republic of Palau
CAPITAL CITY	Melekeok
CURRENCY	US Dollar (USD)
MEMBERSHIP	PIF, SPC
GOVERNMENT	Constitutional government in free association with the US
POPULATION	21,093
POP. DENSITY	46/km²; 119/mi²
GDP	124.5 Million US$
LANGUAGE(S)	Palauan, English
ETHNICITY	Palauan 70%, Filipino 15%, Chinese 6%, Carolinian 1%
RELIGION	Roman Catholic 42%, Evangelical 23%, Modekngei 9%, Seventh-day Adventist 5%
CLIMATE	Tropical

The western group of islands in the widely scattered Caroline Islands chain, Palau is a collection of coral islands and atolls. The largest, Babeldaob, is thickly forested with uplands, volcanoes, rivers and waterfalls. The islands' population is a mix of indigenous Polynesian and Asian clans and European and Japanese settlers. Palau's colonial history includes periods under Spanish, German and then Japanese rule, each of whom capitalized on Palau's abundant resources of bauxite and fish. Following the Second World War the islands became part of the Trust Territory of the Pacific Islands after which the struggle for independence began. Tourism and fishing remain the mainstays of an economy which also exports coconuts and their by-products.

THE ROCK ISLANDS
The Rock Islands, a chain of over 70 islets, are situated about 30 kilometres south of the city of Koror.

FEDERATED STATES OF MICRONESIA

Situated to the north of Papua New Guinea, the eastern islands of the Caroline Islands archipelago are an independent federal republic with close ties to the US.

The 607 islands are spread over some 2,900 kilometres in the Pacific and are organized into four territorial groups: the Yap Islands, the Chuuk Islands, the Pohnpei and the Kosrae. These islands vary in geography from smaller coral atolls to larger, mountainous and volcanic islands. The only significant natural resources come from fishing and the economy of the islands is generally restricted by a lack of development and the remoteness of their location. The population is dominated by indigenous peoples, with some American and Japanese immigrants.

FACT FILE

LOCAL NAME	Federated States of Micronesia
CAPITAL CITY	Palikir
CURRENCY	US Dollar (USD)
MEMBERSHIP	G77, PIF, SPC
GOVERNMENT	Democratic Federated Presidential Republic; Constitutional government in free association with the US
POPULATION	111,594
POP. DENSITY	159/km²; 412/mi²
GDP	277 Million US$
LANGUAGE(S)	English, Chuukese, Kosrean, Pohnpeian, Yapese, Ulithian, Woleaian, Nukuoro, Kapingamarangi
ETHNICITY	Chuukese 49%, Pohnpeian 24%, Kosraean 6%, Yapese 5%, Yap (outer islands) 5%
RELIGION	Roman Catholic 50%, Protestant 47%
CLIMATE	Tropical

YAP ISLANDS
A traditional men's house, where male villagers could gather and unmarried men slept.

OCEANIA

MARSHALL ISLANDS

9° 00' N, 168° 00' E | KM² 181 | MI² 70 | UTC+12

A collection of twenty-nine atolls and five islands, the Marshall Islands are spread across a wide area about half way between Australia and Hawaii.

The atolls are typically low-lying coral rings which encircle a lagoon; those furthest south are covered in thick vegetation and all except ten of the Marshall Islands are inhabited. The first European, the British sea captain John Marshall, arrived in 1788. The islands then passed from German to Japanese and then American rule. Between 1946 and 1958 the islands became the site for US nuclear testing and 66 nuclear weapons were detonated, including the largest H-bomb, Bravo. Independent since 1986, the Marshall Islands still rely upon American aid.

Subsistence farmers and fishermen make up the majority of the population, with tuna, copra and coconut oil being the only significant exports.

MAJURO
A view of the shoreline and a reef close to the main city of Majuro.

FACT FILE

LOCAL NAME Republic of the Marshall Islands
CAPITAL Majuro
CURRENCY US Dollar (USD)
MEMBERSHIP G77, PIF, SPC
GOVERNMENT Democratic Presidential Republic in Free Association with the USA
POPULATION 60,660
POP. DENSITY 335/km²; 867/mi²
GDP 115 Million US$
LANGUAGE(S) Marshallese, English
ETHNICITY Marshallese 92%, mixed Marshallese 6%
RELIGION Protestant 55%, Assembly of God 26%, Roman Catholic 8%, Bukot nan Jesus 3%, Other Christian 6%
CLIMATE Tropical

US PACIFIC DEPENDENCIES

A collection of uninhabited islands and atolls in the Pacific Ocean, the US Pacific Dependencies are neither culturally nor geographically linked.

Consisting of Baker and Howland Islands, Jarvis Island, Palmyra Atoll, Kingman Reef, Johnston Atoll and the Midway Islands, all of the dependencies are considered to be of scientific and strategic interest and as such are overseen by the US. Attempts to settle the islands were abandoned during the Second World War and now the only inhabitants are temporary, mainly marine scientists and military personnel. Howland Island is remarkable for being the refuelling station sought by aviator Amelia Earhart when she disappeared in 1937. The Midway Islands were a crucial refuelling point for the American fleet during the Second World War and became the site of a significant victory over the Japanese. Johnston, Jarvis and Howland have traditionally all been important sources of guano, used for plant fertilizer and gunpowder.

NAURU

0° 32' S, 166° 55' E | KM² 21 | MI² 8 | UTC+12

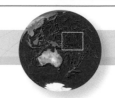

The smallest island nation in the world and the smallest independent republic, Nauru is one of three phosphate rock islands in the Pacific Ocean.

Surrounded by coral reefs, through which sixteen shipping canals have been carved, the population of almost 14,000 live within districts around the coast of the island. The interior phosphate plateau, once dominated by mining, is now a wasteland. A British and German mining consortium controlled Nauru from 1888 until the First World War; following this the country came under the administration of Australia, with the exception of a short period of Japanese occupation during the Second World War. Phosphate exports once provided incredible wealth, but with diminishing reserves the economy has begun to shrink. Environmental damage has left few natural resources and the population relies upon imported processed foods and Australian aid, provided in return for housing a detention centre for Australian immigrants.

FACT FILE

LOCAL NAME Republic of Nauru
CAPITAL CITY No official capital (government offices in Yaren district)
CURRENCY Australian Dollar (AUD)
MEMBERSHIP C, PIF, SPC, not WB member, not IMF member
GOVERNMENT Republic
POPULATION 13,770
POP. DENSITY 656/km²; 1721/mi²
GDP 60 Million US$
LANGUAGE(S) Nauruan, English (government and commerce)
ETHNICITY Nauruan 77%, Tuvaluan 4%, Kiribati 1%, Other Pacific Islander 12%, Chinese 4%
RELIGION Nauru Congregational 35%, Roman Catholic 33%, Nauru Independent Church 10%
CLIMATE Tropical

KIRIBATI

1° 25' N, 173° 00' E | KM² 811 | MI² 313 | UTC+12

The Republic of Kiribati consists of three groups of small coral atolls spread across a wide area; the shifting of the International Date Line in 1995 has made Kiribati the easternmost country in the world.

The three separate archipelagos were unified as Kiribati in 1983, following the independence of the Gilberts from Britain and the Line Islands and Phoenix Islands from the US. The extensive Micronesian population consider themselves 'Gilbertese' and the Gilberts are the main island group. Phosphate mining provided wealth early in the twentieth century but was abandoned in 1979 when reserves on Banaba dried up; since then the mainly agriculturally based economy has relied upon coconuts, copra and fish and residents are now subsistence farmers. The easternmost island, Caroline, was renamed Millennium Island when it became the first place on earth to experience sunrise in the new millennium.

TABITEUEA, GILBERT ISLANDS
Islanders farming seaweed near the shore.

FACT FILE

LOCAL NAME Republic of Kiribati
CAPITAL CITY Tarawa
CURRENCY Australian Dollar (AUD)
MEMBERSHIP C, PIF, SPC
GOVERNMENT Republic
POPULATION 110,356
POP. DENSITY 136/km²; 353/mi²
GDP 348 Million US$
LANGUAGE(S) I-Kiribati, English
ETHNICITY Micronesian 99%
RELIGION Roman Catholic 55%, Kiribati Protestant Church 36%, Mormon 3%
CLIMATE Tropical Maritime

OCEANIA

POLYNESIA

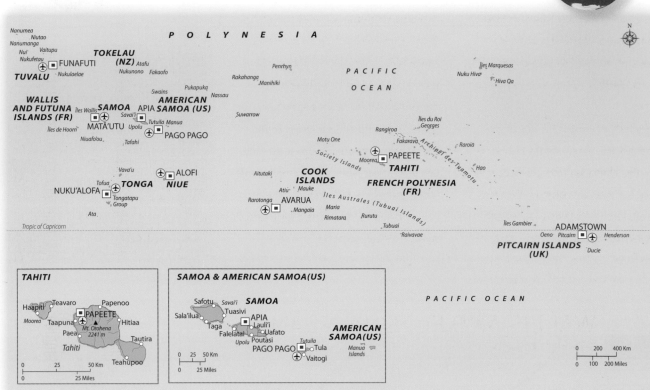

Consisting of over 1,000 islands in the south-west Pacific, Polynesia was first established in 1756 as a term to cover the cultural and anthropological connections between the peoples of the Pacific islands.

The term Polynesia has since come to refer to the large region extending from Hawaii to the north, New Zealand in the south-west and Rapa Nui (Easter Island) further east. Polynesian peoples have inhabited the Pacific islands for thousands of years, developing diverse societies and cultures, which intermingled as they travelled and traded over the successive centuries. Famed for their navigational skills, they crossed vast expanses of the Pacific Ocean in out-rigger canoes. Spanish explorers during the late eighteenth century heralded the beginnings of European colonization, with Christian missionaries in particular focusing their efforts on Polynesia. As a consequence of this, the majority of the islands have retained little of their traditional way of life.

SAVAI'I, SAMOA
Sea turtles swimming in the Pacific Ocean off the coast of Samoa.

TUVALU

8° 00' S, 178° 00' E | KM² 26 | MI² 10 | UTC+12

This group of four reef islands and five atolls is one of the least populated independent countries in the world, only the Vatican City and Nauru being smaller.

The islands and atolls of Tuvalu are all extremely low-lying, with the highest elevation at only 15 metres; consequently rising sea levels are a serious threat to the country. The Polynesian population was keen to separate from the mainly Micronesian Gilbert Islands, with whom they were politically tied when part of the British Empire. Separation came in 1975 and independence from Britain followed three years later. A lack of natural resources, a sparse population and little opportunity for generating savings or investment makes the country very dependent on foreign aid. One of its major sources of income, the sale of stamps as collector's items, was recently supplemented by the leasing of its internet domain, 'tv', for $50 million.

FACT FILE

LOCAL NAME	Tuvalu
CAPITAL CITY	Funafuti
CURRENCY	Australian Dollar (AUD); Tuvaluan Dollar
MEMBERSHIP	C, PIF, SPC, not WB member, not IMF member
GOVERNMENT	Parliamentary Democracy with a Constitutional Monarchy
POPULATION	12,177
POP. DENSITY	468/km²; 12,18/mi²
GDP	26.7 Million US$
LANGUAGE(S)	Tuvaluan, English, Samoan, Kiribati (on Nui Island)
ETHNICITY	Tuvaluan 94%, part Tuvaluan 5%
RELIGION	Ekalesia Kelisiano Tuvalu Church 91%, Other Christian 6%
CLIMATE	Tropical

WALLIS AND FUTUNA ISLANDS

13° 18' S, 176° 12' W | KM² 274 | MI² 106 | UTC+12

The two island groups of Wallis and Futuna are French overseas collectivities in Polynesia, but are distinct from French Polynesia.

The three volcanic islands of Uvea (Wallis), Futuna and Alofi are traditional chiefdoms, with the capital of Mata-Utu on Uvea. Alofi is uninhabited, mainly due to the lack of freshwater supplies although popular legend has it that the population was eaten by the rival cannibal clans on Futuna. In 1842 the French declared a protectorate over the islands in response to an internal rebellion; they eventually came under the authority of New Caledonia. In 1961 the islands became an overseas territory of France, but cultural tensions between the European form of jurisdiction and traditional tribal laws were sparked in 2005 when the king overruled French law. Subsistence farming and fishing is the mainstay of the economy, with aid and overseas remittances providing further support.

WALLIS
The lagoon on Wallis is one of the most beautiful and best preserved in the world.

FACT FILE

LOCAL NAME	Territory of Wallis and Futuna Islands
SOVEREIGN STATE	France
CAPITAL/MAIN CITY	Mata-Utu
CURRENCY	Comptoirs Français du Pacifique Franc (XPF)
MEMBERSHIP	SPC
GOVERNMENT	French Overseas Collectivity
POPULATION	15,237
POP. DENSITY	56/km²; 144/mi²
GDP	60 Million US$
LANGUAGE(S)	Wallisian, Futunan, French
ETHNICITY	Polynesian
RELIGION	Roman Catholic 99%
CLIMATE	Tropical

OCEANIA

TONGA

20° 00' S, 175° 00' W | KM² 748 | MI² 289 | UTC+13

Forty-six of Tonga's 169 islands are inhabited and the archipelago is the furthest south of the Polynesian islands.

The majority of Tonga's islands are formed from coral limestone, with some more mountainous volcanic islands to the west. The main island, Tongatapu, is home to the capital city, Nuku'alofa and the Royal Palace. Despite having become a British protectorate in 1875, Tonga never lost its own governance and as such remains the only independent monarchy in the Pacific. Although the islands had been visited by various European explorers during the eighteenth and nineteenth centuries, only missionaries remained; Tonga has since adopted a 'Western' style of governance and administration. Tonga exports mainly agricultural goods such as vanilla, squash, coconuts and bananas and the only other major source of income is tourism.

FACT FILE

LOCAL NAME Kingdom of Tonga
CAPITAL CITY Nuku'alofa
CURRENCY Pa'anga (TOP)
MEMBERSHIP C, G77, PIF, SPC, WTO
GOVERNMENT Constitutional Monarchy
POPULATION 100,895
POP. DENSITY 135/km²; 349/mi²
GDP 526 Million US$
LANGUAGE(S) Tongan, English
ETHNICITY Tongan 95%
RELIGION Christian 97% (Free Wesleyan Church 37%, Roman Catholic 16%, Latter-day Saints 17%, Free Church of Tonga 11%, Church of Tonga 7%, Other Christian 9%)
CLIMATE Tropical

SAMOA

13° 35' S, 172° 20' W | KM² 2,944 | MI² 1,137 | UTC-11

The western portion of the Samoan island chain, and until 1997 called Western Samoa, the territory comprises two main islands – Savai'i and Upolu.

Samoa's islands are mountainous and rainforested with narrow, low coastal plains and are home to a number of active volcanoes. The Samoan islands, including American Samoa, had been the subject of a three-way struggle for control between America, Britain and Germany during the nineteenth century. Britain eventually relinquished its claim in return for territorial gains in Africa, the Solomon Islands and Tonga. Western Samoa became a German territory until it was seized by New Zealand in 1914. When Samoa finally achieved independence in 1962 it was the first Polynesian state to do so. Maintaining traditional family-oriented communities, the vast majority of Samoans are of Polynesian descent and rely on fishing and agriculture. Although the economy still receives aid from New Zealand, it has experienced growth, with tourism, investment and offshore banking becoming increasingly important.

SAVAI'I ISLAND
The Afu Aau waterfall on Savai'i Island.

FACT FILE

LOCAL NAME Independent State of Samoa
CAPITAL CITY Apia
CURRENCY Tala (SAT)
MEMBERSHIP C, G77, PIF, SPC, WTO (observer)
GOVERNMENT Parliamentary Republic
POPULATION 188,752
POP. DENSITY 64/km²; 166/mi²
GDP 1.029 Billion US$
LANGUAGE(S) Samoan, English
ETHNICITY Samoan 93%, Euronesians (persons of European and Polynesian blood) 7%
RELIGION Congregationalist 35%, Roman Catholic 20%, Methodist 15%, Latter-day Saints 13%, Assembly of God 7%, Seventh-day Adventist 4%
CLIMATE Tropical

AMERICAN SAMOA

14° 20' S, 170° 00' W | KM² 199 | MI² 77 | UTC-11

The five main islands of American Samoa are rugged and mountainous with volcanic interiors and low coastal plains.

The eastern portion of the Samoan island chain, American Samoa became an overseas territory of the USA in 1899. Occupied by Polynesian tribes for over three thousand years, the three Manu'a islands within American Samoa had once been the centre of an empire which ruled over a number of Polynesian islands. American Samoans are now considered US nationals but without the right to vote in presidential elections, they instead elect their representative Governor. Despite this American status, American Samoa remains traditionally Polynesian, with 90 per cent of the land under communal ownership and the population abiding by customs and laws dictated by family chiefs. Tuna fishing and processing is the main economic activity on the islands, supported by tourism.

FACT FILE

LOCAL NAME Territory of American Samoa
SOVEREIGN STATE United States
CAPITAL/MAIN CITY Pago Pago
CURRENCY US Dollar (USD)
MEMBERSHIP SPC
GOVERNMENT Unincorporated and unorganized territory of the US
POPULATION 64,827
POP. DENSITY 326/km²; 842/mi²
GDP 510.1 Million US$
LANGUAGE(S) Samoan, English, Tongan
ETHNICITY Native Hawaiian and other Pacific Islander 92% (including Samoan 88%), Asian 3%
RELIGION Christian Congregationalist 50%, Roman Catholic 20%
CLIMATE Tropical Maritime

PAGO PAGO
A view of of Pago Pago, captial of American Samoa.

NIUE

19° 02' S, 169° 52' W | KM² 260 | MI² 100 | GMT +/- | UTC-11

The large coral island of Niue with its steep limestone cliffs and high central plateau is known to locals as 'The Rock'.

FACT FILE

LOCAL NAME Niue
CAPITAL/MAIN CITY Alofi
CURRENCY New Zealand Dollar (NZD)
MEMBERSHIP PIF, SPC
GOVERNMENT Self-governing Parliamentary Democracy in free association with New Zealand
POPULATION 1,444
POP. DENSITY 6/km²; 14/mi²
GDP 7.6 Million US$
LANGUAGE(S) Niuean, English
ETHNICITY Niuen 80.6%, Pacific islander 10.5%, Caucasian 4.7%, mixed 4%
RELIGION Ekalesia Niue 63%, Latter-day Saints 9%, Roman Catholic 7%, other Christian 4%
CLIMATE Tropical

Inhabited by Polynesian tribes since AD 900, Niue's remoteness, inhospitable coastline and unwelcoming inhabitants made it notoriously difficult for European explorers to land. Niue eventually became a Christian country owing to the persistence of missionaries in the area. Annexed by New Zealand in 1901, it was granted the right to self-governance in 1974. Niue has since been dependent upon aid from New Zealand to support its economy, particularly since the devastation caused by the typhoon of 2004 which damaged much of the island's infrastructure and its capital city, Alofi. Most Niuans are subsistence farmers, and grow their own food. Cash crops such as passion fruits, coconuts, limes and honey are exported.

AVALKI CAVE
The Avalki Cave is sacred to the Niueans.

TOKELAU ISLANDS

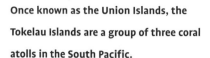

9° 00' S, 172° 00' W | KM² 10 | MI² 4 | UTC-11

Once known as the Union Islands, the Tokelau Islands are a group of three coral atolls in the South Pacific.

The islands of Atafu, Nukunonu and Fakaofo are all low-lying atolls enclosing large lagoons. Despite having a population of only about 1,400 Tokelau is overcrowded, with little arable land and few natural resources. The ocean and lagoons provide seafood, which is the islanders' staple fare. In 1863 the native population was decimated by

FACT FILE

LOCAL NAME Tokelau

SOVEREIGN STATE New Zealand

CAPITAL/MAIN CITY Fakaofo, Nukunonu and Atafu are main settlements

CURRENCY New Zealand Dollar (NZD)

MEMBERSHIP PIF (observer), SPC

GOVERNMENT Self-administering territory of New Zealand

POPULATION 1,433

POP. DENSITY 143/km²; 358/mi²

GDP 1.5 Million US$

LANGUAGE(S) Tokelauan, English

ETHNICITY Tokelauan 74%, part Tokelauan/ Samoan 11%, Part Tokelauan/Tuvaluan 5%

RELIGION Christian 100% (Congregational Christian 62%, Roman Catholic 34%, Other Christian 3%)

CLIMATE Tropical

Peruvian slave traders who arrived on the islands and removed all the men. The islands then became the focus of emigration for Polynesian and European travellers who repopulated the islands with the remaining women. In 1948 the administration of the islands was passed from the UK to New Zealand, and the residents are currently working towards achieving the status of free-association with New Zealand, similar to that of Niue and the Cook Islands.

COOK ISLANDS

21° 14' S, 159° 46' W | KM² 236.7 | MI² 91 | GMT +/- | UTC-10

A self-governing territory in free-association with New Zealand, the Cook Islands are some of the more economically developed of the South Pacific islands.

Consisting of fifteen small coral islands, the seven northern islands are sparsely populated low-lying atolls, while the eight southern islands are home to the majority of the population. Rarotonga is the largest of these hilly and fertile volcanic islands and is the administrative centre of the archipelago. Named after the British navigator James Cook who first sighted them in 1773, the islands became a British Protectorate in 1888, in order to avoid French colonization. Administration was transferred to New Zealand in 1901 and self-governance came in 1965. Exported goods include black pearls, traditionally manufactured goods such as woven baskets and textiles and citrus fruits. Tourism is a growing sector.

ATIU ISLAND
Lush tropical rain forest vegetation on Atiu Island, which lies about 200 kilometres north-east of Rarotonga.

FACT FILE

LOCAL NAME Cook Islands

CAPITAL CITY Avarua

CURRENCY NZ Dollar (NZD)

MEMBERSHIP PIF, SPC

GOVERNMENT Self-governing Parliamentary Democracy in free association with New Zealand

POPULATION 12,271

POP. DENSITY 52/km²; 135/mi²

GDP 183.2 Million US$

LANGUAGE(S) English, Maori

ETHNICITY Cook Island Maori (Polynesian) 88%, part Cook Island Maori 6%

RELIGION Cook Islands Christian Church 56%, Roman Catholic 17%, Seventh-day Adventists 8%, Latter-day Saints 4%, Other Protestant 6%

CLIMATE Tropical Oceanic

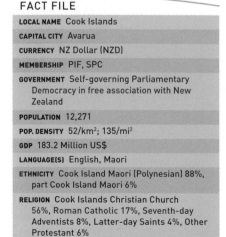

FRENCH POLYNESIA
15° 00' S, 140° 00' W | KM² 4,167 | MI² 1,609 | UTC-10

The five archipelagos that make up French Polynesia consist of 118 volcanic islands and coral atolls spread over an area of 2,500,000 square kilometres of ocean.

The largest and most populous island of French Polynesia is Tahiti, part of the Society Islands group. The other archipelagos are the Austral, Bass, Gambier, Marquesas, and the Tuamotu Islands. Tahiti is the location of the capital city of the territory, Papeete. Before the establishment of the French Protectorate in 1889, the island groups were independent of one another and organized into petty chieftainships. European discovery in the sixteenth century heralded the arrival of Christian missionaries from Spain, England and France; the divisions between Catholics and Protestants ignited French interest. Makatea, one of the three

phosphate rock islands in the Pacific, was intensively mined until 1967. Tahitian black pearls are an important export commodity, and the developed economy also relies upon deep-sea fishing. The location for a number of military bases, the islands were controversially used for French nuclear testing during the 1990s.

FACT FILE
LOCAL NAME	French Polynesia
SOVEREIGN STATE	France
CAPITAL	Papeete
CURRENCY	Comptoirs Français du Pacifique Franc (XPF)
MEMBERSHIP	PIF (associate member), SPC
GOVERNMENT	Overseas Collectivity of France
POPULATION	266,178
POP. DENSITY	64/km²; 165/mi²
GDP	4.58 Billion US$
LANGUAGE(S)	French, Tahitian
ETHNICITY	Polynesian 78%, Chinese 12%, Local French 6%, Metropolitan French 4%
RELIGION	Protestant 54%, Roman Catholic 30%
CLIMATE	Tropical

MARQUESAS ISLANDS
A stone statue on Nuku Hiva in French Polynesia.

PITCAIRN ISLANDS
25° 04' S, 130° 06' W | KM² 47 | MI² 18 | UTC-9

The last of the United Kingdom's once large number of Pacific colonial territories, the four Pitcairn Islands are Pitcairn, Henderson, Ducie and Oeno.

The Pitcairns are hot, humid tropical islands formed of volcanic rock. They each have rugged mountainous interiors with high, rocky cliff coastlines. The isolation and general inaccessibility of the islands has made them almost uninhabitable; only Pitcairn has a human population,

of presently just fewer than 50 people. The Pitcairn Islanders are famously the

FACT FILE
LOCAL NAME	Pitcairn Islands
SOVEREIGN STATE	United Kingdom
CAPITAL/MAIN TOWN	Adamstown
CURRENCY	New Zealand Dollar (NZD)
GOVERNMENT	British Overseas Territory
POPULATION	48
POP. DENSITY	1/km²; 3/mi²
GDP	N.A.
LANGUAGE(S)	English, Pitkern
ETHNICITY	Descendants of the *Bounty* mutineers and their Tahitian wives
RELIGION	Seventh-day Adventist 100%
CLIMATE	Tropical

descendants of the mutinous sailors of the the *Bounty* and their Tahitian companions, who settled in 1790 under the leadership of Fletcher Christian. The islands officially became a colony of the British Empire in 1838. The tiny economy relies upon fishing, agriculture and the sale of postage stamps. In 2004 six men were imprisoned on the island following investigations into institutionalized child abuse leading to one quarter of the island's labour force being lost.

OCEANIA

ANTARCTICA

Height (m)

9000
6000
5000
4000
3000
2000
1500
1000
500
200
100
0
below sea level
-2000
-4000
-5000
-6000
-7000
-8000
-10000

Stereographic
1 : 48 000 000

0   500   1000 Km

0   500 Miles

Situated almost entirely within the Antarctic Circle and surrounded by the waters of the Southern Ocean, Antarctica is the fourth-largest, most isolated and most inhospitable continent on the planet.

On average Antarctica is the world's highest, coldest and windiest landmass. It is also the driest, for despite the fact that around 70 per cent of the world's fresh water is contained within its ice sheets, the Antarctic interior receives so little precipitation (less than 50 millimetres a year) that it may be regarded as a desert. The lowest temperature ever recorded on Earth, −89°C, was at Vostok Station in Antarctica in 1983.

ANTARCTIC SUNSHINE
Seals bask in the sun. During the height of the Antarctic and Arctic summers the sun never dips below the horizon and so both territories can be called lands of the midnight sun.

Although the existence of a southern continent had been the subject of speculation since ancient times, Antarctica remained undiscovered until the nineteenth century and largely unexplored until the early years of the twentieth century, when adventurers from several countries mounted expeditions to the South Pole. The seasoned Arctic explorer Roald Amundsen was the first to reach the geographic South Pole in December 1911, while the ill-fated British party led by Captain Robert Scott arrived a month later and perished on the return journey. Several nations laid claim to Antarctic territory in the first half of the twentieth century, but the Antarctic Treaty of 1959 suspended any further claims; it also prohibited military activity and the exploitation of natural resources, and fostered environmental protection and scientific cooperation. There are no permanent settlements on the Antarctic continent, although about twenty countries maintain scientific research facilities there, working in such fields as meteorology, astronomy, biology and ecology; of these countries, relatively few make a territorial claim and they are listed in the pages that follow. However, tourism is booming, with flights over and short visits by ship to the continent and its adjacent islands now supplemented by tourists engaging in extreme sports, all of which raises fears of environmental damage to the territory.

KING PENGUIN
The King Penguin breeds at the northern edge of Antarctic territory.

BRITISH ANTARCTIC TERRITORIES

The British Antarctic Territory consists of a sector south of latitude 60° South and between the longitudes of 20° West and 80° West in the west of the Antarctic continent, taking in the Antarctic Peninsula, Ronne Ice Shelf and Weddell Sea, as well as the South Orkney and South Shetland Islands. However, much of the territory is also claimed by Argentina and Chile. Britain first laid claim to the area in 1908, and the territory was administered as a dependency of the Falkland Islands until 1962, when it

was designated as a UK Overseas Territory in its own right following the implementation of the Antarctic Treaty. The British Antarctic Survey maintains three research stations within the territory, two of which are permanently manned.

A second UK Overseas Territory in the region is South Georgia and the South Sandwich Islands; South Georgia lies just outside the maximum extent of sea ice in the south Atlantic Ocean, while the South Sandwich Islands lie within this zone in an

area of the Southern Ocean that is ice-free in the Antarctic summer months. Britain also claimed South Georgia and the South Sandwich Islands in 1908 and administered them from the Falkland Islands until 1985, when they became a separate territory. The British Antarctic Survey maintains two research stations in this territory, and other summer residents include the curators of the museum in Grytviken that records South Georgia's history as a whaling station.

ARGENTINE ANTARCTICA

Argentine Antarctica consists of a sector south of latitude 60° South and between the longitudes of 25° West and 74° West, covering much of the British Antarctic Territory (including the Antarctic Peninsula), which Argentina does not recognise. Argentina founded its first permanently staffed research base in Antarctica in

the South Orkney Islands in 1904, before establishing its wider territorial claim during the 1950s. Having originally claimed South Georgia in 1927, Argentine forces occupied the island in 1982, an action that was the first act of the conflict with Britain over the Falklands. Argentina maintains numerous research facilities within its

Antarctic claim, the largest of which is Esperanza, where in 1978 Emilio Marcos Palma became the first person to be born on the continent.

PRIMAVERA RESEARCH STATION
Argentina's Primavera research station consists of a collection of huts on Alejandrina Island.

ANTÁRTICA (CHILE)

Overlapping the territorial claims of Britain and Argentina between the meridians of 53° West and 90° West, and from latitude 60° South to the South Pole, Chile's Antarctic claim was established in 1961. It was administered from the Magallanes Province until 1975, when the Antártica Chilena Province was established. Chile's first Antarctic base was set up on Greenwich Island in 1947, but the nation's territorial claim actually predates the discovery of the Antarctic mainland, and is founded on the fifteenth-century Treaty of Tordesillas, which divided Spanish and Portuguese territorial claims and provisionally included all undiscovered southern territories. Today, Chile maintains a permanent settlement at Villa Las Estrellas on King George Island that

HUMPBACK WHALE
Humpbacks are found in all the world's oceans.

includes a school, a hospital, a church, a bank and a post office.

THE ROSS DEPENDENCY (NEW ZEALAND)

Named after the British explorer Sir James Clark Ross, who discovered the Ross Sea in 1841, the Ross Dependency occupies the area between the meridians of 160° East and 150° West, and from latitude 60° South to the South Pole. This includes the Ross Sea, the Ross Ice Shelf, Ross Island, Scott Island, the Balleny Islands, Roosevelt Island and part of Edward VII Land and Victoria Land. The territory was claimed by Britain and entrusted to New Zealand in 1923, by which time numerous scientific expeditions had already taken place in the region, including the attempts to reach the South Pole by Captain Robert Scott, Ernest Shackleton and Roald Amundsen. New Zealand's only research facility in the Ross Dependency is the Scott Base, which was founded on Ross Island in 1957.

THE ROSS ICE SHELF
The Ross Ice Shelf is the largest in Antarctica.

ADÉLIE LAND (FRANCE)

Flanked on either side by the Australian Antarctic Territory, Adélie Land is a segment of Antarctica situated south of latitude 66° South and between longitudes 136° East and 142° East. It forms part of the French Southern and Antarctic Territories, which also includes a number of islands and archipelagos in the southern Indian Ocean. The coast of Adélie Land was discovered in 1837 by the French explorer Jules Dumont d'Urville, who named the region after his wife, although the first French base, Port Martin, was not established until 1950. This base was destroyed by fire, and then replaced two years later by the research station Dumont d'Urville on the Ile des Pétrels, which has been permanently manned since 1956. Adélie Land is dominated by an ice-clad plateau, although strong katabatic (cool, downward-driven) winds tend to keep parts of the coast relatively ice-free.

ADÉLIE PENGUIN
The Adélie penguin is the smallest of all the species of penguin living in the Antarctic.

AUSTRALIAN ANTARCTIC TERRITORY

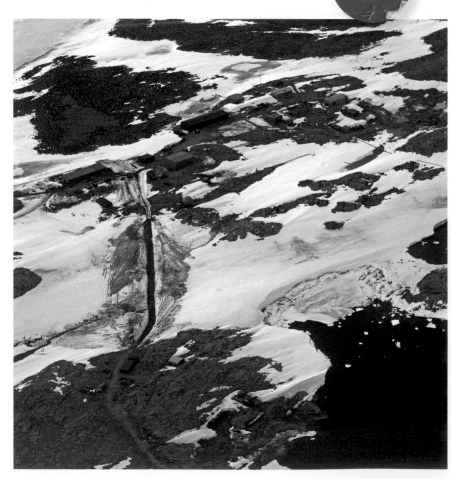

The largest claim in Antarctica, the Australian Antarctic Territory occupies much of eastern Antarctica, and consists of the territory south of latitude 60° South and between the longitudes of 45° and 160° East, except for the French sector of Adélie Land. Originally claimed by Britain, the territory was transferred to Australia in 1933, and the borders with Adélie Land were officially delineated in 1938. Australia maintains three Antarctic research facilities within its territorial claim: Mawson, established in 1954; Davis, opened in 1957, and Casey, constructed during the 1960s. However, the country's first base in the region was established in 1947 on the subantarctic Heard Island, which, with the McDonald Islands, was transferred from British to Australian sovereignty the same year.

CASEY RESEARCH STATION
Casey Station is occupied throughout the year.

NORWEGIAN ANTARCTIC TERRITORY

The Norwegian Antarctic Territory consists of Dronning ('Queen') Maud Land, Bouvet Island and Peter I Island. Dronning Maud Land, constituting the continental part of Norway's claimed Antarctic territory, is the sector lying between longitudes 20° West and 45° East; although no northerly or southerly parameters have been officially designated, it is commonly accepted that the territory extends from the South Pole to latitude 66° South. Named by Roald Amundsen after Queen Maud, the English princess who became the wife of King Haakon VII of Norway, the region was first explored by Hjalmar Riiser-Larsen in 1930 and formally claimed by Norway eight years later, and become a Norwegian dependency in 1957. Norway maintains two research stations, Troll and Tor, in Dronning Maud Land. The subantarctic Bouvet Island, lying in the South Atlantic Ocean between Antarctica and southern Africa, is one of the world's most remote islands, while Peter I Island is the only claimed Antarctic territory between 90° West and 150° West.

ICEBERGS
Antarctic icebergs are identified and named by the National Ice Center. An iceberg must measure at least 10 nautical miles along the long axis and be located south of 60° S latitude.

ARCTIC

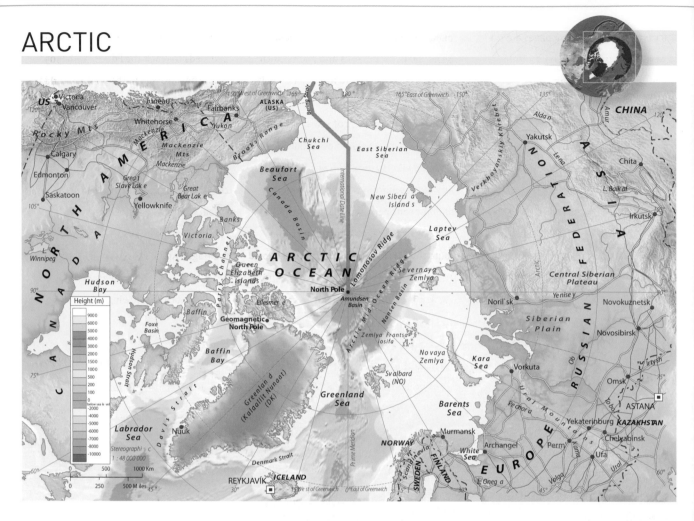

Height (m)
9000
6000
5000
4000
3000
2000
1500
1000
500
200
100
below sea le vel
-2000
-4000
-5000
-6000
-7000
-8000
-10000

Stereographi c
1 : 48 000 000

Unlike the Antarctic, which is an ice-clad continental landmass surrounded by the Southern Ocean, the Arctic region consists of a polar ice cap floating in the Arctic Ocean and the territories lying north of the Arctic Circle, which almost entirely encircle the Arctic Ocean.

The Arctic territories comprise parts of the mainland of Norway, Sweden, Finland, Russia, the US state of Alaska and Canada. Greenland, Iceland, and numerous smaller islands and archipelagos are mainly or totally within the Arctic Circle. The territories

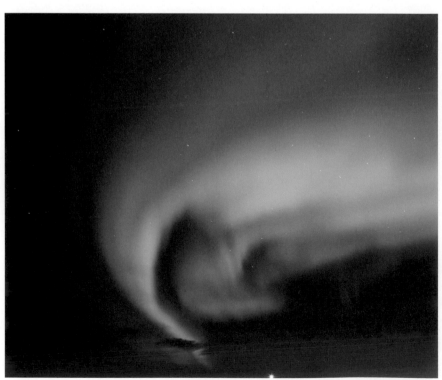

AURORAE
Spectacular light shows caused by solar winds can be seen in the skies over the polar regions.

discussed in the following pages are the lesser-known islands whch lie within the Arctic Circle. Although under a UN treaty, nations with an Arctic coastline are restricted to an economic zone of 200 nautical miles, the shrinking of the polar ice cap as a consequence of global warming is opening up new shipping channels and raises the possibility of mineral extraction from the seabed. This has led Russia, the USA, Canada and Norway to claim sectors extending to the North Pole; Russia planted a flag on the seabed below the Pole in August 2007 to symbolise its claim.

Despite the harsh climate of the Arctic, where winter temperatures may fall as low as −40°C, the region is home to numerous plant and animal species such as polar bears, seals, arctic foxes and plants, such as grasses and lichens, and has been inhabited by humans, such as the Inuit and Sami peoples, for thousands of years. However, exploration of the region essentially began with the Vikings during the ninth century, and increased from the fifteenth century as Europeans began to search for the 'Northwest Passage', a northern trading route to Asia. The Norwegian explorer Roald Amundsen completed the first successful navigation of the passage between 1903 and 1906, by which time the focus of Arctic exploration had shifted towards reaching the North Pole itself. This feat was accomplished by the American Robert Peary, who traversed the ice cap with dogs and sleds to reach the Pole in April 1909. Since the outbreak of the Second World War, a number of scientific stations have been established in the Arctic, with major areas of study including geology, meteorology, biology and oceanography. In recent years, climatology, and particularly the effects of global warming, have become of primary concern, partly because of the threat to the fragile Arctic ecosystem, but mainly because of the global impact of rising sea levels as the ever-growing areas of the polar ice melt.

POLAR BEAR
Polar bears are born on land but spend much of their time on the ice, where they wait to prey on seals as they come to the surface.

THE CANADIAN ARCTIC ARCHIPELAGO

Extending over an area of more than one million square kilometres between Alaska and Greenland, the Canadian Arctic archipelago comprises the largest island group on Earth. It also contains several of the largest islands in the world, including Baffin Island, which is renowned for its seabird colonies and other wildlife, and is home to the largest human settlement in the archipelago, the Inuit community of Iqaluit. The terrain throughout the archipelago consists generally of low-lying tundra, although there are mountainous areas, particularly in the east. Following the sixteenth-century explorations of Martin Frosbisher, who sailed in search of the Northwest Passage, the archipelago was originally claimed by Britain, with sovereignty being transferred to Canada between 1880 and 1895. However, Norway maintained claims to some of the most northerly islands until 1930, and the status of Hans Island remains disputed with Denmark. Disagreements have also arisen over the status of the maritime territories in the region, with Canada claiming sovereignty over all of the north-western passages off its northern coast and a sector extending to the North Pole, despite these waterways being designated by treaty as international waters.

IQALUIT
The settlement of Iqaluit is located on the southern coast of Baffin Island.

RUSSIAN ARCTIC ISLANDS

Russia's Arctic islands, scattered across a vast area of the Arctic Ocean from the Chukchi Sea off eastern Siberia to the Arctic coast of European Russia, are dominated by four major island groups: the New Siberian Islands, Severnaya Zemlya, Franz Josef Land and Novaya Zemlya, which consists of Severny Island and Yuzhny Island. In addition to these archipelagos, the territory contains a number of large isolated islands, including Kolguyev Island and Wrangel Island, as well as numerous smaller islands off the Russian coast. Most of the large islands are heavily glaciated; the exception are the New Siberian Islands, although the shallow, low-salinity seas of the broad Siberian Shelf on which they lie are prone to extensive and prolonged freezing. Severnaya Zemlya is the world's most recently discovered island, having remained unmapped until 1933, while Franz Josef Land was annexed from Austria in 1926. Novaya Zemlya, however, has been known to the Russians since as early as the tenth century, and became permanently inhabited during the 1870s, when indigenous Nenets people were resettled there to prevent Norwegian expansion. Since 1954, however, it has been used for nuclear testing. Russia maintains several military and scientific facilities on its Arctic islands.

NORWEGIAN ARCTIC ISLANDS

The Norwegian Arctic Islands consist of the Svalbard archipelago, which is located around 650 kilometres north of Norway, and Jan Mayen Island, which lies between Norway and Greenland, around 900 kilometres west of the Norwegian coast. The Svalbard archipelago comprise nine major islands, the largest of which is Spitsbergen. Although Spitsbergen was known in Viking times, it was rediscovered during the sixteenth century, following which it became an important base for whaling. Coal mining, which remains the area's principal economic activity, began during the late nineteenth century, and the islands were formally recognised as part of Norway during the 1920s. The largest settlement on the islands is Longyearbyen, which has a population of approximately 2,000 inhabitants Most recently, Spitsbergen has become home to the Svalbard Global Seed Vault, a repository designed to store the seeds of as many known plant species as possible.

Like Svalbard, Jan Mayen Island is rugged and extensively glaciated. Although it too may have been known in earlier times, it was discovered during the early seventeenth century, and became a Dutch whaling base. The island was annexed by the Norwegian Meteorological Institute in 1922 and became sovereign territory in 1930. Today its only inhabitants are scientists and military personnel.

KONGSFJORDEN, SPITSBERGEN
Kongsfjorden is on the west coast of Spitsbergen.

INDEX

HOW TO USE THE INDEX

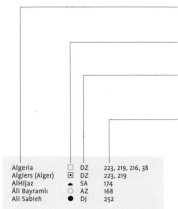

Place name every place found in the maps is indexed, whether a city or other geographic feature.

Symbol a simple icon set indicates what sort of place is indexed

ISO Country Code tells you what country that place belongs to. Places that belong to more than one may have several codes, while those belonging to none are not coded. See the table ISO Country Codes on page 334 for the list of countries.

Page reference one or more page references take you to a map location; where relevant, the country map is listed first with the region map second, followed by the continent map and then the map in the world map section.

INDEX SYMBOLS

Continent/Region	◘
Country	☐
Administrative division	■
Capital	☑
City/Town	●
Place	○
Landscape	▲
Wetland	◉
Mountain	▲
Mountain Range	▲▲
Glacier	▲
River/Lake	⌣
Ocean/Sea	▼
Ocean topography	▽
Cape/Peninsula	▽
Island	⌒

Algeria	☐	DZ	223, 219, 216, 38
Algiers (Alger)	☑	DZ	223, 219
AlHījaz	▲	SA	174
Āli Bayramlı	○	AZ	168
Ali Sabieh	●	DJ	252

A Coruña	●	ES	138
Aachen	●	DE	130
Åalborg	●	DK	113
Aalst	○	BE	124
Aarau	●	CH	132
Aba	●	CN	184, 235
Abādān	○	IR	194
Ābādeh	○	IR	194
Abaji	○	NG	235
Abakaliki	○	NG	235
Abancay	●	PE	95
Abau	○	PG	282, 281
Abaya	⌣	ET	253
Abbé	⌣	DJ	252
Abbeville	●	FR	127
'Abd al 'Azīz, Jabal	▲	SY	169
'Abd al Kūrī	⌒	YE	175
Abdali	○	KW	172
Abéché	●	TD	244, 242
Abengourou	●	HR	239
Åbenrå	●	DK	113
Aberdeen	○	CN	187
Aberdeen	●	UK	118
Aberystwyth	○	UK	118
Abhā	●	SA	164, 174
Abidjan	●	HR	239, 229
Abilene	●	US	62
Abnūb	○	EG	225
Aboisso	●	HR	239
Abomey	●	BJ	236
Abong Mbang	○	CM	245
Abou Déia	○	TD	244
Abou Goulem	○	TD	244
Absaroka	▲▲	US	54
Absaroka Range	▲▲	US	56
Abu Ballâs	▲	EG	225
Abu Dhabi (Abū Zabī)	☑	AE	176, 164, 162, 34
Abu Hamed	○	SD	227
Abū Kamāl	○	SY	169
Abū Rujmayn, Jabal	▲	SY	169
Abū Sunbul	○	EG	225
Abu Zabad	○	SD	227
Abū Zanima	○	EG	225
Abuja	☑	NG	235, 229
Abuná	⌣	BR	97, 96
Abyad	○	SD	227
Acajutla	○	SV	72
Acapulco	●	MX	68, 66
Acaray, Represa de	⌣	BR	97
Acarigua	○	VE	91
Acaş	○	RO	155
Accra	☑	GH	237, 229
Achaguas	○	VE	91
Achill	⌒	IE	121
Achnasheen	○	UK	118
Acklins	⌒	BS	75
Aconcagua, Cerro	▲	AR	103
Açores, Arquipélago dos	⌒		137
Acoua	○	FR	264
Acquaviva	○	SM	141
Acri	○	IT	142
ACT	■	AU	276
Acurenam	○	GQ	248
Ad Dahnā'	▲	SA	174, 164
Ad Dakhla	●	EH	222
Ad Dammān	●	SA	174, 164
Ad Dīwanīyah	●	IQ	173
Ad Dūr	○	BH	177
Ada	○	GH	237
Adacao	○	US	285
Adam, Mount	▲	UK	105
Adamawa Highlands	▲		242
Adamstown	☑		290

Adana	●	TR	166, 164
Adapazarı	●	TR	166
Adare	○	IE	121
Addis Ababa (Ādīs Ābeba)	☑	ET	253, 250, 216, 38
Addu Atoll	⌒	MV	200
Adelaide	⌒	CL	296, 46
Adelaide	●	AU	276, 274
Adélie Land	▲	FR	296, 46
Aden ('Adan)	●	YE	175, 164
Aden, Gulf of	▼		164, 162
Adh Dhayd	○	AE	176
Ādīgrat	○	ET	253
Adilang	○	UG	256
Adirondack Mountains	▲▲	US	60
Adıyaman	●	TR	166
Adjud	○	RO	155
Adjumani	○	UG	256
Admiralty	⌒		281
Adrar	●	DZ	223
Adrar des Ifoyas	▲	ML	233
Adrar Tamgak	▲	NE	234
Adré	○	TD	244
Adriatic Sea	▼		142, 135
Adycha	⌣	RU	159
Aegean Sea	▼		135, 106
Ærø	⌒	DK	113
Afabet	○	ER	252
Afghanistan	☐	AF	195, 192, 162, 30
Afmadow	○	SO	254
Africa	◘		216, 217
Afrīn	○	SY	169
Afune Yosēf	▲	ET	253
Afyon	●	TR	166
Agadez	●	NE	234, 229
Agadir	●	MA	220
Agalega Islands	⌒	MU	265
Agalta, Sierra-de	▲▲	HN	71
Āgaro	○	ET	253
Agartala	●	IN	197
Agboville	●	HR	239
Ağdam	○	AZ	168
Agen	○	FR	127
Agger	○	DK	113
Agios Nikolaos	●	GR	148
Agnibilékrou	○	HR	239
Agogo	○	GH	237
Agordat	○	ER	252
Agra	●	IN	197
Ağri	●	TR	166
Agrigento	○	IT	142
Agrihan	⌒		285
Agrinio	○	GR	148
Agua	▲	GT	70
Aguadilla	○	US	78
Aguelhok	○	ML	233
Ahalts'ikhe	○	GE	167
Ahmadabad	●	IN	197
Ahuachapán	○	SV	72
Aigialousa	○	CZ	168
Aiguá	○	UY	102
Aileron	○	AU	276
Aïn Ben Tili	○	MR	230
Airai	○	PW	285
Aires	○	CR	73
Aitana	▲	ES	138
Aitape	○	PG	282
Aitutaki	⌒		290
Aix-en Provence	●	FR	127
Aizawl	●	IN	197
Ajaccio	●	FR	127
Ajdābiyā	●	LY	224, 219
Ajka	○	HU	154

'Ajlūn	○	JO	172
'Ajmān	●	AE	176
Ajmer	○	IN	197
Akelamo	○	ID	212
Akhalk'alak'i	○	GE	167
Akiéni	○	GA	247
Akilok	○	UG	256
Akimiski	⌒	CA	49, 19
Akita	○	JP	190
Akjoujt	○	MR	230
Aknoul	○	MA	220
Akobo	⌣		253
Akobo	○	SD	227
Akola	○	IN	197
Akonolinga	●	CM	245
Akron	○	US	58
Aksai Chin	■	CN/IN	197, 178, 162
Aksaray	●	TR	166
Aksu	⌣		178
Aksu	●	CN	184
Āksum	○	ET	253
Aktau	●	KZ	180
Aktobe	●	KZ	180, 178
Akure	●	NG	235
Akureyri	○	IS	114
Al 'Uwaynāt	○	LY	224
Al 'Amārah	●	IQ	173
Al 'Aqabah	●	JO	172
Al 'Arīsh	●	EG	225
Al 'Ayn	●	AE	176
Al Abraq	○	KW	172
Al AḤmadī	●	KW	172
Al Bāb	○	SY	169
Al Bahr Al Abyad	⌣	SD	227
Al Baydā	●	LY	224
Al Baydā'	○	YE	175
Al Buraymī	●	AE	176
Al Dhafrah	▲	AE	176
Al Farwānīyah	●	KW	172
Al Fāw	○	IQ	173
Al Fayyūm	●	EG	225
Al FuḤayḤīl	●	KW	172
Al Fujayrah	●	AE	176
Al Ghaydah	●	YE	175
Al Ghurdaqah	●	EG	225
Al H‿illah	●	IQ	173
Al Ḥadīthah	○	IQ	173
Al Haffah	○	SY	169
Al Hammām	○	EG	225
Al Harrah	○	EG	225
Al Harūj al Aswad	▲	LY	224
Al Hazm al Jawf	○	YE	175
Al Hasakah	●	SY	169
Al Hījaz	▲	SA	174, 164
Al Hoceima	●	MA	220
Al Humrah	▲	AE	176
Al Huwaylah	○	QA	177
Al Ismāīlīyah	●	EG	225
Al Jāfūrah	▲	SA	174
Al Jaghbūb	○	LY	224
Al Jahrah	●	KW	172
Al Jamalīyah	○	QA	177
Al Jawf	○	LY	224
Al Jubayl	○	SA	174
Al Karak	○	JO	172
Al Kāzimīyah	○	IQ	173
Al Khalīf	○	OM	175
Al Khāliş	○	IQ	173
Al Khārija	●	EG	225
Al Kharrārah	○	QA	177
Al Khasab	○	OM	175
Al Khatam	▲	AE	176
Al Khawr	●	QA	177
Al Khums	●	LY	224

Al Khuwayr	○	QA	177
Al Kir'ānah	○	QA	177
Al Kūfah	○	IQ	173
Al Kūt	●	IQ	173
Al Līth	○	SA	174
Al Liwā'	▲	AE	176
Al Madīnah	●	SA	162, 34
Al Mafraq	○	JO	172
Al MaḤwīt	○	YE	175
Al Mālikīyah	○	BH	177
Al Mamtalah	○	BH	177
Al Manşūrah	●	EG	225
Al Maqwā'	○	KW	172
Al Marj	●	LY	224
Al MiḤrāḍ	▲	SA	174
Al Minyā	●	EG	225
Al Mudawwarah	○	JO	172
Al MuḤarraq	●	BH	177
Al Muqdādīyah	○	IQ	173
Al Qāmishlī	●	SY	169
Al Qasr	○	EG	225
Al Qaţrānah	○	JO	172
Al Qayşūmah	○	SA	174
Al Qunayţirah	○	SY	169
Al Quşayr	●	EG	225
Al Quwayrah	○	JO	172
Al Rabbād	▲	AE	176
Al Samha	●	AE	176
Al Shaţrah	○	IQ	173
Al Uqaylah	○	LY	224
Al Wafī	○	OM	175
Al Wafrah	○	KW	172
Al Wakrah	●	QA	177
Al Wusayl	○	QA	177
Al-Bu'ayrāt	○	LY	224
Ala - Too	▲	KG	182
Alabama	■	US	54
Alabama	⌣	US	62, 54, 49
Alai Range	▲▲	KG	182
Alajuela	●	CR	73
Alamogordo	○	US	56
Alamor	○	EC	94
Alanās	○	SE	111
Åland	⌒	SE	111
Åland	⌒		112
Alantika Mountains	▲▲	CM	245
Alaska	■	US	56, 48
Alaska Range	▲▲		56, 48
Alaska, Gulf of	▼	US	56, 54
Alausí	○	EC	94
Alaverdi	○	AM	167
Alazeya	⌣	RU	159
Alba Lulia	○	RO	155
Albacete	●	ES	138
Albania	☐	AL	147, 135, 106, 26
Albany	●	US	60, 54
Albany	⌣	CA	50
Albany	○	AU	276
Alberdi	○	PY	101
Albert	⌣		256, 246
Alberta	■	CA	50
Albi	○	FR	127
Albina	●	SR	93
Alborán Sea	▼		137
AlBudayyi	○	BH	177
Albuquerque	●	US	56, 54
Alcácer do Sal	○	PT	136
Alcañices	○	ES	138
Alcañiz	○	ES	138
Alcántara	○	ES	138
Alchevs'k	○	UA	157
Aldabra Islands	⌒	SC	264
Aldan	⌣	RU	159, 107
Alderney	⌒		120

INDEX

INDEX

INDEX

INDEX

The International Organization for Standardization has allocated country codes of 2 and 3 characters. Country codes in the index and in the maps use the ISO alpha 2 convention. The list of 199 countries below includes seven that are not members of the United Nations and they are marked with an asterisk.

This table shows a list of political and economic membership organisations whose titles are abbreviated in the Fact Files. For organisations such as the UN where the majority of countries are members, the Fact File only records exceptions to membership.

Conuntry Name	ISO Alpha 2 code	Conuntry Name	ISO Alpha 2 code
Afghanistan	AF	Libya (Libyan Arab Jamahiriya)	LY
Albania	AL	Liechtenstein	LI
Algeria	DZ	Lithuania	LT
Andorra	AD	Luxembourg	LU
Angola	AO	Macedonia, Republic of	MK
Antigua and Barbuda	AG	Madagascar	MG
Argentina	AR	Malawi	MW
Armenia	AM	Malaysia	MY
Australia	AU	Maldives	MV
Austria	AT	Mali	ML
Azerbaijan	AZ	Malta	MT
Bahamas	BS	Marshall Islands	MH
Bahrain	BH	Mauritania	MR
Bangladesh	BD	Mauritius	MU
Barbados	BB	Mexico	MX
Belarus	BY	Micronesia, Federated States of	FM
Belgium	BE	Moldova	MD
Belize	BZ	Monaco	MC
Benin	BJ	Mongolia	MN
Bhutan	BT	Montenegro	ME
Bolivia	BO	Morocco	MA
Bosnia and Herzegovina	BA	Mozambique	MZ
Botswana	BW	Myanmar	MM
Brazil	BR	Namibia	NA
Brunei Darussalam	BN	Nauru	NR
Bulgaria	BG	Nepal	NP
Burkina Faso	BF	Netherlands	NL
Burundi	BI	New Zealand	NZ
Cambodia	KH	Nicaragua	NI
Cameroon	CM	Niger	NE
Canada	CA	Nigeria	NG
Cape Verde	CV	*Niue	NU
Central African Republic	CF	Norway	NO
Chad	TD	Oman	OM
Chile	CL	Pakistan	PK
China	CN	Palau	PW
Colombia	CO	*Palestinian Territory, Occupied	PS
Comoros	KM	Panama	PA
Congo, Democratic Republic of the	CD	Papua New Guinea	PG
Congo, Republic of the	CG	Paraguay	PY
*Cook Islands	CK	Peru	PE
Costa Rica	CR	Philippines	PH
Côte d'Ivoire	HR	Poland	PL
Croatia	CU	Portugal	PT
Cuba	CY	Qatar	QA
Cyprus	CZ	Romania	RO
Czech Republic	CI	Russian Federation	RU
Denmark	DK	Rwanda	RW
Djibouti	DJ	Saint Kitts and Nevis	KN
Dominica	DM	Saint Lucia	LC
Dominican Republic	DO	Saint Vincent and the Grenadines	VC
East Timor (Timor-Leste)	TL	Samoa	WS
Ecuador	EC	San Marino	SM
Egypt	EG	Sao Tome and Principe	ST
El Salvador	SV	Saudi Arabia	SA
Equatorial Guinea	GQ	Senegal	SN
Eritrea	ER	Serbia	RS
Estonia	EE	Seychelles	SC
Ethiopia	ET	Sierra Leone	SL
Fiji	FJ	Singapore	SG
Finland	FI	Slovakia	SK
France	FR	Slovenia	SI
Gabon	GA	Solomon Islands	SB
Gambia	GM	Somalia	SO
Georgia	GE	South Africa	ZA
Germany	DE	Spain	ES
Ghana	GH	Sri Lanka	LK
Greece	GR	Sudan	SD
Grenada	GD	Suriname	SR
Guatemala	GT	Swaziland	SZ
Guinea	GN	Sweden	SE
Guinea-Bissau	GW	Switzerland	CH
Guyana	GY	Syria (Syrian Arab Republic)	SY
Haiti	HT	*Taiwan, Republic of China	TW
Honduras	HN	Tajikistan	TJ
Hungary	HU	Tanzania, United Republic of	TZ
Iceland	IS	Thailand	TH
India	IN	Togo	TG
Indonesia	ID	Tonga	TO
Iran, Islamic Republic of	IR	Trinidad and Tobago	TT
Iraq	IQ	Tunisia	TN
Ireland	IE	Turkey	TR
Israel	IL	Turkmenistan	TM
Italy	IT	Tuvalu	TV
Jamaica	JM	Uganda	UG
Japan	JP	Ukraine	UA
Jordan	JO	United Arab Emirates	AE
Kazakhstan	KZ	United Kingdom	UK
Kenya	KE	United States of America	US
Kiribati	KI	Uruguay	UY
Korea, Democratic People's Republic of	KP	Uzbekistan	UZ
Korea, Republic of	KR	Vanuatu	VU
*Kosovo	None	*Vatican City State (Holy See)	VA
Kuwait	KW	Venezuela (Bolivarian Republic of)	VE
Kyrgyzstan	KG	Vietnam	VN
Laos (Lao People's Democratic Republic)	LA	Western Sahara	EH
Latvia	LV	Yemen	YE
Lebanon	LB	Zambia	ZM
Lesotho	LS	Zimbabwe	ZW
Liberia	LR		

source:http://www.un.org/en/members/index.shtml#s

Abbreviation	Member Organization
AC	Arctic Council
APEC	Asia-Pacific Economic Cooperation
ASEAN	Association of South East Asian Nations
AU	African Union
BSEC	Organization of the Black Sea Economic Cooperation
Benelux	Union in Western Europe
C	Commonwealth of Nations
CAN	Andean Community of Nations (Comunidad Andina)
CARICOM	Caribbean Community
CBSS	Council of the Baltic Sea States
CE	Council of Europe
CEI	Central European Initiative
CEMAC	Monetary and Economic Community of Central Africa
CEPGL	Economic Community of the Great Lakes Countries
CIS	Commonwealth of Independent States
COMESA	The Common Market for Eastern and Southern Africa
CP	Colombo Plan
D-8	Developing 8 countries
EAC	East African Community
EAEC	Eurasian Economic Community
EAPC	Euro-Atlantic Partnership Council
ECO	Economic Cooperation Organization
ECOWAS	Economic Community of West African States
EU	European Union
G-5	Group of 5 nations
G-8	Group of 8 nations
G-10	Group of 10 nations
G-15	Group of 15 nations
G-20	Group of 20 nations
G-24	Group of 24 nations
G-77	Group of 77 nations
GCC	Gulf Cooperation Council
GUAM	GUAM - Organization for Democracy and EconomicDevelopment
IAEA	International Atomic Energy Agency
IBRD	International Bank for Reconstruction and Development
IMF	International Monetary Fund
LAIA	Latin American Integration Association
LAS	League of Arab States
NAM	Non-Aligned Movement
NATO	North Atlantic Treaty Organization
OAPEC	Organization of Arab Petroleum Exporting Countries
OAS	Organization of American States
OECD	Organization for Economic Cooperation and Development
OECS	Organization of Eastern Caribbean States
OIC	Organization of the Islamic Conference
OPEC	Organization of the Petroleum Exporting Countries
PIF	Pacific Islands Forum
RG	Rio Group
SAARC	South Asian Association for Regional Cooperation
SADC	South African Development Community
SELA	Latin American and Caribbean Economic System
SPC	The Secretariat of the Pacific Community
UN	United Nations
WB	World Bank
WTO	World Trade Organization

FACT FILE

Local Name
The name by which local people call their country

Capital City
The main city of the country, normally the seat of government

Currency
Name of the currency and the abbreviation given by ISO alpha 3 convention

Membership
List of strategic political or economic organizations of which the country is a member. See the table on *page 334* of membership organizations to decode the abbreviations used

Government
The type of political regime ruling the country

Population
Latest available number of inhabitants

Pop. Density
Average number of people living in a square mile or kilometre

GDP
The total value of production expressed in USD

Language(s)
The main languages spoken in the country, with official language(s) shown first

Ethnicity
The ethnic origins or types of the inhabitants: note that very small percentages of ethnic minorities have been left out and the percentages shown may not add up to 100 per cent because often country census information that is available simply gives the balancing figure as 'unspecified' or 'other'. The threshold for recording ethnic percentages is 3 per cent, below which they are rarely shown unless they have particular interest – most often in the case of indigenous populations where the editors consider that the reader will be interested

Religion
Statistics for religious membership are handled in a similar way to ethnicity

Climate
Generally climate description follows the Koppen classification; the information presents averages which may be based on substantial variants of temperature and rainfall because of elevation or other localized climatic factors

Regional Divisions
A summary of the main levels of regional organization of the country

Dependencies
Territories that are outside of the mainland or main borders of the country, but fall under its sovereign rule; often historical colonies

Economic Activities
Key commercial activities of the country

Natural Resources
Mineral and other resources that are significant to the global market

There are almost 300 fact files in this encyclopedic atlas; they are a concise way of presenting country information in a consistent manner that makes it easy to compare country with country and to have a clear understanding of the key facts. Compiling this information presents many challenges because it constantly changes. Generally the entries are consistent with the CIA Factbook but in many cases the data here is more up to date.

There are variations in the fact files: half-page country entries have a short version with no administrative or economic details; many dependent territories have a separate entry from their sovereign state and these fact files are slightly different. States of the USA have a simplified version.

The entries are explained in detail left and below:

Even if it is a dependency, the flag shown is local when there is one

The name commonly used by the international community

The longitude and latitude of a notional centre point of the country

Area in square kilometres

Area in square miles

Universal Coordinated Time +/- hour; shows the time difference between UTC at the prime or Greenwich Meridian (commonly known as Greenwich Mean Time) at the country capital. A band is shown when a country has more than one time zone

Shows the country in solid red on globe background

ACKNOWLEDGEMENTS

The publisher would like to thank the following libraries and photographers
for their kind permission to reproduce their photographs in this book.

Corbis

11b, 13, 51, 52, 53, 54, 57, 59t, 59b, 60, 61, 62, 63, 64, 65, 67, 68, 69, 70, 71, 72, 73, 74, 75, 76, 78, 79,
81, 82, 84, 85, 86, 87, 90, 91, 92, 94, 95, 96, 98, 99, 102, 103, 104, 105, 108, 110, 111, 112, 113, 114, 115,
116, 117, 118, 119, 120, 121, 122, 123, 124, 125, 126, 127, 129, 130, 131, 132, 133, 134, 135, 136, 138, 139, 140,
141, 143t, 144, 146,147, 148, 149, 152, 153 154, 155, 156, 157, 158, 160, 161t, 161b, 164, 165, 166, 168, 169,
171, 172, 173, 174, 176, 177, 179, 180, 183, 184, 185, 186, 187, 188, 189, 191t&b, 193, 194, 195, 196, 198,
199, 201, 202, 203, 205, 206, 208, 209, 210, 211, 212, 213, 214, 215, 220, 223, 224, 225, 226, 227, 230,
232, 234, 235, 236, 238, 240, 241, 243b, 244, 246, 247, 248, 251, 253, 254, 255, 256, 257, 258, 260,
264, 265, 269, 270, 271, 272, 276, 277, 279, 280, 281, 282, 285, 286, 287t&b, 288, 289, 290, 291, 292,
293t&b, 294, 295, 298, 302, 303, 304, 305

Digital Vision

6, 7, 8l, 8r, 9t, 9b, 55, 250, 266, 267 t&b, 287,
296, 297, 300t

Getty Images

12, 89, 101, 128, 157, 181, 200, 207, 218, 219, 228, 229, 231, 233, 237, 239, 243t (and 4), 249, 259, 261,
263, 299, 299, 300b, 301

NASA

11t, 11b

Cover images:
Main globe image: The blue globe © SOT/Getty Images
Small images from left to right:
Grand Canyon © Rosemary Calvert/Getty Images
Taj Mahal © Pete Turner/Getty Images
Victoria Falls © John Giustina/Getty Images
Eiffel Tower © Elke Van de Velde/Getty Images
Pyramid with Sphinx © Andrew Holt/Getty Images
Sydney Opera House © Fraser Hall/Getty Images

Thank you to Lynn Neal and Caroline Alder for their work on the maps.